HANDBOOK OF BUILDING CRAFTS IN CONSERVATION

FRONTISPIECE
TO THE
PRACTICAL BUILDER.

THE HOUSE OF FULTON ALEXANDER ESQ.

at Patrick near Glasgow

London Published by T. Kelly, 17, Paternoster Row, August 1, 1823

HANDBOOK OF BUILDING CRAFTS IN CONSERVATION

A commentary on Peter Nicholson's
The New Practical Builder and Workman's Companion, 1823

Edited by

Jack Bowyer
Dipl. Arch. (Leeds)

HUTCHINSON
LONDON MELBOURNE SYDNEY AUCKLAND JOHANNESBURG

 VAN NOSTRAND REINHOLD COMPANY
NEW YORK CINCINNATI TORONTO LONDON MELBOURNE

Hutchinson & Co. (Publishers) Ltd
An imprint of the Hutchinson Publishing Group
24 Highbury Crescent, London N5 1RX

Hutchinson Group (Australia) Pty Ltd
30—32 Cremorne Street, Richmond South, Victoria 3121
P.O. Box 151, Broadway, New South Wales 2007

Hutchinson Group (NZ) Ltd
32—34 View Road, PO Box 40—086, Glenfield, Auckland 10

Hutchinson Group (SA) (Pty) Ltd
PO Box 337, Bergvlei 2012, South Africa

First published 1981

© Jack Bowyer 1981

Line drawings © Hutchinson & Co. (Publishers) Ltd 1981
Drawn by Illustra Design Ltd

Filmset and printed in Great Britain by
BAS Printers Limited, Over Wallop, Hampshire

British Library Cataloguing in Publication Data
Handbook of building crafts in conservation.
    1. Historic buildings — Great Britain —
Conservation and restoration
    I. Bowyer, Jack   II. Nicholson, Peter,
b. 1765. New practical builder and workman's
companion
720'.28   NA109.G7

ISBN 0 09 142210 8

Copyright © 1981 by Jack Bowyer

Library of Congress Catalog Card Number: 81—50643

ISBN 0—442—2135—3

Printed in Great Britain

Published by Van Nostrand Reinhold Company
135 West 50th Street, New York, NY 10020, USA

16 15 14 13 12 11 10 9 8 7 6 5 4 3 2 1

Contents

The Contributors

Douglas Garland   Manager, Cathedral Works Organization, Chichester

Peter Minter   Director, The Bulmer Brick and Tile Co. Ltd

William Nash   Head of Department of Construction, Southampton Technical College

Giles Munby   Master Carpenter

Harry Munn   Joinery Manager, G. E. Wallis and Sons Ltd, Maidstone

David Wallis   Director, G. E. Wallis and Sons Ltd, Maidstone

Dennis Tyrrell   Senior Lecturer in Plumbing, Croydon College

Alan Foster   Director, John Williams & Co., London

Charles Brown   Architect in private practice, Hinton Brown Langstone, Warwick

Brian Pegg   Technical Director, Bobac Ltd, London

Donald Stagg   Senior Lecturer in Building Crafts, Hammersmith and West London College

Ian Bristow   Architect in private practice, London

Editor's Introduction
The life and work of Peter Nicholson

Born at Prestonkirk, East Lothian, on 20 July 1765, Peter Nicholson was educated at the village school where he showed great aptitude for mathematics. Leaving school at the age of twelve he worked for his father, a stonemason, but deciding that this trade was not to his liking, was soon apprenticed to a cabinet maker at Linton, Haddingtonshire. During the period he worked as a journeyman in Edinburgh and continued his studies in mathematics. Such was his application that, on moving to London, he was able to set up an evening school in Berwick Street, Soho. This venture was such a success that he was encouraged to prepare his first publication, *The Carpenter's New Guide*, for which he engraved his own plates. This book illustrated an original method for the construction of groins and niches of complex form.

Having established himself as both craftsman and writer, Nicholson proceeded, as did so many of his eighteenth century contemporaries, to set himself up in practice as an architect. This he did in Glasgow in 1800, removing however to Carlisle in 1805 when, on the recommendation of Thomas Telford, he was appointed architect to the county of Cumberland. Having supervised the construction of the new court house, designed by Sir Robert Smirke, he returned to London in 1810 to produce his *Architectural Dictionary* and to recommence his educational work, giving private lessons in mathematics, land surveying, mechanical drawing and similar subjects.

In 1827 he began a work called *The School of Architecture and Engineering* but the bankruptcy of his publisher prevented more than five of the projected twelve numbers from appearing. This venture cost Nicholson a great deal of money and as a result he moved to Morpeth in Northumberland in 1829 to occupy a small property he had inherited. In 1832 he returned to educational work, opening a school in Newcastle-upon-Tyne. This does not however appear to have been financially successful for in July, 1834 a local subscription raised £320 on his behalf. His abilities were nevertheless recognized by his fellow townsmen who elected him in 1835 president of the Newcastle Society for the Promotion of the Fine Arts.

He died in Carlisle on 18 June 1844 and is buried in Christ Church graveyard. Twice married, he was survived by his son Michael Angelo by his first wife and by his second wife, son and daughter.

Nicholson's work as an architect produced a number of interesting projects — Castleton House and Corby Castle, both near Carlisle; additions to the University of Glasgow; a coffee-house at Paisley and the layout for the new town of Ardrossan in Ayrshire. It is, however, through his publications that he is best known. His devotion to mathematics, and his proven ability in the subject, enabled him both to simplify old methods and to invent new ones. These he applied to building and formulated rules which enabled joiners to make handrails more simply and with less wastage of material. For this work the Society of Arts awarded him their gold medal in 1814.

He was the first to describe, both in text and illustration, methods for hanging doors and shutters and he showed that Greek mouldings were, in fact, conic sections and the volutes of Ionic capitals were logarithmic spirals. His invention of the centrolinead, used in the preparation of perspective drawings, gained him a silver medal in 1815 from the Society of Arts.

Apart from the publications previously mentioned Nicholson wrote articles for Reeves's *Cyclopedia* on architecture, masonry, carpentry, perspective and projection and also on carpentry for Brewster's *Edinburgh Encyclopedia*. He prepared many of his own plates for these works. His best known publication is, however, *The New and Improved Practical Builder and Workman's Companion*. This incorporated all his innovation described above with many more in both text and fine copper plates. Originally published in 1823, the work was reprinted in 1837 under the editorship of T. Tredgold, and again in 1847, 1848–50, 1853 and in 1861 with a portrait by William Derby.

1. Masonry

Douglas Garland

COLUMNS

Originally columns were very much a load-bearing feature, and now usually encompass a load-bearing steel or concrete member. When used in this way the well-established practice of working the beds slightly convex is necessary to prevent 'flushing' or 'spalling' of the arrises. Joints should always be raked back, final pointing only being done after the stone has accepted its full loading.

Several methods exist for calculating the entasis, or curve, necessary to prevent the parallel sides of the column from appearing hollow. The Concoid of Nicomedes is the most usual. This system leaves the choice of base dimension and height to the designer; and to achieve an elegant proportion, reference to actual examples in buildings of merit is recommended.

Lathes adapted for and designed for the stone trade, now deal with all circular work. The stone will be sawn to the size required for a column stone, with a small allowance. Steel plates are set into the top and bottom bed to receive the lathe centres, and the corners of the stone are taken off by hand with a pitching tool before placing on the lathe. Even with care it is most unusual for the stone to be perfect in its dimensions and for the steel plates to be precisely at the centre of each bed, and so an allowance is necessary to take up minor discrepancies and to allow the operator, not only to bring the face of the column to its correct profile, but also to trim the beds to ensure that they are perfectly parallel.

The decorative vertical flutes cut into the face of the column have several forms, the most common being a simple hollow terminating at its extremes with a rounded 'stop end'.

Because of the entasis introduced into a column, each stone forming the column will have a slightly smaller top than bottom bed, and a curve to its face. Therefore the machine working the flutes, either by planing or grinding, will need adjustment by hand to bring the flutes to a true line.

The sub-division of a column into individual stones will usually be determined by the available bed heights of the chosen stone. Examples of stone columns worked in other than their natural bed can be seen, used particularly for decorative effect, in interior situations. When used on the exterior of a building in either a load-bearing or semi-load-bearing situation, however, the natural bed is used.

PILASTERS

Of classical origins the pilaster is now a common feature in stone buildings. The term has come to describe any projection or thickening of the wall face which is not substantial enough to be called a buttress. While mainly decorative a pilaster

11

CHAPTER VI.

———◆———

MASONRY.

MASONRY, practically considered, is the art of shaping and uniting stones for the various purposes of building. It, therefore, includes the hewing of stones into the various forms required, and the union of them, either by joints, level, perpendicular, or otherwise; or by the aid of cement, or of iron, lead, &c. The operations of masonry require much practical dexterity, with some skill in geometry and mechanics.

In treating on this subject, it will be necessary to divide it into several branches, and first we shall notice that local necessity was its parent, and that the fluctuations of the art have always marked the rise and fall of empires.

In Egypt, Greece, and Italy, the greater works of masonry included some which were almost incredible in their extent; and their materials were equally so, if considered in detail. These countries seem to have been favoured in every way, in order to be eternized; for they abounded in porphyries and marbles, which promoted magnificence in their structures, without peculiar contrivance in arrangement. Modern masonry consists rather in the piling stones to a great height, than in covering an extent of plan; but this requires equal skill, if it be not productive of equal magnificence.

V.—ORNAMENTAL MASONRY.

COLUMNS.—These comprise, generally, a conoidal shaft, with a small diminution towards their upper diameter, amounting, generally, to about one-sixth less than the lower diameter. The proportion of columns, from the Egyptians, varied but little; the columns of this people, in their larger temples, amounting only to about four and a half diameters in height. Those of Greece, as in the *Parthenon*, at Athens, are little more than five. In the best Roman examples, the proportion was increased to upwards of seven diameters. The columns of *all* the Grecian remains are fluted, though in different manners. The Doric shafts have their flutes in very flat segments, finished to an arris: sometimes flutings of the semi-ellipsis shape, with fillets, were adopted.

The genius of an architect is generally displayed in the application of columns. The Greeks surrounded their public walks with them; their porticos carried this kind of splendour to its highest pitch; as in them may be found the whole syntax of architecture and masonry. To construct a temple, in the Greek manner, required the greatest taste and judgment, combined with a perfect knowledge of architecture. The Parthenon, at Athens, exhibits, or rather did exhibit, the most elaborate display of masonry in the world.

The comparatively perfect state in which the monuments of Greece remain, is a proof of the great judgment with which they were constructed. The famous Temple of Minerva would have been entire to this day, if it had not been destroyed by a bomb. The *Propylea*, which was used as a magazine for powder, was struck by lightning and blown up. The Temple of Theseus, having escaped accidental destruction, is almost as entire as when first erected. The little choragic monument of Thrasybulus, as well as that of Lysicrates, are also entire. These instances should impress on modern architects the utility of employing large blocks, and of uniting them

strengthens a wall if correctly bonded. However, if the design and execution of the bonding is of poor quality, the wall may be weakened.

The general coursing heights given to the adjacent ashlar are carried through the pilaster and the length of stones chosen to bond should be generous. The inclusion of L-shaped stones at internal and external angles, alternating with normal coursing is of further value. With the exception of the plinth and capping courses to the pilaster, the remainder may be quite plain and both the rectangular or 'L'-shaped ones cut by diamond saw. A useful refinement of the diamond saw is the twin blade type, the blades of which can be inclined to any desired angle. Thus with one blade set vertical at the appropriate height above the table, and the other set horizontal to this height the waste stone is removed in one pass of the table.

If further decoration is required to a pilaster, the sunk and moulded panel is the most popular. The stones to be sunk and moulded would each have this information detailed on the card allocated to it in the normal production sequence, together with details of the required moulds and templates. The face to be sunk would then be reduced on a grinding machine. If shaped wheels were available to the reverse of the required moulding, these could be run either immediately, or after the face was sunk. Alternatively it may be economic to retain the wide grinding wheel in position on the machine until all the stones required are dealt with, and only then change the wheel to a moulding one. The factor to be decided would be which labour — changing the stone or changing the machine part — was most practical and economical in the situation.

PARAPETS

Because of its exposed position in the upper portion of the building the design, selection of stone, execution and fixing of a parapet calls for the greatest care. Parapets were traditionally used to form a final stabilizing element to the cornice. Although part of that duty may now be taken by the plates and bolts that attach the stones to the steel and concrete framed structure, the relationship of the plinth course to the cornice, in the form of bonding and attachment with non-ferrous fixings, is still important.

The upper course of a parapet is now termed a capping or a coping, rather than a cornice. Its central course is a subject for a wide variation of design ranging from a solid form with sunk panels, to the elegant rows of circular balusters, with their intermediate baluster die-stones, which are probably the most commonly seen throughout our cities.

The plinth course is ideally suited to production on the planing machine, especially if carrying several moulded members. This also applies to the capping

with the greatest accuracy; without which masonry is not superior to brick-laying. The core of the rubble-work of the Grecian walls is impenetrable to a tool; which is an additional proof of the care which was taken in cementing their masonry.

The joining of columns in free-stone, has been found more difficult than in marble; and the practice used by the French masons, to avoid the failure of the two arrisses of the joint, might be borrowed with success for con-structing columns of some of our softer kinds of free-stone. It consists in taking away the edge of the joints, by which means a groove is formed at every one throughout the whole column. This method is employed only in plain shafts. It appears to have been occasionally used by the antients, though for a different purpose; *viz.* to admit the shaft to be adorned with flowers, and other insignia, on the occasion of their shows and games. In the French capital, they affix rows of lamps on their columns, making use of these grooves to adjust them regularly, which produces a very good effect.

The shafts of columns, in large works, intended to be adorned by flutes, are erected plain, and the flutings chiselled out afterwards. The antients commonly formed the two extreme ends of the fluting previously, as may be seen in the remaining columns of the Temple of Apollo, in the Island of Delos; a practice admitting great accuracy and neatness. The finishing the detail of both sculpture and masonry on the building itself, was an universal practice among the antients: they raised their columns first in rough blocks, on them they placed the architraves and friezes, and sur-mounted the whole by the cornice; finishing down only such parts as could not be got at in the building; hence, perhaps, in some measure, arose that striking proportion of parts, together with the beautiful curvature and finish given to all the profiles in Grecian buildings.

PILASTERS, in modern design, are frequently very capriciously applied. They are vertical shafts of square-edged stone, having but a small projec-tion, with capitals and bases like columns; they are often placed by us on the face of the wall, and with a cornice over them. In Greek architecture,

course, with its 'weathered' sloping upper surface, moulded sides, and drip details to the bottom bed.

If circular work is required then the size of the balusters will be appropriate for a small lathe, with hand held tools resting on a fixed bar adjusted to the required distance from the cutting point. A template of the required profile is fixed immediately to the rear of the stone to be turned and by means of calipers, reverses, and with an 'eye' — which only experience can develop — the operator with skill, and not a little strength, brings the stone to its required form.

At intermediate positions with a balustrade are baluster die-stones. They begin, finish and generally divide the work, giving strength and beauty. On to these were worked half balusters in the solid. It has become generally accepted practice to produce the half baluster by cutting it from a whole circular one and to attach it to the die by means of non-ferrous fixings set in epoxy resin.

ASHLAR

Early buildings with walls formed of inner and outer skins of ashlar with a central core of rubble were usually of random coursing. Smaller stones were selected and dressed on five sides, with the back left rough, and the irregular depth of each stone assisted in the bonding of two skins to the central core.

The introduction of the reciprocating frame saw with the facility to slab large blocks mechanically, reduced the masons' task to working the beds and joints, together with correcting the sawn face — as was often necessary. Further progress to the circular carborundum and diamond saws has made the production of ashlar stones an entirely mechanical process. A modern ashlar plant has saws whose twin blades, set at a predetermined width, can deal with the required height whilst a second pair of blades trims the length. Four or five drills can be aligned to cut the holes for lifting pins, and the eventual non-ferrous fixings that will hold the stone firmly in its final position in a building. Even in modest workshops with less sophisticated facilities the production of ashlar stones is no longer a mason's task.

A familiar term in current use is 'ashlar cladding' where the main structure is either brick, steel or concrete, and the stonework is attached to it as a decorative finish. The selection of the appropriate fixing depends on the material to which the stone is to be attached, the thickness of the stone, and on the mason's individual preference (Figure 1.1).

Thus ashlar has developed into a regular course of stonework, each stone of predetermined dimension, and with the necessary recesses for non-ferrous fixings accurately positioned. The finish to facework varies from the hand-

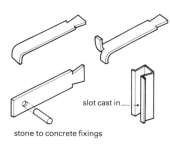

slot cast in

stone to concrete fixings

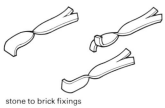

stone to brick fixings

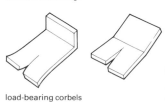

load-bearing corbels

Figure 1.1

they are to be met with commonly on the ends of the walls, behind the columns, in which application their face was made double the width of their sides; their capitals differing materially from those of the accompanying columns, and somewhat larger at bottom than at top, but without any *entasis* or swell.

PARAPETS.—Parapets are very ornamental to the upper part of an edifice. They were used by the Greeks and Romans, and are composed of three parts; viz. the *plinth*, which is the blocking course to the cornice; the *shaft* or *die*, which is the part immediately above the plinth; and a cornice, which is on its top, and projects in its moulding, sufficiently to carry off the rain-water from the shaft and plinth. In buildings of the Corinthian style, the shaft of the parapet is perforated in the parts immediately over the apertures in the elevation, and balustrade-enclosures are inserted in the perforations. The architects have devised the parapet with reference to the roof of the building which it is intended to obscure.

ASHLARING is a term used by masons to designate the plain stone work of the front of a building, in which all that is regarded is getting the stone to a smooth face, called its *plain work*. The courses should not be too high, and the joints should be crossed regularly, which will improve its appearance, and add to its solidity.

CILLS.—These belong to the apertures of the doors and windows, at the bottom of which they are fixed; their thickness varies, but is commonly about one inch and a half; they are also fluted on their under edges, and sunk on their upper sides, projecting about two inches, in general, beyond the ashlaring.

CORNICE.—This forms the crown to the ashlaring, at the summit of a building; it is frequently the part which is marked particularly by the architect, to designate the particular order of his work; hence *Doric, Ionic,* and *Corinthian,* cornices are employed, when, perhaps, no column of either is used in the work; so that the cornice alone designates the particular style of the building. In working the cornice, the top or upper side should be splayed away towards its front edge, that it may more readily carry off the

dressed finish to either a 'sawn' or a 'fine rubbed' finish. Compression or movement joints are recommended at each storey height. These take up the movement of the building frame, or backing, and relieve pressure to the face stonework. The joints are filled with a comparatively soft and elastic mastic compound in place of the normal mortar, and should be positioned immediately below the bonder or supported course. It is important in this last process that the stone and structural expansion joints coincide. As a general guide, in continuous lengths of cladding the provision of open vertical joints at approximately 8 m intervals should prove adequate to allow for possible thermal movement. The joints are sealed with a material that has elastic and adhesive qualities; polysulphide compounds are particularly suitable.

One general feature common to all ashlar stones is the setting of them in their natural bed in order that the natural strata of the stone is in compression.

SILLS

The usual design for a window sill is a splayed or chamfered top, terminated at each end by a raised stooling forming a level bed to receive the jamb stones. Wide windows requiring mullions also need a raised stooling. For many years the planing machine was used as a means to speed production, the operator would cut a recess at the beginning and end of a chamfer or splay to provide a starting and finishing point for the machine tool. The introduction of the grinding machine with either a carborundum or diamond wheel virtually eliminated this process as the grinding wheel, once set at the required angle, is brought down in the correct position on the sill to make its own entry, and at the end of its pass leaves only a small concave part for the mason's attention. In a similar way throatings to the underside, and grooves for waterbars at the top bed, are ground out by wheels of appropriate shapes.

In position the sill is subject to load stress from the jambs at its extreme ends. To avoid breakage, it is usual to place a mortar bed only under the portion accepting the loading, and to point up the remainder after loading is accepted.

CORNICE

Depending on the type of stone and the design selected, a cornice may need to be worked with its bed plane vertical, or 'end bedded'. A pronounced bed strata running through an overhanging feature such as a dentil would cause a weakness and eventual failure if the normal bed plane were used. Local knowledge of each particular stone is best sought in this situation.

Whatever size or design, the basic moulding to this course, including the

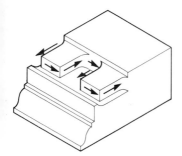

Figure 1.2 *Modillion cornice showing path of milling machine cutter*

weathered upper surface, is best dealt with on the fixed head planing machine. The larger varieties need a machine with a side tool box in addition to the main top one. Further embellishments such as dentils and modillions are usually worked by masons, but the milling machine has been adapted for working with stone in the more sophisticated machine workshops. Its rotating cutter can be induced to move at 90° to the main line of direction thus eliminating all handwork, with the exception of the internal angles which a rotating cutter leaves circular (Figure 1.2).

The cornice is subject to further enrichment by repetitive foliage carvings on the cyma-recta and cyma-reversa mouldings and the ever popular 'egg and dart' (symbol of life and death) cut into the ovolo. These are hand cut, and the carver prepares a stencil to aid the accurate and speedy marking-on of long runs. A saddle joint is necessary if the upper weathered surface is not covered, which would add to the cost as it inhibits the sweep of the planing machine. In the majority of buildings the cornice is now lead or asphalt covered; lead is preferred. It should be dressed over the nose of the cornice and extend a further 5 mm to form a drop at the extreme edge of this member. Asphalt cannot be brought down over the nose and has a marked tendency to lift at the extreme edge exposing the nose moulding and forming a moisture trap. If asphalt is used a lead strip should still be dressed over the nose, and brought back into a keyed groove run in the weathered surface to hold the asphalt.

The cornice is seldom a self-balancing member in modern structures being secured by metal fixings, introduced into either its joints or top bed, which bolt it securely to the main frame and run in neat cement grout when positioned.

RUSTICATING

The addition of the fillet or splay to give the 'rustic' effect is best applied by a grinding machine, when the stone has been sawn to its correct dimensions. If the square or rectangular form is chosen this should be placed on the top edge of each stone (Figure 1.3(a)). If detailed as at Figure 1.3(b), water is likely to enter the joint.

Added emphasis of the main wall surface by this treatment usually means that additional texturing is required to the faces of the quoin stones. The most popular texture is 'rock faced' in which the stone is cut full on its face and the mason, using a pitching tool for the beds and joints, makes a rough irregular surface. Alternatives are 'reticulated' and 'vermiculated' patterns in which bands of stone are left plain and the panels between are sunk and left rough. The reticulated pattern has a polygonal effect and the vermiculated, has irregular curved panels. Both these textures are hand worked.

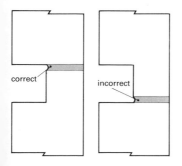

correct   incorrect

Figure 1.3(a) Figure 1.3(b)

ARCHITRAVES

The decorative mouldings to the architrave are usually attached to an adjoining stone in the natural form of bonding. By selecting stones of similar size they can be grouped and produced together, first by sawing to the required size (but left over long if to be put onto a planing machine), and then either by grinding or planing to profile, with the internal mitres finished by hand.

In a restoration programme the projecting mouldings such as architraves are among the first features needing replacement. They can often be cut back carefully and pieced in to the required depth without disturbing the main bonding to the stonework – the line of jointing to the pieces coinciding with the internal lines to mouldings.

Archivolts may not necessarily be attached to the archstones. If worked independently they are suitable for production by a planing machine with a secondary table which, by attachment to an off-centre pivot, describes an arc and can deal with curved mouldings. These machines are not found in every stoneworks but are invaluable where the harder range of stones is worked.

BLOCKING COURSE

Similar in function to a parapet for stabilizing the cornice and terminating the upper order of a building, blocking courses vary greatly in detail from a plain unadorned stone to highly decorative examples with mouldings and sunk panels.

The blocking course receives the lead or asphalt covering to the cornice upper surface, and leadwork from roof or gutter detail at its rear. Its final stability is therefore of particular importance. Any of the several forms of building movement will be reflected at this level, and adequate anchorage both to the cornice and to each other is essential. Replacement of all or part of this course can only be undertaken with a full understanding of the upper courses and their method of anchorage. With its constant height and width, this course is a good subject for modern stone-working machinery.

FASCIA

As with the architrave this term has acquired a slightly different meaning from its origins in the classic order; its most common use now is for the area over large windows. In this position the structural weight is carried by steel or concrete head courses and the fascia attached by load-bearing fixings. The fascia usually projects from the main ashlar face; either at the bottom bed, or by means of a short section of ashlar, detailed at the bottom of the stone, and the projection

water.   At the joint of each of the stones of the cornice, throughout the whole length of the building, that part of each stone which comes nearest at the joints, should be left projecting upwards a small way; a process by workmen called *saddling* the joints; this is done to keep the rain-water from entering them, and washing out the cement.   These joints should be chased or indented, and such chases filled with lead, and even when dowels of iron are employed, they should be fixed by melted lead also.

RUSTICATING, in architecture and masonry, consists in forming horizontal sinkings, or grooves, in the stone ashlaring of an elevation, intersected by vertical or cross ones; perhaps invented to break the plainness of the wall, and denote more obviously the bond of the stones.   It is often formed by splaying away the edge of the stone only; in this style, the groove forms the elbow of a geometrical square.   Many architects omit the vertical grooves in rustics, so that their walls present an uniform series of horizontal sinkings.   There are many examples, both antient and modern, of each kind.

ARCHITRAVES adorn the apertures of a building, projecting somewhat from the face of the ashlaring; they have their faces sunk with mouldings, and also their outside edges.   When they traverse the curve of an arch, they are called *archivolts*.   They give beauty to the exterior of a building, and the best examples are among the Greek and Roman buildings.

BLOCKING COURSE.—This is a course of stone, traversing the top of the cornice to which it is fixed; it is commonly, in its height, equal to the projection of the cornice.   It is of great utility in giving support to the latter by its weight, and to which it adds grace.   At the same time, it admits of gutters behind it to convey the superfluous water from the covering of the building.   The joints should always cross those of the cornice, and should be plugged with lead, or cramped on their upper edges with iron. The Romans often dove-tailed such courses of stone.

FASCIA is a plain course of stone, generally about one foot in height, projecting about an inch before the face of the ashlaring, or in a line with the plinth of the building: it is fluted or *throated* on its upper edge, to prevent the water from running over the ashlaring; its upper edge is sloped with its drip taken away from a bed joint. If the normal ashlar face is to be resumed above the fascia the upper surface will need weathering to direct water away from the bed joint.

This comparatively simple course, whether built in or attached to a structure, is repetitive and easily produced. The constant height and thickness is ideal for repetitive sawing to the initial rectangle, and further mouldings or sinkings can be applied by a multi-headed machine with a series of grinding wheels, each set to carry out one operation.

PLINTHS

The thickening of the wall at plinth level originally helped to spread the loading of the wall on to the foundations. The plinth is subject to abrasive wear from passing traffic and chemical action from the ground, and the upper weathered or moulded surface to droplets of water from the drip courses at various levels above. The best quality stone should be used, even if this necessitates a change from the stone used elsewhere in the building.

The modern departure from load-bearing stone walls to cladding has somewhat diminished the significance of the plinth, but attack from soluble salts and abrasion still occurs. In common with most modern features the need for a constant depth and height of stonework gives the diamond sawing schedules a regular pattern and simplifies production. Mouldings are applied after sawing either by a planing or a grinding machine, as appropriate, with the occasional break in the building line forming an external or internal mitre for hand dressing.

IMPOSTS

The impost is a type of capital and is usually inserted at the top of a pier to an opening. The top bed is level and not to be confused with the springing stones or skewbacks which commence an arch. The moulding is an overhanging one with a weathered top splay back to the building or wall line. In machine production impost stones are worked upside down to give free access to the mouldings. These are applied by a planing machine to the length of the stone, the short return end being dressed by hand.

ARCHES

When stones are placed in an arch they are in compression from their side joints. For this reason it is accepted practice to select the stone with the bed normal to the curve of the arch; the stone is then described as 'end bedded' (Figure 1.4).

Dotted lines indicate natural bed of stone

Figure 1.4

22

downwards for the same purpose. It is commonly inserted above the windows of the ground-stories; *viz.* between them and those of the principal story.

A PLINTH, in masonry, is the first stone inserted above the ground: it is in one or more pieces, according to its situation, projecting beyond the walls above it about an inch, with its projecting edge sloped downwards, or moulded, to carry off the water that may fall on it.

IMPOSTS.—These are insertions of stone, with their front faces generally moulded; when left plain, they are prepared in a similar manner to the facias. They form the spring-stones to the arches in the apertures of a building, and are of the greatest utility.

VIII.—DESCRIPTION OF THE SECTIONS OF ARCHES.
(Plate LXXVI.)

To describe a Parabolic Arch, the span and height of the arch being given—

Method 1.—*Figures* 1 and 2.—Let AB be the span: Bisect AB in the point C, and draw CD perpendicular to AB. Make CD equal to the height of the arch. Produce CD to E; making DE equal DC, join EA, EB. In AE set off the distances A1, A2, A3, &c., so that the parts may be all equal; and, in EB, set off the parts E1, E2, E3, &c., so that the differences may be all equal. Join the corresponding points 1,1; 2,2; 3,3; &c. and the intersections of the several lines will form the parabola required.

Fig. 1 is adapted to a segment, where the rise of the arch is considerable. Fig. 2 is adapted to the head of an aperture, where the radius of curvature of the arch is very great, or where the deflection of the curve from a straight line is but small.

Method 2.—*Figure* 3.—AB and CD being as before, draw DE parallel to AB, and AE parallel to CD. Divide AC into any number of equal parts, and AE into the same number. From the points 1, 2, 3, &c. in AE, draw

23

PLATE LXXVI

MASONRY.

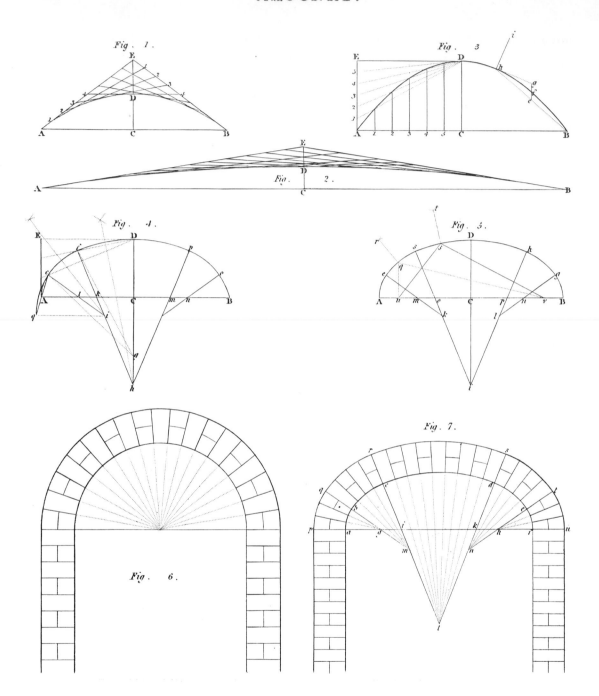

lines to D, intersecting perpendiculars to A, drawn from the points 1, 2, 3, &c., in AC. Through the points of intersection draw the curve AD. In the same manner draw the curve BD.

To draw a straight line perpendicular to the curve from a given point h, (*fig.* 3,) as a joint.

In the curve take any other point, as B, at pleasure, and join B*h*. Bisect B*h* in *e*, and draw *eg* perpendicular to AB, intersecting the curve in the intermediate point *f*. Make *fg* equal to *fe*; join *eg*, and draw *hi* perpendicular to *eg*; then *hi* will be the joint required.

A PRACTICAL METHOD *of describing the* CURVE *of an* ARCH, *and of drawing the joints.* (*Figure* 4.)

Let AB be the axis major. Bisect AB in C, and draw CD perpendicular to AB, and make CD equal to the semi-axis minor. Draw DE and AE, respectively parallel to AB and CD. Divide AC and AE each into three equal parts. Produce DC to *g*, and make C*g* equal to CD. Draw lines from the points of division in AE to the point D, to intersect other lines in *ef*, drawn from *g* through the points of division in AC; then, *e* and *f* will be points in the curve.

Bisect *f*D by a perpendicular, meeting D*g* produced in *h*, and join *hf*, intersecting AC in *k*. Bisect *ef* by a perpendicular, meeting *gh* in *i*. Draw *iq* parallel to AB. From *i*, with the radius *if*, describe the arc *fq*. Join *q*A, and produce *q*A to meet the arc *fq*: join the point of meeting, and the point *i* intersecting AB in *l*.

From *h*, with the radius *h*D, describe an arc D*f*; from *i*, with the radius *if*, describe an arc *fe*; and from *l*, with the radius *lc*, describe the arc *c*A.

By placing the centres in the same position, the other half, DB, of the semi-elliptic arc, ADB, will be described.

To DRAW *a* TANGENT *to a semi-elliptic arch, the axis-major being horizontal.* (*Figure* 5.)

Find the focii *u* and *v*. Let *s* be a point in the curve: join *su* and *sv*.

Draw st, bisecting the angle usv, and st will be the joint required. In the same manner any other joint, qr, will be found.

Or, by finding the position of the centres, and that of the lines for describing the curve, as in *fig.* 4, the joints may be drawn, as qr from k, st from i.

Figure 6 is a semi-circular arch, with the joints marked out.

Figure 7 a semi-elliptic arch, with the joints also marked out, and the centres for drawing them as before.

IX.—STONE-CUTTING, &c.

A SEMI-CIRCULAR RIGHT ARCH. *(Plate* LXXVII.*)*

LET ABCD, *(figure* 4,*)* be the plan of the arch. Divide the opening into two equal parts by the perpendicular EF; from E, with the radius of the intrados, describe the semi-circle AFB; and, from the same point E, with the radius of the extrados, describe the semi-circle GHI. Divide the arch GHI, of the extrados, into five equal parts, and draw the radiating lines ko, lp, mq, nr, for the joints, which will form the heads of the arch-stones.

The horizontals and perpendiculars are not drawn as in the last example, because the stones may be formed without making a mould for each stone, by having the head of the arch-stone and thickness of the wall only, in the following manner:

Choose a stone of sufficient length to answer the thickness of the wall, and of such breadth and depth as to answer the other dimensions. Reduce the side intended for the intrados to a plane surface, on which draw the two parallel lines ab, cd, *(fig.* 1,*)* distant from each other the space between the joints of the intrados; then square one end, as, ac to $abcd$, and parallel to ac draw bd, at a distance equal to the thickness of the wall. Square the other end of the stone, and on the head apply the mould $pqml$, *(fig.* 4,*)* so that its extremities pq may coincide with ca, *(fig.* 1,*)* when applied to one head, and with bd when applied to the other; then hollow out the intrados, and cut the joints or beds according to the traces, as exhibited at *figure* 2.

PLATE LXXVII

MASONRY.

Fig.1.

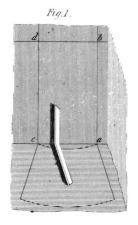

Fig.2.

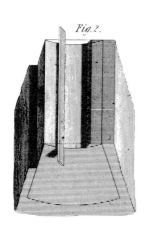

Fig.3.

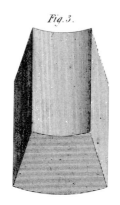

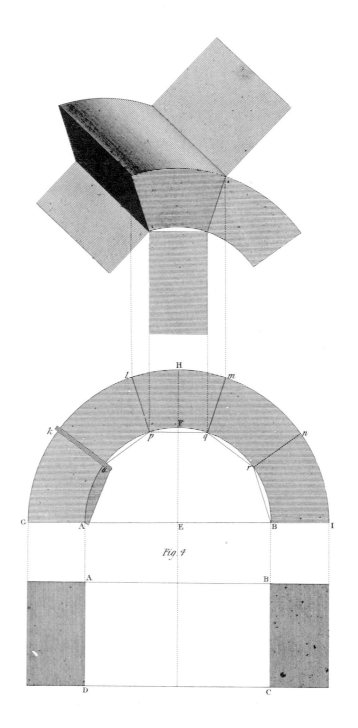

Fig. 4

MASONRY.

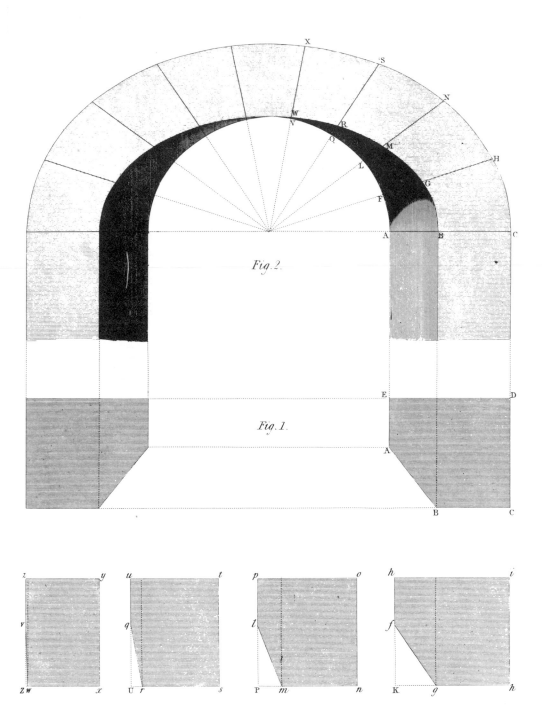

Fig. 2.

Fig. 1.

PLATE LXXIX.

MASONRY.

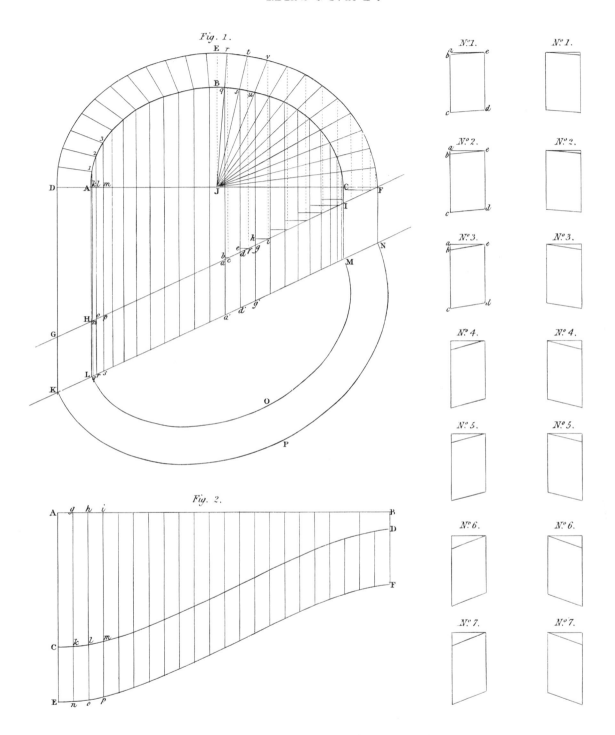

Fig. 1.

Fig. 2.

Nº 1.

Nº 1.

Nº 2.

Nº 2.

Nº 3.

Nº 3.

Nº 4.

Nº 4.

Nº 5.

Nº 5.

Nº 6.

Nº 6.

Nº 7.

Nº 7.

Figure 3 exhibits a stone entirely finished, and all the others are formed after the same manner ; but, instead of forming the heads on the stones themselves, a bevel, such as shewn in *fig.* 4, *k o* A′, may be used with advantage.

The higher part of *fig.* 4 represents an arch-stone, accompanied with the moulds of each side, which will explain the application more particularly.

The middle part of *figure* 4 shows the arch complete, with all the stones supporting one another.

THE ELLIPTICAL ARCH, WITH SPLAYED JAMBS. *(Plate* LXXVIII.*)*

To find the angles of the joints formed by the front and intrados of an Elliptical Arch, erected on splayed jambs.

Figure 1, on the plate, is the plan of the Imposts.

Figure 2, the Elevation.

The impost A′B′C′D′E′ is the first bed ; *f g h i k*, the second ; *l m n o p*, the third ; *q r s t u*, the fourth ; *v w x y z*, the fifth : The other beds are the same in reverse order. The breadth of all these beds is the same as that of the arch itself. The lengths *k* K, *n* P, *s* U, *x* Z, of the front lines of the moulds of the beds are respectively equal to the lines HF, NL, SQ, XV, on the face of the arch. And also, *h g, n m, s r, x w,* on the fronts of the moulds equal to the corresponding distances HG, NM, SR, XW, on the face of the arch. The distances *k f, p l, u q, z v,* are each equal to the perpendicular part AE of the impost.

TO FIND THE JOINTS OF AN ARCH IN MASONRY.

Let ABC *(Plate* LXXIX.*)* be the *intrados,* and DEF be the *extrados,* of the arch. Draw DK, AL, CM, FN, perpendicular to the base DF, of the arch. Make the angle DFG equal to the angle which the wall makes with the jambs of the arch, and draw KN, at a distance from GF, equal to the thickness of the wall; then the plan of the wall is represented by GFNK; the abutment on one side, or springing base, is represented by GHLK, and that on the other side by FIMN. Let J be the centre of the given arch.

Divide ABC, the intrados of the arch, into as many equal parts as the arch-stones are in number. Through the points 1, 2, 3, &c., draw lines $1q$, $2r$, $3s$, &c., cutting the one side KN of the wall at q, r, s, &c., and the other side at n, o, p, &c.

In *figure* 2, draw the straight line AB, and make AB equal to the stretch out of the arc ABC, and let Ag, gh, hi, be equal to the distances on the arc ABC. Draw the perpendiculars ACE, gkn, hlo, &c. Make AC equal to AH, *figure* 1; gk equal to kn, *figure* 1; hl equal to lo, *figure* 1; im equal to mp, *figure* 1; and so on: then through the points C, k, l, m, &c., to D, draw the curve line CD. Likewise make AE, gn, ho, ip, &c. respectively equal to AL, kq, ms, &c. *(fig.* 1.); then, through all the points E, n, o, p, &c. to F, draw the curve EF, which will complete the whole developement of the intrados of the arch.

The parts $CknE$, $klon$, $lmpo$, &c., are the heads, or exact forms, of the ends of the stones of the arch, and therefore the moulds of the ends of the arch-stones must be made to correspond to these figures.

To find the bevels of the joints of the stones.—Let q, s, u, *(fig.* 1.) be the points of division on the intradosal line, next to the crown of the arch.

From the centre J, and through the points q, s, u, &c., draw the lines Jr, Jt, Jv, &c., then qr, st, uv, &c. will represent the joints of the arch. From the points q, s, u, &c., draw qa, sd, ug, &c., parallel to AH, cutting GF in the points a, d, g, &c.; and, from the points r, t, v, &c., draw rc, tf, vi, &c., parallel to AH, cutting GF in the points c, f, i, &c. Draw bc, ef, hi, &c. parallel to DF.

Then, to find the bed of the stone answering to the joint qr, draw the straight line abc, No. 1, and make ab equal to ba, *figure* 1. Draw ae perpendicular to ac, and make ae equal to qr, *figure* 1; and make ac, No. 1, equal to GK or HI, &c. In No. 1, draw cd parallel to be, and ed parallel to ac; then will the figure be formed of the bed of the stone.

PLATE LXXX.

MASONRY.

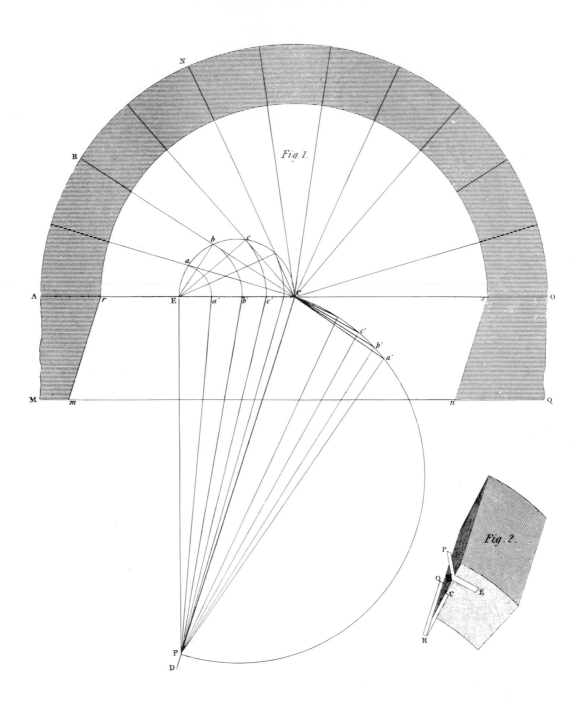

Fig. 1.

Fig. 2.

In the same manner we may form No. 2, to the joint *st*; and No. 3, to the joint *uv*; and so on.

Nos. 1, 2, 3, 4, 5, &c. are the forms of the moulds for the beds of the right-hand arch-stones; and Nos. 1, 2, 3, &c. reversed on the right-hand, are the moulds for the beds of the arch-stones on the left-hand: viz. No. 1, and No. 1, are the two bed-moulds next to, and on each side of, the crown; No. 2, and No. 2, are the second equi-distant bed-moulds from the crown.

In working the stones, the beds ought to be numbered the same as the moulds, in order that the arch-stones may be readily applied together.

The stone-cutter may first work one of the beds, and cut the form of the mould upon the bed of the stone.

OBLIQUE CIRCULAR ARCH. *(Plate* LXXX.*)*

Let ABNO *(figure* 1.*)* be the face of an oblique arch, of which *rsmn* is the plan; AM*rm*, OQ*sn*, the imposts; *rm* and *sn* being the jambs.

Suppose, then, that the obliquity of the arch were given, with the number of stones requisite for its construction, the figure of the stones may be obtained by the following construction:—

Find the centre C, of the span *rs,* which join with the points of division in the arch, by the straight lines CB, CN, &c. At the point C, in *rs,* make the angle *r*CD equal to the given obliquity; in CD take any point, as P, and from P, draw PE, meeting *r*C perpendicularly in E: Upon EC describe the semi-circle E*abc*C, cutting the joints produced in the points *a, b, c:* with the distances E*a*, E*b*, E*c*, describe arcs meeting EC in the points *a', b', c'*; join P*a'*, P*b'*, and P*c'*, then will P*a'r*, P*b'r*, and P*c'r*, be the angles of the faces of the stones to which they are referred.

Again, to find the angle of the bed: upon PC describe the semi-circle P*a''b''c''*C; and, from C, with the distances C*a*, C*b*, C*c*, cut the semi-circle in *a'' b'' c''*; join P*a''*, P*b''*, and P*c''*, then PC*a''*, PC*b''*, and PC*c''*, will be the angles of the bed.

CALCULATION.—In the triangle PCE we have given the angle at C equal to the obliquity, and the side, CP, any magnitude at pleasure; hence the sides PE and EC can be found: then, in the triangle ECa, we have given the angle at C, and the side EC to find Ea equal to Ea'; lastly, in the triangle EPa' we have given the sides PE, Ea', to find the angle Pa'E, which is the angle made by the face of the stone and its bed.

The general formula is cot. req. ang. $=$ cot. obliquity $\times$ sin. $\frac{180° \times m}{n}$, where n is the number of stones in the arch, and m any multiplier in the natural series, 1, 2, 3, &c.

The angle formed by two contiguous boundaries of the bed is found exactly as the last.

The formula is cos. req. ang. $=$ cos. obliquity $\times$ cos. $\frac{180° \times m}{n}$.

As a particular example, suppose the obliquity to be 73°, and the number of stones 11, and the respective angles will be exhibited in the following Table :—

	Divisions of the Arch.	Face Angles.	Bed Angles.
1	16°,, 21',, 49$\frac{1}{11}$''	85°,, 4',, 37''	73°,, 42',, 29''
2	32 ,, 43 ,, 38$\frac{2}{11}$	80 ,, 36 ,, 52	75 ,, 45 ,, 41
3	49 ,, 5 ,, 27$\frac{3}{11}$	76 ,, 59 ,, 23	78 ,, 57 ,, 42
4	65 ,, 27 ,, 16$\frac{4}{11}$	74 ,, 27 ,, 31	83 ,, 1 ,, 25
5	81 ,, 49 ,, 5$\frac{5}{11}$	73 ,, 9 ,, 46	87 ,, 36 ,, 55

The angles for the remaining divisions being the supplements to those in the table, it is unnecessary to give them here.

To apply the formulæ to a numerical Example, we will take the first division in the table—

Formula first : $\begin{cases} \text{Cot. } 73° \dots \dots \dots \dots \text{ Log.} -1.485339 \\ \text{Sin. } 16°,, 21',, 49\frac{1}{11}'' \quad \text{—} \quad 9.449836 \\ \text{Cot. } 85 \,,\, 4 \,,\, 37 \quad .. \quad \text{—} \quad 8.935165 \end{cases}$

Formula second : $\begin{cases} \text{Cot. } 73° \dots \dots \dots \dots \text{ Log.} -1.465935 \\ \text{Cos. } 16°,, 21',, 49\frac{1}{11}'' \quad \text{—} \quad 9.982042 \\ \text{Cos. } 73 \,,\, 42 \,,\, 29 \quad .. \quad \text{—} \quad 9.447977 \end{cases}$

34

PLATE. LXXXI.

MASONRY.

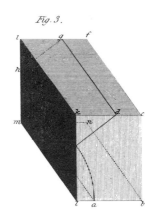

Fig. 3.

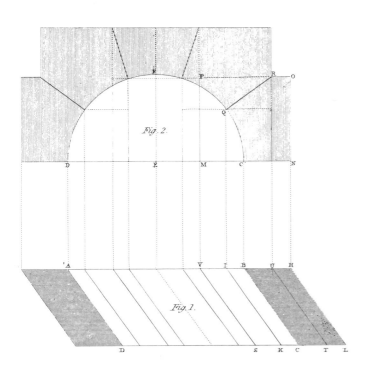

Fig. 2.

Fig. 1.

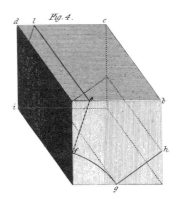

Fig. 4.

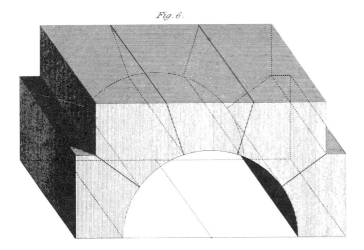

Fig. 6.

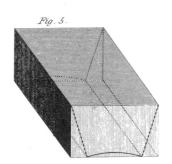

Fig. 5.

35

One of the stones, when finished, will appear as in *figure* 2; where PDE and QRC are the two angles requisite in its construction; PDE being the angle of the face, and QRC the angle of the bed.

———————

OBLIQUE ARCH. *(Plate* LXXXI.*)*

Let ABCD, *(fig.* 1,*)* be the plan, parallel to which draw D'C', *(fig.* 2,*)* on which, as a diameter, describe the semi-circle D'FC'; divide the arc D'FC' into as many equal parts as the proposed number of stones to be in the arch, which, in the present instance, is five. Draw the joints of the face tending to the centre E; draw also the horizontals and perpendiculars of the intradoses marked by dotted lines in the figure.

To form the first arch-stone.—On the impost HBCL make a bed to a stone, that will suit the plan of the bevel HIKL, and work the four adjacent sides each at right angles to HIKL. Apply the mould MNOP *(fig.* 2.*)* to the two ends, so that MN may coincide with KL and IH; the stone being thus guaged, make the upper and under beds parallel to each other. The stone, being now brought to the square, as seen at *fig.* 3, apply the mould C'NORQC', *(fig.* 2.*)* so that NO may coincide with *bc,* and C'N with *ab.* Draw *dg, eh,* and *ap,* parallel to the arris *kl,* then work off the joint *dghe* and the intrados *aehpa,* and the first arch-stone will be finished.

Having made the upper surface of the second stone, as in *fig.* 4, apply to it the mould STUV, *(fig.* 1,*)* forming the parallelogram *abcd, (fig.* 4.*)* Then work off the four adjacent sides to a right angle with it, then guage the stone to its depth, and work off the lower horizontal surface; apply the mould of the head to the ends of the stone, as in working the first arch-stone, and draw the receding lines, then work the joints and the intrados as before, and the stone will be finished.

The key-stone, exhibited in *figure* 5, is wrought in the same manner, and the whole arch, as completed, is represented by *figure* 6.

A SEMI-CIRCULAR ARCHED PASSAGE, BETWEEN TWO SEMI-CIRCULAR ARCHED VAULTS. *(Plate LXXXII.)*

To form the curve of intersection, and cut the stones for this arch.—Let AB be the thickness of the wall in which the passage is to be made, BC and A*t* the two semi-circular arches; EL the opening of the passage; by which the arch GH*c* is described, which divide into any number of parts, at pleasure. Through the points of division draw the lines H*t*, K*p*, *w*N, which, with the semi-circular arches, will form mixt angles, that serve to give the heads of the stones the proper projection, to intersect the semi-circular vaults.

To mark in the plan, the meeting of the passage with the said semi-circular vaults, let fall the perpendiculars CO, SI, QR, &c., which, by their intersecting or meeting the lines RT, IV, OF, &c., will give the points R, I, O, &c., through which trace the curves POR and EFL.

To trace one of the first stones; square the bed and one side of a stone, take the thickness of the wall AB, which lay along the arris of the stone, and, at each of the said lines draw two others on the bed, square to the arris; with a bevel take the mixt angle ZAN, by which dress the two heads, square in themselves; on the upper bed trace the versed sine G*b*, and on the side the sine *bw*, then work out the sheeting with the curve G*w*, and cut the joints square to the sheeting curves; that is, the joint of the semi-circular vault by the mixt angle AN*r*, and that of the passage by the bevel MG*a*.

The other stones are cut exactly in the same manner, excepting that the bevel *n*QC is used to cut the sweep of the second stones, and the bevel *spv* for the key. The rest is so plain as to require no explanation.

PLATE LXXXII.

MASONRY.

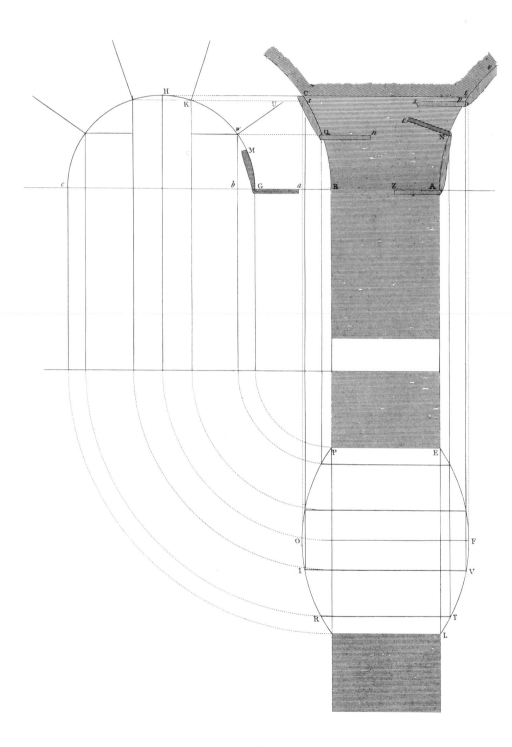

In the many forms of arch one factor remains constant in setting out – the joints are 'normal' to the curve of the arch and radiate from the striking point, or points. This gives the arch its stability and is also aesthetically pleasing. When the arch form is used in the construction of a bridge or flying buttress consideration has to be given to its loading – too heavy a mass over one position may result in lifting elsewhere.

The method of producing archstones varies according to their design. In arches with a constant curve and equal division of joints, each stone is identical to its neighbour. Lengths of stone can be run on the planing machine to the face mould profile, and subsequently cut to the required depth to the arch. In the more complex forms, and with unequal divisions of joints, each stone has to be treated separately. Most workshops have a diamond saw that has a secondary turntable. This upper table can be locked in any position during its rotation in addition to the normal 90°. These intermediate angles allow the chosen angled cut to be achieved without movement of the stone itself. The smooth joints produced by modern saws lack the adhesive qualities of the mason-worked joints, which are dressed slightly hollow and with a degree of roughness. Introducing joggles and roughening the surface at sawn joints will help adhesion.

An example of the different approach necessary in machine production can be seen in the working of stones to an oblique or skew arch. Templates for hand production were designed first to dress the stone to the correct dimension from face to back of arch and then determine its obliquity (Figure 1.5(a)). As it is now possible to profile a stone precisely by machinery, the templates are made to obtain the true profile through the arch and afterwards to adjust the face and back to the correct oblique angle (Figure 1.5(b)).

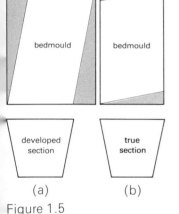

bedmould   bedmould

developed section   true section

(a)   (b)

Figure 1.5

RAKING MOULDINGS

Once a moulding has changed direction as in a pediment its form remains constant. It is at the moment of change that the chief interest lies; the mouldings change profile when developed on a different plane and by either their height or depth being adjusted. Figure 1.6 shows a typical method of working. The stone is sawn on its bottom and top beds with one square and one raking joint; the return end being left overlength to accommodate the break of the planing machine. The initial angle of planing is given at A and completes the raking ogee section; a secondary pass is then made at B when the throat is omitted, so that it does not cut through its own nosing when returned. The return end C and the pocket D are completed by hand dressing. The saving with the use of machinery is obviously greater in a hard stone than in a soft, and so it is very

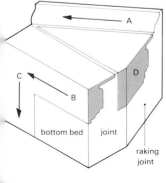

A

C

D

B

bottom bed   joint

raking joint

Figure 1.6

39

X.—RAKING MOULDINGS. *(Plate* LXXXIV.*)*

RAKING MOULDINGS more frequently occur in Masonry than in Joinery: hence we give the following design in consistency with the plan of our work.

Figure 1 is a complete design of a cornice, having part of the ogee level, and part inclined, as happens in the level cornice of a building, with a pediment in the front: $a, b, c, d, e,$ is the moulding at the angle of the break, or projecture, of the pediment, which moulding is given in order to find the right section of the inclined ogee in the pediment. Let af and ee be two parallel lines which terminate the breadth of the raking or inclined moulding; and let ak and el be the parallel lines terminating the breadth of the moulding which is level.

At a convenient place draw $p\,t$ parallel to the edge $a\,k$ of the level ogee: In the given moulding, $a, b, c, d, e,$ take any number of points, $b, c, d,$ and draw $bg,\ ch,\ di,$ parallel to $af,$ or ee; also draw $ap,\ bq,\ cr,\ ds,$ and $et,$ perpendicular to $ak,$ or $el,$ meeting $p\,t$ in the points q, r, s: also, at any convenient distance from $af,$ draw $p't'$ parallel thereto, and transfer the distances $p\,q,$ $q\,r,\ r\,s,\ s\,t,$ to p′q′, q′r′, r′s′, and s′t′, and draw p′A, q′B, r′C, s′D, t′E, perpendiculars to $t'p',$ or $af,$ meeting the lines $af,\ bg,\ ch,\ di,\ e$e, in the points A, B, C, D, and E, and a curve, being drawn through these points, will be the right section of the raking-moulding.

To find the section through mitre t''e *of the two inclined sides,* draw $t''p''$ perpendicular to t''e, and transfer the distances $ts,\ sr,\ rq,\ qp,$ to $t''s'',\ s''r'',$ $r''q'',\ q''p''.$ Draw s″d, r″c, q″b, p″a, perpendicular to $t''p'',$ also draw fa, qb, hc, id, perpendicular to t''e. Then the curve through the points a b c d e will be the common section of the two raking-mouldings, as required.

Figure 2 is a *reverse ogee,* which is traced on the same principle as the ogee, *figure* 1.

PLATE LXXXIV

MASONRY.

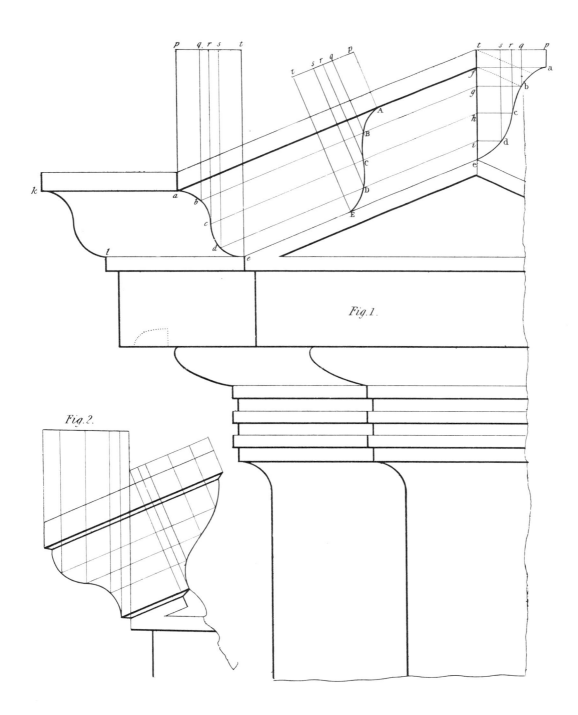

Fig.1.

Fig.2.

much a matter of judgement whether further relieving cuts or profiling is done. The decision will also be influenced by the ratio of hand- to machinery-work in the workshop at the particular time.

TERMS

The majority of terms used in the original text are in common use, with possible local variations. There are some notable exceptions whose common usage demands their inclusion, although the list may not be comprehensive.

Arcade   A range of arches supported on piers or columns, attached to or free-standing from a wall

Arris   The edge formed by the meeting of two surfaces

Bead   A small cylindrical moulding which can be enriched to form the bead and reel decoration

Boasting   A surface finish to masonry achieved with the mallet and the wide boasting chisel

Boning   Testing a surface for accuracy of plane

Bracket   A projecting member designed to support. Built into the wall, its height is usually greater than its width or projection. It is often a subject of decoration and enriched with volutes and scrolls

Canopy   A roof-like covering to a niche

Capital   The crowning feature of a column or pilaster

Cavetto   A simple concave moulding

Cope, to   To split a stone by inserting wedges into prepared positions

Cusp   The point formed by the intersection of the foils in Gothic tracery

Dressings   Mouldings which protrude beyond the wall face

Drip stone   The projecting course over doorways and windows, which throws off water; also known as label or hood moulding

Embrasure   An opening in a parapet between two merlons

Fillet   A narrow flat band used to separate two mouldings

Finnial   The upper or final portion of a pinnacle or other diminishing feature

Gargoyle   A projecting water spout often grotesquely carved, to throw off water from the roof area

Grout   Cement or mortar mix made thin by the addition of water to enable it to flow into joints and cavities

Merlon   The upstanding part of an embattled parapet

AN EXPLANATION OF TERMS, AND DESCRIPTION OF TOOLS, USED IN MASONRY; INCLUDING THE COMPOSITION OF CEMENTS, OR MORTAR, &c.

ABUTMENT.—A term used both in carpentry and masonry. An explanation of it, as used in carpentry, may be found on referring to page 218. In masonry, the *abutments* of a bridge mean the walls adjoining to the land, which support the ends of the extreme arches or roadway.

APERTURE.—An opening through a wall, &c. which has, generally, three straight sides; of these, two are perpendicular to the horizon, and the other parallel to it, connecting the lower ends of the vertical stones or *jambs*. The lower side is called the *cill,* and the upper side the *head*. The last is either an arch or a single stone. If it be an arch, the aperture is called an *arcade*. Apertures may be circular or cylindrical; but these are not very frequent.

ARCH.—Part of a building suspended over a hollow, and concave towards the area of the same.

ARCHIVOLT *of the Arch of a Bridge*.—The curved line formed by the upper sides of the arch-stones in the face of the work; by the *archivolt* is also understood the whole set of arch-stones that appear in the face of the work.

ASHLAR.—A term applied to common or free-stones, as they come out of the quarry. By *ashlar* is also meant the facing of squared stones on the front of a building. If the work be so smoothed as to take out the marks of the tools by which the stones were first cut, it is called *plane-ashlar*: if figured, it may be *tooled ashlar*, or *random tooled*, or *chiselled*, or *boasted*, or *pointed*. If the stones project from the joints, it is said to be *rusticated*.

BANKER.—The stone bench on which work is cut and squared.

BANQUET.—The raised footway adjoining to the parapet on the sides of a bridge.

BATTARDEAU. See *Coffer-dam*.

BATTER.—The leaning part of the upper part of the face of a wall, which so inclines as to make the plumb-line fall within the base.

BEDS *of a Stone*.—The parallel surfaces which intersect the face of the work in lines parallel to the horizon.

In arching, the beds are, by some, called *summerings*; by others, with more propriety, *radiations* or *radiated joints*.

BOND.—That regular connection, in lapping the stones upon one another, when carrying up the work, which forms an inseparable mass of building.

BUTMENT. See *Abutment*.

CAISSON.—A chest of strong timber in which the piers of a bridge are built, by sinking it, as the work advances, till it comes in contact with the bed of the river, and then the sides are disengaged, being constructed for that purpose.

CEMENT *and* MORTAR, *Composition of.*—It is almost superfluous to say, that cement, or mortar, is a preparation of lime and sand, mixed with water, which serves to unite the stones, in the building of walls, &c.

On the proper or improper manner in which the cement or mortar is prepared and used, depends the durability and security of every building: we shall, therefore, here introduce many particulars on this head, discovered by *Dr. Higgins*, but which, not being generally known, have never been reduced into general practice.

For the preparation of every kind of mortar, or cement, the subsequent remarks should always be known. Of *Sand*, the following kinds are to be preferred; first, *drift-sand*, or *quarry-sand*, which consists chiefly of hard quartose flat-faced grains, with sharp angles; secondly, that which is the

Mullions   Vertical stones dividing windows into two or more lights (sections)

Niche   A recess in a wall to receive a statue or ornament

Nosing   The vertical surface of a projecting member. The leading edge of a step

Ovolo   Convex moulding, often carved in classical architecture with egg and dart enrichment

Quirk   A narrow groove or sinking

Respond   A half pillar at the end of an arcade

Reveal   Surface at right angles to the wall at the side of an opening cut through it

Soffit   The underside of a piece of masonry visible when in position

Transome   Horizontal stone dividing a window

Volute   The scroll, or spiral, occurring in Ionic, Corinthian and composite capitals

CEMENTS AND MORTARS

Nicholson wrote his text at a time when materials were obtained locally, and local craftsmen knew how to make best use of their available resources. Modern transport has made a wide variety of materials available and now the final choice is influenced by the material to be laid, the colour and texture required and the situation in which the stone is to be laid.

The rediscovery of 'cement' in the eighteenth century, and the further progress by Joseph Aspdin in the early 1800s with his Portland cement, laid the foundations for our present large and complex cement industry. The availability and consistency of cement have made it a popular building material replacing local limes in many instances, causing a decline in their production and a lack of understanding of their use. Portland cement is a carefully controlled mixture of ingredients such as lime, silica, alumina and iron oxide. Approximately eighty separate operations make up the process of manufacture from the initial crushing of the ingredients, to the rotating kilns where a clinker is formed, and on to the grinding process which reduces the clinker to a fine powder in the rotating tube mills. In the final stages of manufacture gypsum is added to regulate the setting time.

Lime is produced by burning limestone and its quality depends on the composition of the limestone burnt. Lime produced for building purposes falls under a general range of headings, as follows:

Lean lime — a lime that slakes with the addition of water but does not form a good plastic putty. It is obtained from limestone containing more than 5 per cent silica.

Fat lime — a pure calcareous lime which forms a plastic paste or putty, and is obtained from limestone with over 96 per cent calcium carbonate.

Dolomitic lime — obtained from dolomitic or magnesian limestones, and used only in mortars where the presence of magnesia is acceptable.

Hydraulic lime — this lime varies in strength according to the proportions of added silica and alumina. The strongest is classified as eminently hydraulic and the weakest as feebly hydraulic. It is used as a setting agent and is treated and stored like a cement.

The earliest buildings in Britain were built with a lime mix, incorporating local sand, and stonedust, the latter probably generated by the work in hand. A typical wall would be constructed of an inner and outer wall of dressed stone, each with a varying depth into the wall, and with an occasional through bonder. As work proceeded the core to the wall was filled with a mixture of small stones and lime mortar. This type of construction has absorbed remarkably any movement that occurred over the centuries. Lack of adhesion between the two wall surfaces and movement of one or both, results in deterioration to the central core. This can often be corrected by introducing a grouting material, compatible to the original mix, and fed in either under pressure or gravity to fill voids.

Wrought masonry with its larger stones and true bedding surfaces, does not depend on a hard setting mortar. The masons used a mix of three parts stonedust to one part fat lime, and this became known as mason's putty.

The technique of setting each stone changed as stones of several hundredweight needed placing in position. Strips of metal called screeding irons, of the appropriate thickness, were placed at each end of the bed required. Mason's putty was then applied between them, and by drawing a straight edge across the putty a true surface was made.

The screeding irons were removed before the stone was placed. The joints to the stone would be pointed up and a fluid mix (grout) poured in — joggles having been cut into the ends of each stone to aid this process, as well as giving additional stability to the stone. Cladding to buildings has also changed the fixing method so that now the stone depends on a non-ferrous fixing rather than on the mortar used.

Whichever form of stone fixing is used, however, several important factors should be understood and taken into consideration:

1   The choice of sand will be influenced by the colour and texture required, but in general it should be clean and free from impurities. Washed sand should be

freest, or may be most easily freed by washing, from clay, salts, and calcareous, gypseous, or other grains less hard and durable than quartz; thirdly, that which contains the smallest quantity of pyrites or heavy metallic-matter, inseparable by washing; and, fourthly, that which suffers the smallest diminution of its bulk in washing. Where a coarse and fine sand of this kind, and corresponding in the size of their grains with the coarse and fine sands hereafter described, cannot be easily procured, let such sand of the foregoing quality be chosen as may be sorted and cleansed in the following manner :—

Let the sand be sifted in streaming clear water, through a sieve which shall give passage to all such grains as do not exceed one-sixteenth of an inch in diameter; and let the stream of water, and the sifting, be regulated so that all the sand which is much finer than the Lynn-sand, commonly used in the London glass-houses, together with clay, and every other matter specifically lighter than sand, may be washed away with the stream; whilst the purer and coarser sand, which passes through the sieve, subsides in a convenient receptacle, and the coarse rubbish and rubble remain on the sieve to be rejected.

Let the sand, which thus subsides in the receptacle, be washed in clean streaming water through a finer sieve, so as to be further cleansed, and sorted into two parcels; a coarser, which will remain in the sieve, which is to give passage to such grains of sand only as are less than one-thirtieth of an inch in diameter, and which is to be saved apart under the name of *coarse sand*; and a finer, which will pass through the sieve and subside in the water, and which is to be saved apart under the name of *fine sand*. Let the coarse and the fine sand be dried separately, either in the sun, or on a clean iron-plate, set on a convenient surface, in the manner of a sand-heat.

Let *stone-lime* be chosen, which heats the most in slaking, and slakes the quickest when duly watered; that which is the freshest made and closest kept; that which dissolves in distilled vinegar with the least effervescence, and leaves the smallest residue insoluble, and in the residue the smallest quantity of clay, gypsum, or martial matter. Let the lime, chosen according to these rules, be put in a brass-wired sieve, to the quantity of fourteen pounds. Let the sieve be finer than either of the foregoing; the finer the better it will be : let the lime be slaked, by plunging it into a butt filled with soft-water, and raising it out quickly, and suffering it to heat and fume; and, by repeating this plunging and raising alternately, and agitating the lime until it be made to pass through the sieve into the water; and let the part of the lime which does not easily pass through the sieve be rejected : and let fresh portions of the lime be thus used, until as many ounces of lime have passed through the sieve as there are quarts of water in the butt.

Let the water, thus impregnated, stand in the butt closely covered until it becomes clear, and through wooden cocks, placed at different heights in the butt, let the clear liquor be drawn off, as fast and as low as the lime subsides, for use. This clear liquor is called *lime-water*. The freer the water is from saline matter, the better will be the cementing liquor made with it.

Let fifty-six pounds of the aforesaid chosen lime be slaked, by gradually sprinkling the lime-water on it, and especially on the unslaked pieces, in a close clean place. Let the slaked part be immediately sifted through the last mentioned fine brass-wired sieve : let the lime which passes be used instantly, or kept in air-tight vessels; and let the part of the lime which does not pass through the sieve be rejected. This finer and richer part of the lime, which passes through the sieve, may be called *purified lime*.

Let bone-ash be prepared in the usual manner, by grinding the whitest burnt bones; but let it be sifted, so as to be much finer than the bone-ash commonly sold for making cupels.

The best materials for making the cement being thus prepared, take fifty-six pounds of the coarse sand, and forty-two pounds of the fine sand; mix them on a large plank of hard wood placed horizontally; then spread the sand so that it may stand to the height of six inches, with a flat surface on the plank, wet it with the lime-water, and let any superfluous quantity of the liquor, which the sand in the condition described cannot retain, flow away off the plank. To the wettest sand add fourteen pounds of the purified lime, in several successive portions; mixing and beating them up together, in the mean time, with the instruments generally used in making fine mortar: then add fourteen pounds of the bone-ash, in successive portions, mixing and beating all together.

The quicker and the more perfectly these materials are mixed and beaten together, and the sooner the cement thus formed is used, the better it will be. This may be called *coarse-grained water-cement*, which is to be applied in building, pointing, plastering, stuccoing, or other work, as mortar and stucco generally are; with this difference chiefly, that, as this cement is shorter than mortar, or common stucco, and dries sooner, it ought to be worked expeditiously in all cases; and, in stuccoing, it ought to be laid on by sliding the trowel upwards on it. The materials used along with this cement in building, or the ground on which it is to be laid in stuccoing, ought to be well wetted with the lime-water in the instant of laying on the cement. The lime-water is also to be used when it is necessary to moisten the cement, or when a liquid is required to facilitate the floating of the cement.

When such cement is required to be of a still finer texture, take ninety-eight pounds of the fine sand, wet it with the lime-water, and mix it with the purified lime and the bone-ash, in the quantities and in the manner above described; with this difference only, that fifteen pounds of lime, or there-abouts, are to be used instead of fourteen pounds, if the greater part of the sand be as fine as Lynn sand. This may be called *fine-grained water-cement*. It is used in giving the last coating, or the finish, to any work intended to imitate the finer-grained stones or stucco. But it may be applied to all the uses of the *coarse-grained water-cement*, and in the same manner.

When, for any of the foregoing purposes of pointing, building, &c., a cement is required much cheaper and coarser-grained than either of the foregoing, then much coarser clean sand than the foregoing coarse sand, or well-washed fine rubble, is to be provided. Of this coarse sand, or rubble, take fifty-six pounds, of the foregoing coarse sand twenty-eight pounds, and of the fine sand fourteen pounds; and, after mixing these, and wetting them with the cementing-liquor, in the foregoing manner, add fourteen pounds, or somewhat less, of the purified lime, and then fourteen pounds, or somewhat less, of the bone-ash, mixing them together in the manner already described. When the cement is required to be white, white sand, white lime, and the whitest bone-ash, are to be chosen. Gray sand, and gray bone-ash formed of half-burnt bones, are to be chosen to make cement gray; and any other colour of the cement is obtained, either by choosing coloured sand, or by the admixture of the necessary quantity of coloured talc in powder, or of coloured, vitreous, or metallic, powders, or other durable colouring ingredients, commonly used in paint.

This water-cement, whether the coarse or fine-grained, is applicable in forming artificial stone, by making alternate layers of the cement and of flint, hard stone, or bricks, in moulds of the figure of the intended stone, and by exposing the masses so formed to the open air, to harden.

When such cement is required for water fences, two-thirds of the pre-scribed quantity of bone-ashes are to be omitted; and, in the place thereof, an equal measure of powdered terras is to be used; and, if the sand employed be not of the coarsest sort, more terras must be added, so that the terras shall be one-sixth part of the weight of the sand.

When such a cement is required of the finest grain, or in a fluid form, so that it may be applied with a brush, flint-powder, or the powder of any quartose or hard earthy substance, may be used in the place of sand; but in a quantity smaller, in proportion as the flint or other powder is finer; so that the flint-powder, or other such powder, shall not be more than six times the weight of the lime, nor less than four times its weight. The greater the quantity of lime within these limits, the more will the cement be liable to crack by quick drying, and, *vice versá.*

Where the above described sand cannot be conveniently procured, or where the sand cannot be conveniently washed and sorted, that sand which most resembles the mixture of coarse and fine sand above prescribed, may be used as directed, provided due attention be paid to the quantity of the lime, which is to be greater as the quality is finer, and, *vice versá.*

Where sand cannot be easily procured, any durable stony body, or baked earth, grossly powdered, and sorted nearly to the sizes above prescribed for sand, may be used in the place of sand, measure for measure, but not weight for weight, unless such gross powder be specifically as heavy as sand.

Sand may be cleansed from every softer, lighter, and less durable, matter, and from that part of the sand which is too fine, by various methods preferable in certain circumstances, to that which has been already described.

Water may be found naturally free from fixable gas, selenite, or clay; such water may, without any great inconvenience, be used in the place of the lime-water; and water approaching this state will not require so much lime as above prescribed to make the lime-water; and a lime-water sufficiently useful may be made by various methods of mixing lime and water in the described proportions, or nearly so.

When stone-lime cannot be procured, chalk-lime, or shell-lime, which best resembles stone-lime, in the foregoing characters of lime, may be used in the manner described, excepting that fourteen pounds and a half of chalk-lime will be required in the place of fourteen pounds of stone-lime. The proportion of lime, as prescribed above, may be increased without inconvenience, when the cement of stucco is to be applied where it is not liable to dry quickly; and, in the contrary case, this proportion may be diminished. The defect of lime, in quantity or quality, may be very advantageously supplied, by causing a considerable quantity of lime-water to soak into the work, in successive portions, and at distant intervals of time; so that the calcareous matter of the lime-water, and the matter attracted from the open air, may fill and strengthen the work.

The powder of almost every well-dried or burnt animal substance may be used instead of bone-ash; and several earthy powders, especially the micaceous and the metallic; and the elixated ashes of divers vegetables, whose earth will not burn to lime, as well as the ashes of mineral fuel, which are of the calcareous kind, but will not burn to lime, will answer the ends of bone-ash in some degree.

The quantity of bone-ash described may be lessened without injuring the cement; in those circumstances especially which admit the quantity of lime to be lessened, and in those wherein the cement is not liable to dry quickly. The art of remedying the defects of lime may be advantageously practised to supply the deficiency of bone-ash, especially in building, and in making artificial stone with this cement.

As the preceding method of making mortar differs, in many particulars, from the common process, it may be useful to enquire into the causes on which this difference is founded.

When the sand contains much clay, the workmen find that the best mortar they can make must contain about one-half lime; and hence they lay it down as certain, that the best mortar is made by the composition of half sand and half lime.

But with sand requiring so great a proportion of lime as this, it will be impossible to make good cement; for it is universally allowed that the hardness of mortar depends on the crystallization of the lime round the other materials which are mixed with it; and thus uniting the whole mass into one solid substance. But, if a portion of the materials used be clay, or any other friable substance, it must be evident that, as these friable substances are not changed in one single particular, by the process of being mixed up with lime and water, the mortar, of which they form a proportion, will consequently be, more or less, of a friable nature, in proportion to the quantity of friable substances used in the composition of the mortar. On the other hand, if mortar be composed of lime and good sand only, as the sand is a stony substance, and not in the least friable, and as the lime, by perfect crystallization, becomes likewise of a stony nature, it must follow, that a mass of mortar, composed of these two stony substances, will itself be a hard, solid, unfriable, substance. This may account for one of the essential variations in the preceding method from that in common use, and point out the necessity of never using, in the place of sand, which is a durable stony body, the scrapings of roads, old mortar, and other rubbish, from antient buildings, which are frequently made use of, as all of them consist, more or less, of muddy, soft, and minutely divided particles.

Another essential point is the nature and quality of the lime. Now, experience proves that, when lime has been long kept in heaps, or untight casks, it is reduced to the state of chalk, and becomes every day less capable of being made into good mortar; because, as the goodness or durability of the mortar depends on the crystallization of the lime, and, as experiments have proved, that lime, when reduced to this chalk-like state, is always incapable of perfect crystallization, it must follow that, as lime in this state never becomes crystallized, the mortar of which it forms the most indispensable part, will necessarily be very imperfect; that is to say, it will never become a solid stony substance; a circumstance absolutely required in the formation of good durable mortar. These are the two principal ingredients in the formation of mortar; but, as water is also necessary, it may be useful to point out that which is the fittest for this purpose; the best is rain-water, river-water the second, land-water next, and spring-water last.

The ruins of the antient Roman buildings are found to cohere so strongly, as to have caused an opinion that their constructors were acquainted with some kind of mortar, which, in comparison with ours, might justly be called *cement*; and that, to our want of knowledge of the materials they used, is owing the great inferiority of modern buildings in their durability. But a proper attention to the above particulars would soon show that the durability of the antient edifices depended on the manner of preparing their mortar more than on the nature of the materials used. The following observations will, we think, prove this beyond a possibility of doubt:

Lime, which has been slaked and mixed with sand, becomes hard and consistent when dry, by a process similar to that which produces natural *stalactites* in caverns. These are always formed by water dropping from the roof. By some unknown and inexplicable process of nature, this water has had dissolved in it a small portion of calcareous matter, in a caustic state. So long as the water continues covered from the air, it keeps the earth dissolved in it; it being the natural property of calcareous earths, when deprived of their fixed air, to dissolve in water. But, when the small drop of water comes to be exposed to the air, the calcareous matter contained in it begins to attract the fixable part of the atmosphere. In proportion as it does so, it also begins to separate from the water, and to re-assume its native form of lime-stone or marble. When the calcareous matter is perfectly crystallized in this manner, it is to all intents and purposes lime-stone or marble of the same consistence as before. If lime, in a caustic state, is mixed with water, part of the lime will be dissolved, and will also begin to crystallize. The water which parted with the crystallized lime will then begin to act upon the remainder, which it could not dissolve before ; and thus the process will continue, either till the lime be all reduced to an *effete*, or crystalline state, or something hinders the action of the water upon it. It is this crystallization which is observed by the workmen when a heap of lime is mixed with water, and left for some time to macerate. A hard crust is formed upon the surface, which is ignorantly called *frostling*, though it takes place in summer as well as in winter. If, therefore, the hardness of the lime, or its becoming a cement, depends entirely on the formation of its crystals, it is evident that the perfection of the cement must depend on the perfection of the crystals, and the hardness of the matters which are entangled among them. The additional substances used in making of mortar, such as sand, brick-dust, or the like, serve only for a purpose similar to what is answered by sticks put into a vessel full of any saline solution; namely, to afford the crystals an opportunity of fastening themselves upon it. If, therefore, the matter interposed between the crystals of the lime is of a friable brittle nature, such as brick-dust or chalk, the mortar will be of a weak and imperfect kind; but, when the particles are hard, angular, and very difficult to be broken, such as those of river or pit-sand, the mortar turns out exceedingly good and strong. That the crystallization may be the more perfect, a large quantity of water should be used, the ingredients be perfectly mixed together, and the drying be as slow as possible. An attention to these particulars would make the buildings of the moderns equally durable with those of the antients. In the

54

old Roman works, the great thickness of the walls necessarily required a vast length of time to dry. The middle of them was composed of pebbles thrown in at random, and which, evidently, had thin mortar poured in among them. Thus a great quantity of the lime would be dissolved, and the crystallization performed in the most perfect manner. The indefatigable pains and perseverance, for which the Romans were so remarkable in all their undertakings, leave no room to doubt that they would take care to have the ingredients mixed together as well as possible. The consequence of all this is, that the buildings formed in this manner are all as firm as if cut out of a solid rock; the mortar being equally hard, if not more so, than the stones themselves.

CENTRES.—The frame of timber-work for supporting arches during their erection.

COFFER-DAM, or BATTARDEAU.—A case of piling, without a bottom, constructed for inclosing and building the piers of a bridge. A coffer-dam may be either single or double, the space between being filled with clay or chalk, closely rammed.

DRAG.—A thin plate of steel indented on the edge, like the teeth of a saw, and used in working soft stone, which has no grit, for finishing the surface.

DRIFT.—The horizontal force of an arch, by which it tends to overset the piers.

EXTRADOS *of an Arch.*—The exterior or convex curve, or the top of the arch-stones. This term is opposed to the *Intrados,* or concave side.

EXTRÁDOS *of a Bridge.*—The curve of the road-way.

FENCE-WALL.—A wall used to prevent the encroachment of men or animals.

FOOTINGS.—Projecting courses of stone, without the naked superincumbent part, and which are laid in order to rest the wall firmly on its base.

HAMMER.—See *Tools.*

HEADERS.—Stones disposed with their length horizontally, in the thickness of the wall.

JETTEE.—The border made around the stilts under a pier.

IMPOST or SPRINGING.—The upper part or parts of a wall employed for springing an arch.

INTRADOS.—See *Extrados*.

JOGGLED JOINTS.—The method of indenting the stones, so as to prevent the one from being pushed away from the other by lateral force.

KEY-STONES.—-A term frequently used for *bond-stones*.

KEY-STONE.—The middle voussoir of an arch, over the centre.

KEY-STONE *of an Arch*.—The stone at the summit of the arch, put in last for wedging and closing the arch.

LEVEL.—Horizontal, or parallel to the horizon.

MALLET.—See *Tools*.

MORTAR.—See *Cement*.

NAKED, *of a Wall*.—The vertical or battering surface, whence all projectures arise.

OFF-SET.—The upper surface of a lower part of a wall, left by reducing the thickness of the superincumbent part upon one side or the other, or both.

POINT.—See *Tools*.

PARAPETS.—The breast-walls erected on the sides of the extrados of the bridge, for preventing passengers from falling over.

PAVING.—A floor, or surface of stone, for walking upon.

PIERS *in Houses*.—The walls between apertures, or between an aperture and the corner.

PIERS *of a Bridge*.—The insulated parts between the apertures or arches, for supporting the arches and road-way.

PILES.—Timbers driven into the bed of a river, or the foundation of a building for supporting a structure.

PITCH *of an Arch*.—The height from the springing to the summit of the arch.

PUSH *of an Arch*.—The same as *Drift*; which see.

QUARRY.—The place whence stones are raised.

RANDOM COURSES, *in Paving*.—Unequal courses, without any regard to equi-distant joints.

kept from contact with the earth. The careful use of two grades of sand — fine and coarse — is recommended if wide joints are required. The fine sand fills voids and helps to reduce shrinkage.

2   Stonedust, unlike sand, absorbs water and thus a mix containing a large percentage of stonedust with its greater fluid content has a higher shrinkage factor than a sand mix. This may be acceptable where large stones are set on fine beds and the ratio of bed to stone is small. Where generous beds are required with smaller stones, it is wise to keep the amount of stonedust to a minimum. This point is endorsed by the leading authorities in the 'plastic' or 'artificial' stone type of repair. Where an area has to be 'built up' by the application of several coats of material, and cracks or crazing of the surface are unacceptable, they achieve a match to natural stone by careful selection of sands with little or no use of stonedust.

The setting agents chosen have varying characteristics. According to the choice of agent and its proportion to the mix, the bedding material may or may not be suitable for pointing. Cement has a shrinkage factor, but a cement mortar has high early strength. Non-hydraulic limes are comparatively slow in their setting qualities, but add greatly to the 'flow' or workability of a mix. The addition of cement to a lime mix to aid its early and final strength is common practice. Hydraulic limes are in several classifications. An eminently hydraulic lime has the advantage of not shrinking during its curing and is particularly suitable for restoration and conservation work. It is somewhat slower than cement in its initial stages of setting, and when used in pointing in exposed situations the addition of a small quantity of cement may be desirable.

3   While masonry does not need to be saturated with water, it is very necessary to moisten beds and joints in order that the mortars can cure naturally and not be subject to undue suction from a large area of dry stonework. Should the bedding mix not be thought inappropriate for pointing, and if the addition of extra strengthening is considered, it should always be borne in mind that the resultant pointing should never be harder than the material to be pointed. Hard unsympathetic pointing can cause deterioration to the arris of stones and if it remains proud when stonework has eroded it will feed water into the joint causing further damage.

TOOLS

The traditional masonry hand tools remain virtually unchanged in design and method of use. One major introduction is the use of tungsten carbide as a cutting edge. This supplements the forge sharpened tools, and can be secured

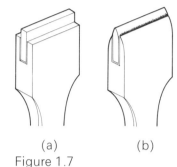

(a)　　　(b)
Figure 1.7

by brazing into a groove on the leading edge of the chisel (Figure 1.7(a)) and sharpened (Figure 1.7(b)) on a soft-grade grinding wheel.

Tungsten is supplied in a variety of grades and the material to be worked should be specified. In general it forms a hard and resilient cutting edge that lasts many days before it needs re-sharpening. With toolsmiths in short supply the tungsten tool is a double boon and with care offers many years' working life.

A recent innovation is the nylon mason's mallet, prompted no doubt by the poor quality of wooden ones on sale. The 'blow' is a little too percussive when compared with a good quality beechwood, but nylon mallets enjoy several advantages. A correctly made wooden mallet has two 'beats', one at each opposing end, while the nylon mallet can be struck anywhere on its circumference. Also the nylon is unaffected by moisture, if neglected on sitework or left in the proximity of water-fed machinery. However, it must be recorded that in general contour and steel content the hand tools marketed today are far inferior to those available to earlier craftsmen.

Compressed air and electrical percussion hammers are a valuable addition to stone working equipment. Compressed air guns are workshop and site tools, and the electrical hammer is used on site when compressed air is not available. These hammers come in a wide range of sizes and are designed for use on delicate features as well as for rough cutting. The generally accepted principle — that on a hard stone a smaller hammer and mallet is used, but struck more often — is carried into the principle of rapid vibratory piston strokes transmitted to the

Gun type compressed air hammer

SAW.—See *Tools.*

SHOOT *of an Arch.*—The same as *Drift;* which see.

SPAN.—The span of an arch is its greatest horizontal width.

STERLINGS.—A case made about a pier of stilts in order to secure it. See the following article.

STILTS.—A set of piles driven into the bed of a river, at small distances, with a surrounding case of piling driven closely together, and the interstices filled with stones, in order to form a foundation for building the pier upon.

STRAIGHT-EDGE.—See *Tools.*

STRETCHERS.—Those stones, which have their length disposed horizontally in the length of the wall.

THROUGH STONES.—A term employed, in some countries, for bond-stones.

THRUST.—The same as *Drift;* which see.

TOOLS *used by Masons.*—The masons' *Level, Plumb-Rule, Square, Bevel, Trowel, Hod, and Compasses,* are similar in every respect to those tools which bear the same name among bricklayers; and which are described hereafter. Those tools, which differ from such as are used by the bricklayer, are as follow :—

The *Saw* used by masons is without teeth, and stretched in a frame nearly resembling the joiner's saw-frame. It is made from four to six feet, or more, in length, according to the size of the slabs, which are intended to be cut by it. To facilitate the process of cutting slabs into slips and scantlings, a portion of sharp silicious sand is placed upon an inclined plane, with a small barrel of water at the top, furnished with a spiggot, which is left sufficiently loose to allow the water to exude drop by drop; and thus, by running over the sand, carries with it a portion of sand into the kerf of the stone. The workman sits at one side of the stone, and draws the saw to and fro, horizontally, taking a range of about twelve inches each time before he returns. By this means, calcareous stones of the hardest kinds may be cut into slabs of any thickness, with scarcely any loss of substance. But, as this method of sawing stone is slow and expensive, mills have been erected in various parts of Great Britain, by which the same process is performed at a

cutting edge of the chisel. Thus the air tool is generally of more value on hard stones than on soft ones. However, it can still be used to good effect on all stones in the hands of a skilled operator and is complementary to, rather than a replacement of, the normal method of working.

Cutting out on site is a particularly good application for the power hammer. In many instances the area to be removed is not at an ideal height for hand working and the power tool can be brought to bear with equal effect from a variety of positions. Current regulations require all electrical hand tools to be 110 volts.

STONE WORKING MACHINERY

Stone working machinery can be divided into four main classes:

1 *Primary saws* that make the initial cuts into the large blocks and convert them to slab form.
2 *Secondary saws* that cut the slabs to the required shape and size.
3 *Moulding machines* that are capable of applying moulded sections and sinkings to pre-sawn stone.
4 *Polishing machines* that are used to bring the surface of marble and granite to its high degree of polish.

1   *Primary saws* can be of three types — wire, circular, and reciprocating frame.

The *wire saw* uses an endless wire strand on to which an abrasive is fed with water; it is of value on materials with an even texture and has a greater application in the quarrying field than in general stone production.

The *circular diamond saw* cuts rather less than half its diameter, as it needs a centre pivot with clamps to hold the blade firmly in position. The result is that with block sizes of up to 1.5 m high, blades range between 2.5 m to 3.5 m in diameter. For many years the diamond has been used as a cutting agent. At first metal segments approximately 10 mm long were placed around the circumference of a blade, and single diamonds were placed in each segment, each in a slight different position to its predecessor so that the whole width of the blade was covered in six or seven segments. Modern blades still retain the metal segment, but each is impregnated with industrial diamonds. The density of the diamonds and the composition of the metal segment is adjusted to suit the particular stone to be cut. The blade revolves at a high peripheral speed and is kept clean and cool by jets of water played on to the leading edge and sides. The original design, in which blocks of stone were brought against the rotating blade by a moving table, has given way to the table or in some instances tables, remaining stationary while the blade traverses, suspended from a heavy beam

much cheaper rate, and in some of these mills every species of moulding upon stone is produced.

Masons make use of many *chisels*, of different sizes, but all resembling, or nearly resembling, each other in form. They are usually made of iron and steel welded together; but, when made entirely of steel, which is more elastic than iron, they will naturally produce a greater effect with any given impulse. The form of masons' chisels is that of a wedge, the cutting-edge being the vertical angle. They are made about eight or nine inches long. When the cutting-edge is broader than the portion held in the hand, the lower part is expanded in the form of a dove-tail. When the cutting-edge is smaller than the handle, the lower end is sloped down in the form of a pyramid. In finishing off stone, smooth and neat, great care should be taken that the arris is not splintered, which would certainly occur, if the edge of the chisel were directed outwards in making the blow: but, if it be directed inwards, so as to overhang a little, and form an angle of about forty-five degrees, there is little danger of splintering the arris in chipping.

Of the two kinds of chisels, which are the most frequently made use of, *the tool* is the largest; that is to say, in the breadth of its cutting-edge; it is used for working the surface of stone into narrow furrows, or channels, at regular distances; this operation is called *tooling*, and the surface is said to be *tooled*.

The *Point* is the smallest kind of chisel used by masons, being never more than a quarter of an inch broad on its cutting-edge. It is used for reducing the irregularity of the surface of any rough stone.

The *Straight-Edge* is similar to the instrument among carpenters of the same name; it being a thin board, planed true, to point out cross-windings and other inequalities of surface, and thus direct the workmen in the use of the chisel.

The *Mallet* used by the mason differs from that of any other artisan. It is similar to a bell in contour, excepting a portion of the broadest part, which is rather cylindrical. The handle is rather short, being only just long enough to be firmly grasped in the hand. It is employed for giving percus-

Twin-blade secondary diamond saw

section. The table is advanced to the correct position for each succeeding cut. With the blade size quoted for these large saws the blade must be of a substantial thickness, and the segments on its circumference slightly wider than the blade to give clearance. A cut of some 20 to 25 mm in width is usually made. With this amount of stone lost during a cut it is not usual to cut slabs of less than 150 mm thickness.

The *reciprocating frame saw* was developed from the original system of hand sawing. The basic design comprises a series of metal blades set in a frame some 2 m wide by 4 m long. This frame is given its cutting motion by a beam set eccentrically on a fly-wheel. Early frame saws had steel blades tensioned by steel wedges. Water and abrasive materials were fed into the cuts, the frame itself swung from pivots, in a semi-circular movement some 750 mm long, and by means of a worm drive was gradually lowered into the stone. Cutting speed varied according to the materials and could be adjusted, but on medium grade stone 200 mm per hour would be average.

The modern frame saw has blades whose bottom edge has a series of diamond segments as described for the circular saw. Tension for all the blades is by hydraulic pressure and the swinging motion of the frame has been changed to a horizontal cutting action. Using water only, the result is a faster cutting action and an improved surface on the material, both in accuracy and finish. Cutting speeds of 400 mm per hour are average. The speeds quoted can appear deceptively slow, but according to the width of the stone and the thickness of each stone required, some ten to twenty blades may be cutting together.

sive force to chisels, by striking them with any part of the cylindrical surface of the mallet.

The Hammer used by masons is generally furnished with a point or an edge like a chisel. Both kinds are used for dividing stones, and likewise for producing those narrow marks or furrows left upon hewn-stone work which is not ground on the face.

VAULT.—A mass of stones so combined as to support each other over a hollow.

UNDER BED *of a Stone.*—The lower surface, generally placed horizontally.

UPPER BED *of a Stone.*—The upper surface, generally placed horizontally.

VOUSSOIRS.—The arch-stones in the face or faces of an arch; the middle one is called the *key-stone*.

WALL.—An erection of stone, generally perpendicular to the horizon; but sometimes *battering*, in order to give stability.

WALLS, *Emplection.*—Those which are built in regular courses, with the stones smoothed in the face of the work. They are of two kinds, Roman and Grecian, as already noticed. The difference is, that the core of the Roman emplection is rubble; whereas in the Grecian emplection, it is built in the same manner as the face, and every alternate stone goes through the entire thickness of the wall. *See pages* 306, 307.

Walls, Isodomum ; those wherein the courses are of equal thickness, compact, and regularly built; but the stones are not smoothed on the face.

Walls, Pseudo-Isodomum ; those which have unequal courses. *See page* 306.

Above   *Secondary diamond saw with blade inclined*

Above right   *Milling machine adapted for stone cutting*

The width of cut is an important factor and at 6 to 8 mm offers a far smaller wastage factor than the large circular saw. Frame saws using steel blades and abrasives are still found in use in the sandstone and granite yards; each area by the simple expedient of trial and error finding the best and most economical way to deal with its natural materials.

2   *Secondary saws* are available in a wide range. The blades are almost universally of the impregnated diamond segment type, (except in some sandstone areas) and diameters range from 300 mm to 1.5 m. Design varies from single blade saws which can turn their tables 90° in order to square a stone, to saws with twin blades for batch cutting. Others have blades that can be adjusted to any angle for splay cutting and can be lifted to carry out checking. For granite the blade cannot be brought across at its full depth, and step cutting with the blade brought down some 30 mm at each pass, can be carried out by machines on a pre-set automatic programme.

3   *Moulding machines* can be divided into two classes, those that have a 'dry' cutting action and those using a revolving abrasive wheel with a wet application. Planing machines have a dry cutting action, using a moving table passing under a rigid head on which a tool box or boxes are placed. The several stones to be machined are first roughly profiled, with a round-nosed tool and when all the surplus material is removed, cutting tools ground to the reverse of the mouldings required, bring the stone to the desired shape. Mouldings

Above   Balusters being turned on a hand lathe

Above right   Profile cutting with diamond grinding wheel

following a shallow curve can be planed if a machine is available which has a secondary table placed on the first and actuated by an adjustable off-centre pivot. All stones for profiling on a planing machine must be cut overlength to allow for the 'break' which occurs when the tool passes the end of the stone. Cutting tools to a planing machine are nearly all tungsten carbide tipped, the rest are tool-steel ground and tempered.

The *stone lathe* can be a small machine, used on items such as balusters, with the operator guiding the tool by hand, or a machine large enough to turn a column base some 2 m or so in diameter and equipped with a rigid tool box. The cutting operation is similar to the planing machine with a round nosed wasting tool removing the surplus stone and roughly outlining the moulding profile. Carefully ground reverse shapes to the mouldings are then applied to cut the final perfect shape.

Grinding machines may have a grinding wheel of a carborundum composition, which is normal if a moulding profile is to be obtained, or have a series of diamond segments on its edge. Grinding is a wet operation similar to sawing, and in fact most grinders use a saw blade as well as grinding wheels during their operation. These machines are generally used for less complex and smaller mouldings than are planing machines. Advantages over the planing machine are that a stone to be ground can be cut the correct length, and the grinding wheel can be set to enter the surface of a stone and make a sunk panel without any preparatory hand cutting.

4   *Polishing machines* such as the simple Jenny Lind hand-guided polisher with its one revolving head, are still very much in use after decades of service. The revolving head can be changed as required to the correct grade of carborundum and if a high polish is to be obtained, a felt polishing head together with a mild abrasive, such as salts of sorrell, follows the cutting head. This type of polisher is confined to smaller workshops or those with only an occasional need for polishing. Workshops that deal entirely with materials that have a polished finish employ large multi-head polishing machines. The material is fed on a conveyer-belt system through the machine which is usually totally enclosed. Progressing from coarse grade wheels on to fine ones and finally to the polishing stage, the stone is brought from a sawn finish to a polished surface in one continuous operation. Edges to slabs are polished with a similar machine.

CONSERVATION AND RESTORATION

In caring for a stone building it is not sufficient to recognize a defect — the cause should always be investigated. An example might be the discovery of open joints at a parapet. Is this simply the eventual failure of the mortar, or is there movement in the parapet itself? Inspection of adjacent stonework for sign of fracture, a check on joint sizes for any undue irregularity or presence of ferrous fixings, plus a check for overall alignment would each help to establish the correct answer. The age of the building itself is a guide, there being a time when all materials need replacement. A knowledge of the reasonable lasting qualities of particular materials and stones must be gained.

The intrusion of water, with attendant damage by saturation and frost is one of the main faults encountered in routine maintenance. Particular attention should be paid to stones with water-shedding members, joints at uncovered cornices, copings and other projecting courses being particularly vulnerable. Shallow weathering courses form lodgement for vegetation; this should be removed by applying a residual algicide. Gutters, lead flashings and all items concerned with the disposal of rainwater are potential sources of damage.

Several factors influence the extent of repairs in a major restoration programme but the number of years before any further work is envisaged is probably the most important. Financial considerations of necessity control the overall quantity, but when costly scaffolding is erected it may be prudent to use it to the full rather than leave items that will soon need attention.

Stone replacement varies from minor piecing in to the replacement of complete areas or courses. If available the original stone should be used, except where the original stone has failed within an unacceptable time scale, or in particularly vulnerable situations. Stone of similar visual appearance but of a known superior quality can then be introduced.

If stonework is to be pieced in, then as far as possible the line of joint should be at an internal angle on a moulded member so that the visual pattern of original jointing is not lost. Pieces should be of a reasonable depth, and whenever practical a degree of undercut should be made to form a key. The function of all solid stones should be fully understood before their removal and where necessary support should be given to the affected areas.

The style of original work should be noted and matched. Attention to detail in such items as the length of stones in relation to bed height, surface finish, width and texture of beds all contribute to a successful repair. The re-dressing of eroded stone is of doubtful value. It is not always appreciated that the natural weathering surface a stone develops when placed in situation does not take place again if the stone is dressed back. The practice of recutting old stone for re-use is discouraged for this reason. However, this must be qualified by saying that 'stone' is a very wide term and that some of the harder stones respond better to this treatment than the middle to soft range. Also, cutting back on site under difficult conditions may prove almost as costly as new stonework, especially if moulded items are included.

Stone cleaning is a recognized form of building care. Stonework benefits from the removal of accumulated sooty deposits, details once obliterated become visible and latent defects in the structure are often brought to light. Washing by the water spray method, together with brushing and scraping heavily encrusted areas is acknowledged as the best system. Penetration of water into open joints must be guarded against and the operation must take place in frost-free conditions. Abrasive blasting, and chemical cleaning are both approved methods but great care is needed in their use and the choice is best determined by the type of stone to be cleaned and the degree of soiling. Detail can be lost by excessive or unsympathetic blasting and success depends on the understanding of and care taken by the operator.

Research into the impregnation of stone with a preservative has so far been inconclusive, but effort is being expended towards finding a suitable solution that is inconspicuous and effective.

2. Brickwork
Peter Minter and William Nash

HISTORICAL DEVELOPMENT

Since the original publication of Nicholson's *Practical Builder*, the brickmaking industry has undergone numerous changes, some technical, some due to fashion and some to political problems and the waging of two world wars.

The years preceding the publication had seen a steady development in the use of brick as a building material and consequently an improvement in the techniques employed in the manufacture. In Tudor times moulded brickwork was produced by cutting and rubbing. Its final surface finish was of a roughish texture and in the palaces, churches and houses of the period, precision was not really being sought or achieved. With the change in style to the 'Classical' and a greater awareness of fashion, there were new demands on the brickmaker. Bricks were wanted in larger numbers and over a much wider area and had to conform to ever tightening standards with regard to quality, colour and texture. Their use now went further than a simple building material; they were used to influence style, to create design by the use of contrasting colours and textures, and these themselves could be enhanced by the type of jointing and pointing used in the laying. A feature would be made of certain aspects of a building incorporating a number of moulded bricks, or bricks whose size differed from the standard. In this respect the influence of stone still showed strongly and if brick was to be the material chosen for a decorative feature, it was often made to a size resembling stone.

A clean, fine textured clay was now used, together with a fine sand, and served to accentuate the contrast between wall and window or wall and arch. In the same way the use of corbelling served to throw water from the face of a building and added both design and contrast. A need grew for the use of brick in structural situations (such as arches) and care was exercised to ensure that the brickwork was finished in such a way as to give both strength and aesthetic appeal. The arches of the 'Classical' period had been for the most part cut and rubbed from a 'brick rubber' — a brick made from clean washed clay free from impurities, which enabled the bricklayer to cut and gauge his arch. This work required a high degree of skill and patience to transform, by cutting and rubbing the block of fired clay to the required shape. With the need for more and cheape buildings to serve the interests of an expanding commercial empire came the need for more houses. The brick industry, for this is what it had become, looked for ways to produce large numbers of bricks and the 'specials' to be used with them. Mechanization was increasing and both facing and common bricks were being produced by machine.

The mechanization of brick production first became general in the Midlands and northern parts of the country where the clays were more suitable for

CHAPTER VIII.

BRICKLAYING:

INCLUDING AN ABSTRACT OF THE BUILDING ACT, 14th Geo. III. c. 78.

BRICKLAYING is the art of Building with Bricks, or of uniting them, by cement or mortar, into various forms for particular purposes.

The BRICKS of the antients were of various forms and sizes, and their triangular bricks were peculiarly adapted to certain figures, but modern bricks, of English make, are commonly of one form, 9 inches long, by $4\frac{1}{2}$ broad, and $2\frac{1}{2}$ deep.

Bricks are made of a species of clay or loamy earth, either pure or with various mixtures; they are shaped in a mould, and, after some drying in the sun or air, are burnt to a hardness. The more pure the earth of which it is formed, the harder and firmer the brick will be. The bricks generally known to our modern builders are of several sorts: that is to say, *Marls*, of two qualities, *Gray-Stocks*, and *Place-Bricks*, besides two or three foreign kinds, occasionally imported. Bricks vary in quality, according to the quality of the material of which they are composed, the manner in which the clay is tempered, and the diffusion of the heat while burning.

The finest kind of Marls, called *Firsts*, are those usually selected for arches over doors and windows: those less fine, called *Seconds*, are commonly used for the fronts of buildings. The Gray-Stocks are of the next quality, and are generally of a good earth, well wrought, with little mixture, sound, and durable. Place-Bricks are too frequently poor and brittle, badly

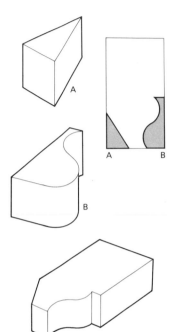

Figure 2.1 *Window label mould*

machine making techniques than those of the southern and eastern counties. Hand moulding, however, continued everywhere and was in fact extended to cover the making of many of the specials that had previously been produced by cutting and rubbing. A vital part of the work now involved the carpenter and joiner whose skill produced the many and varied moulds from which the special bricks were made. Moulds that have survived from the turn of the century show the high degree of craftsmanship that went into making these moulds. Almost any shape or profile became possible, with the more complicated designs being made in a number of pieces, which were removed after the mould had been filled to allow the brick to be withdrawn. The moulds were usually of a hardwood, to give the carver more scope and far greater durability to the mould itself (Figure 2.1).

MOULDS AND MOULDING

As much conservation work concerns buildings from the fourteenth, fifteenth and sixteenth centuries, precision in the mouldings of specials is not critical. However, face texture is of importance as the roughness of much of the earlier brickwork, together with the passage of time means that replacement brickwork is often all too readily obvious. It is possible to overcome this problem to some extent by the use of different sands at the time of making and the way the moulder rolls his warp; but with the growing requirement for bricks to match 'Georgian' and 'Victorian' brickwork, greater emphasis lies with the mould maker. It is of the utmost importance that the mould is made to a high standard of accuracy if the brick maker is to produce bricks with the exactness and finish to match the original. How to set about producing such a mould, the choice of wood, and how to keep the costs within bounds, are just some of the problems facing the mould maker today.

The hand moulding of bricks has changed very little over the years; it may differ slightly from region to region (as do the words used to describe the process), but the broad principle remains the same. The seam of London Bed Clay at present being worked at Bulmer is dug mechanically where once it was the winter's occupation of the summer makers. The clay, having been allowed to weather (this action of natural weathering helps the process of clay preparation) is pulled down into beds and thoroughly soaked before being tipped into the 'mill' and pugged. The mill consists of a barrel in which a number of paddles, attached to a central shaft, rotate slowly, mixing the wet clay and turning it into a soft, butter-like mass. The clay, working its way through the mill, is extruded from the end of the barrel ready for use by the moulder, being transferred to his table by the 'temperer' by means of a cuckle, an inverted T-shaped tool enabling

burnt, and of very irregular colour. *Burrs* or *Clinkers* are such as are so much overburnt as to vitrify, and run two or three together.

Red Stocks and the *Red Bricks*, called also, from their use, *Cutting Bricks*, owe their colour to the nature of the clay of which they are made; this is always used tolerably pure, and the bricks of the better kind are called by some *Clay Bricks*, because they are supposed to be made of nothing else.

The Gray Stocks, being made of a good earth, well wrought, are commonly used in front in building: the Place Bricks being made of clay, with a mixture of dirt and other coarse materials, and more carelessly put out of hand, are therefore weaker and more brittle, and are introduced where they cannot be seen, and where little stress is laid upon them: the Red Bricks, of both kinds, are made of a particular earth, well wrought, and little injured by mixtures; and they are used in fine work, in ornaments over windows, and in paving. These are frequently cut or ground down to a perfect evenness, and sometimes set in putty instead of mortar; and thus set they make a very beautiful appearance.

These are the kinds of bricks commonly used by us in building, and their difference is owing to variety in the materials. The Place Bricks and Gray Stocks are made in the neighbourhood of London, wherever there is a brick-work; the two kinds of red brick, depending upon a particular kind of earth, can be made only where that is to be had; they are furnished from several places within fifteen or twenty miles of London.

We have already observed, that there are two or three other kinds of brick to be named, which are imported from other countries; and there is also one of the red or cutting brick sort, that is of our own manufacture, and for its excellence deserves to be particularly mentioned; this is the Hedgerly Brick: it is made at a village of that name, of the famous earth called Hedgerly loam, well-known to the glass-makers and chymists. The loam is of a yellow-reddish colour, and very harsh to the touch, containing a great quantity of sand; its particular excellence is, that it will bear the greatest violence of fire without injury: the chymists coat and lute their furnaces with this, and the ovens at glass-houses are also repaired or lined with it

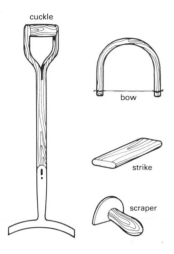

Figure 2.2

Figure 2.3 *Brick barrow*

him to cut and load the table with wet clay and avoid its sticking to the implement (Figure 2.2).

The maker is now ready to mould his brick. He must have close to hand his bin of sand (used as a releasing agent between clay and mould), his mould, strike, water pot, brick boards or platters, and his offbearing or brick barrow on which he will place the freshly made bricks. The mould will have been wetted sufficiently to allow a dusting of sand to adhere to its surfaces and the table will also be covered with sand. The maker pulls, or cuts with his bow, enough clay from his pile to fill the mould. He rolls the clay firmly in the sand on the table so that it forms a mangeable wedge both shorter and narrower than the mould in which it is to be placed. The wedge of clay, known as a warp or clot, is then thrown into the mould, the soft clay expanding outwards to fill the shape of the mould but prevented from sticking to its sides by the sand. The surplus clay is then removed from the top of the mould by means of a 'strike', the frame is removed from its 'stock' and, and with a platter taken from the head of the barrow (Figure 2.3), is given a firm shake which releases the brick, and allows the frame to be lifted away. This process is repeated until a full load has been made.

DRYING AND FIRING

During the summer months, drying takes place in the open air; the bricks are placed or 'pitched' on hacksteds — prepared strips of concrete covered by a low roof to give the 'green' bricks protection from rain and excessive sun. There they are allowed to dry naturally through the action of sun and wind. Bricks can be piled row upon row to a height of some six courses, provided that time is allowed for the underneath row to dry sufficiently to take the weight of the brick placed upon it. It is at this stage that crease marks may be caused, the first row drying and shrinking fast produces a widening gap between one brick and another and the brick then placed on top covering this gap is marked to leave a 'crease'. To assist the drying process, the bricks are often opened out and set at 45° to one another. This gives a better air flow around the brick and exposes more of its surfaces to the air — the process is known as 'skinking'. Once drying is complete the brick is wheeled to the kiln and stacked ready for firing.

With the large number of bricks being fired in any one kiln, the 'setting' or stacking of a particular kiln can present considerable problems. The bricks have to be set in such a way as to allow the free movement of heat within the kiln while at the same time ensuring protection to the moulded faces of the 'special' bricks and maintaining the stability of the bricks during the height of the firing. Once the chamber is filled the doorway is sealed by using a sandwich of bricks where it stands all the fury of their heat without damage. It is brought into London for this purpose, under the name of Windsor loam, the village being near Windsor, and is sold at a high price. The bricks made of this are of the finest red that can be imagined. They are called *Fire-Bricks*, because of their enduring the fire; and are used about furnaces and ovens in the same way as the earth.

The foreign bricks above mentioned are the *Dutch* and *Flemish Bricks* and *Clinkers*: these are all nearly of a kind, and are often confounded together; they are very hard, and of a dirty brimstone colour; some of them not much unlike our Gray Stocks, others yellower. The Dutch are generally the best baked, and Flemish the yellowest. As to the Clinkers, they are the most baked of all, and are generally warped by the heat. These bricks are used for peculiar purposes; the Dutch and Flemish for paving yards, stables, and the like; and the clinkers for ovens.

The fine red cutting English Bricks are twice, or more than twice, the price of the best Gray Stocks; the Red Stocks half as dear again as the gray; and the Place Bricks, as they are much worse, so they are much cheaper, than any of the others.

The Gray Stocks and Place Bricks are employed in the better and worse kinds of plain work; the red stocks, as well as the gray, are used sometimes in this business, and sometimes for arches, and other more ornamental pieces: the fine red cutting bricks are used for ruled and gauged work, and sometimes for paving; but the red stones are more frequently employed when a red kind is required for this purpose.

The Red Cutting Brick, or fine red, is the finest of all bricks. In some places they are not at all acquainted with this; in others, they confound it with the red stock, and use that for it; though, where the fine red brick is to be had pure and perfectly made, the difference is five to three in the sale price between that and the red stock.

The Red and Gray Stock are frequently put in gauged arches, and one as well as the other set in putty instead of mortar: this is an expensive work,

*Brick kiln and bricks
awaiting dispatch*

and sand sufficiently thick to prevent cold air being drawn in or heat being lost from within.

Firing starts with the process of 'tanning', which takes two days. This enables the burner to warm his kiln thoroughly and drive out any damp from both bricks and kiln before he begins the firing proper. During firing, a period of some thirty-eight to forty hours, the burner will be in almost continual attendance, stoking at regular intervals, throughout the day and night, avoiding a too rapid build up of heat and the possibility of 'over firing' any part of the kiln. Experience enables him to 'read' the colour of his fires, the noise and hum of his kiln and the way in which the smoke rises from the chimney. He will get a feel of the way things are going and by using the damper set in the mainflue and by governing the amount of coal fed to the fires at each 'coaling' will control his firing until the heat is down to the bottom of the kiln. Confirmation that this point has been reached is obtained by use of a trail inserted through a check hole in the base of the doorway, this trail fluxing at some 1100°C. When the firing is completed, the kiln is left to cool for three days until the freshly burnt bricks are ready to be 'drawn' from the chamber and stacked ready for delivery.

SPECIALS

The same basic process is used for the making of 'specials', this term being used to cover almost any non-standard brick, bricks with moulded faces or shaped so that together they will form a design or are themselves a complete design.

74

but it answers in beauty for the regularity of the disposition and fineness of the joints, and has a very pleasing effect.

The fine Red Brick is used in arches ruled and set in putty in the same manner; and, as it is much more beautiful, is somewhat more costly. This kind is also the most beautiful of all in cornices, ruled in the same manner, and set in putty.

The Gray Stocks of an inferior kind are also used in brick walls.

The Place Bricks are used in paving dry, or laid in mortar, and they are put down flat or edgewise. If they are laid flat, thirty-two of them pave a square yard; but, if they are placed edgewise, it takes twice that number: in the front work of walls the Place-Bricks should never be admitted, even in the meanest building. That consideration, therefore, only takes place in the other kinds: and the fine Cutting Bricks come so very dear this way, that few people will be brought to think of them; so that it lies, in a great measure, between the Gray Stocks and Red Stocks. Of these the gray are most used; and this not only because they are cheaper, but, in most cases where judgement is preferred to fancy, they will have the preference.

We see many very beautiful pieces of workmanship in Red Brick; but this should not tempt the judicious architect to admit them into the front walls of buildings. In the first place, the colour itself is fiery and disagreeable to the eye; and, in summer, it has an appearance of heat that is very disagreeable; for this reason it is most improper in the country, though the oftenest used there, from the difficulty of getting gray. But a farther consideration is, that, in the fronts of most important buildings, there is more or less stone-work; now, as there should be as much conformity as can be attained between the general nakedness of the wall and those several ornaments which project from it; the nearer they are of a colour, the better they always range together; and if we cast our eyes upon two houses, the one of red, and the other of gray brick, where there is a little stone-work, we shall not be a moment in doubt which to prefer. There is something harsh in the transition from the red brick to stone, and it seems altogether unnatural;

Before these bricks can be produced, considerable background information is needed. What purpose does the brick serve? Is it in a new or old building? Does it have to match up with existing work? Is it rebuilding or repairing? How important is the match? Is it important in an historical sense that as much of the original as possible is retained? This may mean that a comparatively small quantity of bricks will be wanted, and being of different shapes will necessitate the making of a considerable number of moulds. Alternatively, while new moulds will be required, large numbers may be wanted from each mould. This will spread the mould cost but may then require the use of hardwoods in their construction rather than softwoods, to give the mould sufficient life. Will the work be from drawings or a templet? Is one of the original bricks available? If so, this will give a better idea of colour and texture, together with an idea of how it was made and some idea of the problems that faced the original maker. If an arch is being constructed, measurements and perhaps a full sized templet of the arch will be needed from which the work can be set out, scaled up to give necessary shrinkages. How long will the work take? This in itself will depend on a whole number of factors, the availability of drying space, boards on which to place the wet brick, the amount of room available in the kiln, even the 'grind' of clay required for the particular type of brick. Finally, of course, how much is it all going to cost?

The size and shape of a 'special' will present the maker with various problems relating initially to the filling and compaction of the clay within the mould and later the removal of the completed brick. It is important that the warp is both large enough and of the right basic form to fill the main shape when thrown into the mould. It is then possible to add additional clay to fill out the mould, compaction being achieved by picking up and banging the mould a number of times before striking off the surplus clay. This firming of the clay within the mould serves a number of functions. It ensures the brick is made from a homogenous mass of clay and that the design in the brick is properly formed and will keep its shape when removed from the mould. In the case of the simpler shapes and designs in which there is no undercutting, the brick is removed by gently tapping the box to free the clay from its sides and then inverting the brick onto a platter. If, however, there is undercutting in the design, means will have to be devised for dismantling the mould itself in order to release the finished brick. Shrinkages of different clays vary enormously and can be, for example, approximately ten per cent. This will show that some of the larger copings, window mullions, jambs and returns may be shrinking up to 50 mm during the drying process. For the shrinkage to take place without causing excessive cracking or distortion a long slow dry will be needed; in the case of some of the larger pieces, clay may be scooped from the back of the brick, to help the 'dry'.

in the other, the Gray Stocks come so near the colour of stone, that the change is less violent, and they sort better together. Hence, also, the Gray Stocks are to be considered as best coloured when they have least of the yellow cast; for the nearer they come to the colour of stone, when they are to be used together with it, it is certainly the better. Where there is no stone-work, there generally is wood; and this, being painted white, as is commonly the practice, has yet a greater effect with red brick than the stone-work: the transition is more sudden in this than in the other; but, on the other hand, in the mixture of gray bricks and white paint, the colour of the brick being soft, there is no violent change.

The Gray Stocks are now made, of prime quality, in the neighbourhood of London. The late Duke of Norfolk had the bricks brought from his estate, in that county, for building the front of his house, in St. James's-square; but the event shews that his Grace might have been better supplied near at hand, as to colour, with equal hardness.

The greatest advantage that a Gray Stock, which is the standard brick, can have, is in its sound body and pale colour; the nearer it comes to stone the better; so that the principal thing the brick-maker ought to have in view, for the improvement of his profession, is the seeking for earth that will burn pale, and that will have a good body, and to see it has sufficient working. The judicious builder will always examine his bricks in this light, and be ready to pay that price which is merited by the goodness of the commodity.

The utility and common practice of building all our edifices of brick, both in London and the country, arises from motives too obvious to need a definition; since it is generally considered to be much the cheapest, as well as the most eligible substance that can be invented for the purpose, both in point of beauty and duration, and inferior to nothing but wrought stone.

BRICKS ARE LAID in a varied, but regular, form of connection, or *Bond*, as exhibited in *Plate* LXXXV. The mode of laying them for a 9-inch walling, shown in *figure* 1, being denominated *English Bond*; and *figure* 2, *Flemish Bond*. *Figure* 3 is English Bond, in a brick and a half, or 14-inch walling;

This hollowing out will also help to ensure the escape of gasses from within the brick during firing and serve as a 'frog', giving an extra key when the brick is laid.

In the making of a 'rubber' shrinkage would not be of primary importance as the bricklayer would have the responsibility of fashioning his shape from a fired brick. However, when producing bricks gauged to an arch, accuracy is vital in the finished dimensions of the brick. A limited amount of rubbing will have to be done in order to produce a sharp arris, the final face texture being obtained by light rubbing in situ. It is interesting to note that a brick so rubbed, provided it has been properly fired, will keep its original colour and brightness almost indefinitely whereas the brick in its untouched form, although harder, will readily weather in its surroundings, taking up lichens or pollutents from the atmosphere. The difference in the weathering properties of the same clay in this context can probably be explained by the removal of the sand from the face of the rubber. How well the use of this technique has helped to heighten the contrast between the different textures on many of our older buildings, especially those constructed long before the industrial society started polluting the air.

BRICKLAYING

Bricklaying is the art of building with bricks, uniting them with the aid of mortar into various forms for particular purposes. The common practice of building with bricks arises from the fact that a wide variety of colours and textures may be obtained much more economically than by using stone. Bricks are also very durable and will withstand very well the ravages of weather and the sulphates which are present in the atmosphere in urban areas.

Bonding is the term used for formations of bricks laid with their ends along the face or their sides. Those laid with their ends showing are called 'headers' and those showing their length are 'stretchers'. A course is one complete layer of bricks laid between 'stopped ends' or 'quoins'. There are many bonding arrangements that can be used in walling. In conservation work it is most important that the bond patterns are carefully observed before any repairs to walling are carried out. The following are some of the more common patterns mentioned in the *Practical Builder* and in general use:

Stretcher bond is normally used in half-brick thick walls and consists of all the bricks laid as stretchers and the courses laid half-bond with each other.

English bond has alternate courses of headers and stretchers. The lap is formed by either introducing a closer next to the quoin header or starting each stretcher course with a three-quarter bat (Figure 2.4).

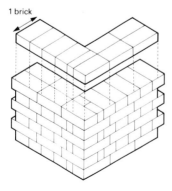

1 brick

Figure 2.4 *An isometric view of a 1-brick quoin in English bond with the top course raised to show the bonding to alternate courses*

78

PLATE LXXXV.

BRICKLAYING

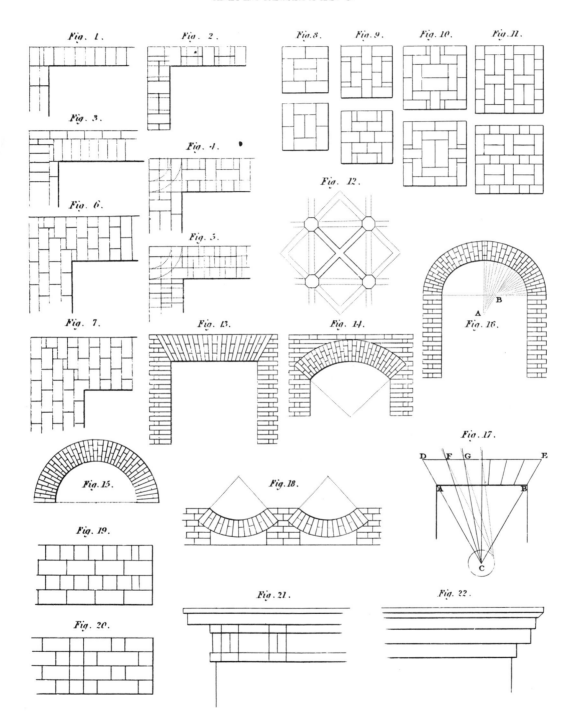

Fig. 1. Fig. 2. Fig. 8. Fig. 9. Fig. 10. Fig. 11. Fig. 3. Fig. 4. Fig. 6. Fig. 5. Fig. 12. Fig. 7. Fig. 13. Fig. 14. Fig. 16. Fig. 15. Fig. 17. Fig. 18. Fig. 19. Fig. 20. Fig. 21. Fig. 22.

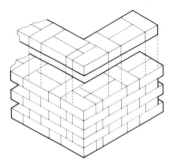

Figure 2.5 *An isometric view of a 1-brick quoin in Flemish bond with the top course raised to show the bonding to alternate courses*

Flemish bond is generally accepted as being a more decorative bond than English, and consists of alternate headers and stretchers in each course with the headers in each course being laid centrally over the stretchers in the course immediately below. The bond is usually formed by the introduction of a closer next to the quoin header, although, if desired, it is possible to use a three-quarter bat at the quoin instead of a stretcher (Figure 2.5).

Dutch bond is somewhat similar to English bond in that it consists of alternate header and stretcher courses, but there are no closers in the header course and the bond is formed by starting each stretcher course with a three-quarter bat. In addition the stretcher courses are laid half-bond to each other; this is effected by placing a header on alternate stretcher courses next to the three-quarter bat. This will create a pattern in which the perpends follow each other diagonally across the wall in an unbroken line.

In some of the older buildings of the William and Mary or Georgian periods it was not uncommon to use 'rubbed' brick on the face of a wall laid in a thin lime putty joint. The interior of the wall would be built of an inferior brick laid in lime mortar. If the bricks were of differing thicknesses then the gauge would be different and often the headers would be snapped into half bats thus forming two skins. Walls greater than one brick in thickness would have the interior of the wall filled with bats or even rubbish. The outer skins would only be bonded into the wall at intervals where the courses coincided. When carrying out work on these buildings, great care must be taken to investigate the construction of the walling, even though the walls may be thick and look substantial — especially if the work necessitates some pulling down before repairs are started. It is common for walls built in this manner to split into two thicknesses along their lengths. Another method of bonding often adopted to overcome this weakness in thicker walls was the single Flemish bond, that is, Flemish bond on the face side but backed up with English bond, the headers in the Flemish bond being laid as full bricks as often as possible in order to 'tie in' the outer skin.

Broken bonds occur where lengths of piers and work below and above window openings does not always allow for perfect bonding. It is often necessary to insert a broken bond into the walling at the centre of the pier or opening. This bond may be a three-quarter bat or an additional header, but never a closer or quarter bat.

MORTARS

Mortars in older buildings were composed of lime and sand, generally in a ratio of 1:3, 1:4 or 1:5. The lime was usually of semi-hydraulic type, although in

and *figure* 4, Flemish Bond, in the same. *Figure* 5 represents another method of disposing Flemish Bond in a 14-inch wall. *Figure* 6, English Bond, in an 18-inch, or two brick thick, wall; and *figure* 7, English Bond, in a two and half brick thick wall.

Figures 8, 9, 10, 11, represent square courses, in pairs, of Flemish Bond. In each pair, if one be the lower course, the other will be the upper course.

The Bricks, having their lengths in the thickness of the wall, are termed *Headers,* and those which have their lengths in the length of the wall are *Stretchers.* By a *Course,* in walling, is meant the bricks contained between two planes parallel to the horizon, and terminated by the faces of the wall. The thickness is that of one brick with mortar. The mass formed by bricks laid in concentric order, for arches or vaults, is also denominated a *Course.*

The disposition of bricks in a wall, of which every alternate course consists of *headers,* and of which every course between every two nearest courses of headers consist of *stretchers,* constitutes *English Bond.*

The disposition of bricks, in a wall, (except at the quoins,) of which every alternate brick in the same course is a *header,* and of which every brick between every two nearest headers is a *stretcher,* constitutes *Flemish Bond.*

It is, therefore, to be understood that *English Bond* is a continuation of one kind throughout, in the same course or horizontal layer, and consists of alternate layers of headers and stretchers, as shown in the plate; the headers serving to bind the wall together, in a longitudinal direction, or lengthwise, and the stretchers to prevent the wall splitting crosswise, or in a transverse direction. Of these evils the first is of the worst kind, and therefore the most to be feared.

A respectable writer on this subject has said, that the old English mode of brick-work affords the best security against such accidents; as work of this kind, wheresoever it is so much undermined as to cause a fracture, is not subject to such accidents, but separates, if at all, by breaking through the solid brick, just as if the wall were composed of one piece.

The antient brick-work of the Romans was of this kind of bond, but the existing specimens of it are very thick, and have three, or sometimes more, courses of brick, laid at certain intervals of the height, stretchers on stretchers, and headers on headers, opposite the return wall, and sometimes at certain distances in the length, forming piers, that bind the wall together in a transverse direction; the intervals between these piers were filled up, and formed panels of rubble or reticulated work;* consequently great substance, with strength, were economically obtained.

It will, also, be understood that *Flemish Bond* consists in placing, in the same course, alternate headers and stretchers, a disposition considered as decidedly inferior in every thing but appearance, and even in this the difference is trifling; yet, to obtain it, strength is sacrificed, and bricks of two qualities are fabricated for the purpose; a firm brick often rubbed and laid in what the workmen term a putty-joint for the exterior, and an inferior brick for the interior, substance of the wall; but, as these did not correspond in thickness, the exterior and interior surface of the wall would not be otherwise connected together than by an outside heading brick, here and there continued of its whole length; but, as the work does not admit of this at all times, from the want of agreement in the exterior and interior courses, these headers can be introduced only where such a correspondence takes place, which, sometimes, may not occur for a considerable space.

Walls of this kind consist of two faces of four-inch work, with very little to connect them together, and what is still worse the interior face often consists of bad brick, little better than rubbish. The practice of Flemish Bond has, notwithstanding, continued from the time of William and Mary, when it was introduced, with many other Dutch fashions, and our workmen are so infatuated with it, that there is now scarcely an instance of the old English Bond to be seen.

The frequent splitting of walls into two thicknesses has been attributed to the Flemish Bond alone, and various methods have been adopted for its prevention. Some have laid laths or slips of hoop-iron, occasionally, in the horizontal joints between the two courses; others have laid diagonal courses of bricks at certain heights from each other; but the effect of the last method is questionable, as, in the diagonal course, by their not being continued to the outside, the bricks are much broken where the strength is required.

Other methods of uniting complete Bond with Flemish facings have been described, but they have been found equally unsuccessful. In *figures* 2 and 4, (*Plate* LXXXV,) the interior bricks are represented as disposed with intention to unite these two particulars; the Flemish facings being on one side of the wall only; but this, at least, falls short of the strength obtained by English Bond. Another evil attending this disposition of the bricks is, the difficulty of its execution, as the adjustment of the bricks in one course must depend on the course beneath, which must be seen or recollected by the workman; the first is difficult from the joints of the under-course being covered with mortar, to bed the bricks of the succeeding course; and, for the workman to carry in his mind the arrangement of the preceding course can hardly be expected from him; yet, unless it be attended to, the joints will be frequently brought to correspond, dividing the wall into several thicknesses, and rendering it subject to splitting, or separation. But, in the English Bond, the outside of the last course points out how the next is to be laid, so that the workman cannot mistake.

The outer appearance is all that can be urged in favour of Flemish Bond, and many are of opinion that, were the English mode executed with the same attention and neatness that is bestowed on the Flemish, it would be considered as equally handsome; and its adoption, in preference, has been strenuously recommended.

In forming English Bond, the following rules are to be observed:

1st, Each course is to be formed of headers and stretchers alternately.

2d, Every brick in the same course must be laid in the same direction: but, in no instance, is a brick to be placed with its whole length along the side of another; but to be so situated that the end of one may reach to the middle of the others which lie contiguous to it, excepting the outside of the stretching-course, where three-quarter bricks necessarily occur at the ends, to prevent a continued upright joint in the face-work.

walls requiring greater strength an eminently hydraulic lime was used. Rubbed work was constructed with a lime putty which was a mixture of lime and water. The lime had to be thoroughly slaked in pits before being mixed with the sand. This mixing had to be done with care ensuring that no lumps of 'free lime' were allowed in the mix. Delayed slaking of lime in a wall could cause serious problems in its stability. A good mortar should be able to resist frost and should develop its durability fairly quickly, particularly in winter. In general, mortar should not have a greater strength than the bricks; if strong dense mortars are used with some types of bricks 'spalling' is likely to occur on the faces of the bricks when they become saturated and subjected to freezing conditions.

The mixtures of the materials greatly depend on where they are to be used. If the work is likely to be subjected to frost soon after being built then it is advisable to enrich the mixes slightly by reducing the sand content by some 10 per cent. A lower percentage of sand should be used for coarse or uniformly fine sand and a larger percentage for well-graded sand. Sand increases in bulk when it becomes damp and it is better, therefore, to weigh the materials to ensure accurate proportions. If volume batching is to be used then it is wise to use gauge boxes rather than resort to measuring by the 'shovelful' (Figure 2.6). When mixing by volume allowance must be made for 'increase of bulking' due to dampness. This increase varies with the type of sand and amount of water, but it can be as much as 30 per cent.

If the facework is to be pointed as the work proceeds, it is necessary to ensure that the same type of sand is used throughout the work, and that careful gauging of the mortar mix is carried out in order to ensure constant colour of the mortar in the facework. Different sands or erratic mixing can result in a patchwork of colours in the facework.

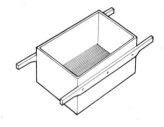

Figure 2.6 *A typical bottomless gauge box for mixing mortar by volume*

METHOD OF WORKING

Brick walling must be of a high standard if it is to be durable and have an attractive appearance. If work is carried out in a slip-shod manner it will be a lasting bad advertisement for both the craftsmen and the builder by whom they are employed and may well have an adverse effect on the business on which both rely.

The main essentials in brickwork are that the work should:
1 be truly plumb or vertical
2 be truly level or horizontal
3 be kept to gauge
4 have perpends in line and truly vertical
5 have a true surface along its face.

3d, A wall, which crosses at a right-angle with another, will have all the bricks of the same level course in the same parallel direction, which completely bonds the angles, as shown by *figures* 1, 3, and 6.

The GREAT PRINCIPLE in the PRACTICE of BRICK-WORK lies in the proclivity or certain motion of absolute gravity, caused by a quantity or multiplicity of substance being added or fixed in resistible matter, and which, therefore, naturally tends downwards, according to the weight and power impressed. In bricklaying, this proclivity, chiefly by the yielding mixture of the matter of which mortar is composed, and cannot be exactly calculated, because the weight of a brick, or any other substance, laid in mortar, will naturally decline according to its substance or quality; particular care should, therefore, be taken, that the material be of one regular and equal quality all through the building; and, likewise, that the same force should be used to one brick as another; that is to say, the stroke of the trowel: a thing or point in practice of much more consequence than is generally imagined; for, if a brick be actuated by a blow, this will be a much greater pressure upon it than the weight of twenty bricks. It is, also, especially to be remarked, that the many bad effects arising from mortar not being of a proper quality should make masters very cautious in the preparation of it, as well as the certain quantity of materials of which it is composed, so that the whole structure may be of equal density, as nearly as can be effected.

Here we may notice a particular which often causes a bulging in large flank walls, especially when they are not properly set off on both sides; that is, the irregular method of laying bricks too high on the front edge: this, and building the walls too high on one side, without continuing the other, often causes the defects. Notwithstanding, of the two evils, this is the least; and bricks should incline rather to the middle of the wall, that one-half of the wall may act as a shore to the other. But even this method, carried too far, will be more injurious than beneficial, because the full width of the wall, in this case, does not take its absolute weight, and the gravity is removed from its first line of direction, which, in all walls, should be perpendicular and united; and it is farther to be considered that, as the walls will have a superincumbent

The basic principles apply for both repair and conservation work but when dismantling it is important never to over-rate the strength or stability of the brickwork and to ensure that walling, and any other structure it may be supporting, is well pinned up with dead raking or flying shores. For small openings it may well be possible to rely on the natural bracketing of the brickwork to carry the walling above the opening, but careful inspection must be carried out first to ensure safe working.

JOINTING AND POINTING

Jointing and pointing are terms given to the final process of finishing a wall to give it a neat appearance. There are two main ways in which joints may be finished off, and each has its advantages and disadvantages. Jointing is the method of finishing off the joints as the work proceeds. A few bricks are laid then the joints are pointed with the aid of a trowel, jointing iron or even a piece of sacking or hessian. The number of bricks which can be laid will depend upon the degree of suction within the bricks, although it is quite common to complete each course and then joint it. The advantages of this method are:

1 That the face joints and bedding mortar are unified, therefore there is less chance of frost damage.
2 It is economical as building and finishing take place together.

The disadvantages are:

1 It is difficult to maintain uniform colour in the joints and a careful watch must be taken over the gauging of the mortar and the type of materials used, particularly the sand.
2 It is difficult to introduce contrasting coloured mortars.
3 If the work is subjected to a heavy rainfall during construction, the joints are difficult to point and it is possible that the facework will be spoilt by mortar running out of the joints down the brickwork.

Pointing is the method whereby the joints of the new work are raked out to a depth of about 15 mm as the work proceeds (Figure 2.7). The raking out is best done with the aid of a piece of wood where soft facing bricks are used, or a cavity wall tie in the case of hard bricks. After the joints have been raked out they should be well brushed out to remove any loose mortar and also to ensure that the arrises are clean. When the walling is completely built and ready for pointing, it should first be scrubbed down with water and a scrubbing brush to remove any dirt or mortar that may be on the face of the wall. Obstinate stains

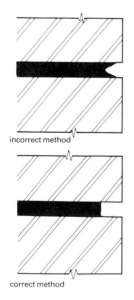

incorrect method

correct method

Figure 2.7 *Raking out joints*

weight to bear, adequate to their full strength, a disjunctive digression is made from the right line of direction; the conjunctive strength becomes divided; and, instead of a whole or united support from the wall, its strength is separated in the middle, and takes two lateral bearings of gravity; each insufficient for the purpose; therefore, like a man overloaded either upon his head or shoulders, naturally bends and stoops to the force impressed; in which mutable state the grievances above noticed usually occur.

Another great defect is frequently seen in the fronts of houses, in some of the principal ornaments of Brick-work, as, arches over windows, &c., and which is too often caused by a want of experience in rubbing the bricks; which is the most difficult part of the branch, and ought to be very well considered: the faults alluded to, are the bulging or convexity in which the faces of arches are often found, after the houses are finished, and sometimes loose in the key or centre bond. The first of these defects, which appears to be caused by too much weight, is, in reality, no more than a fault in the practice of rubbing the bricks too much off on the insides; for it should be a standing maxim (if you expect them to appear straight under their proper weight) to make them the exact guage on the inside, that they bear upon the front edges; by which means their geometrical bearings are united, and all tend to one centre of gravity.

The latter observation, of camber arches not being skewed enough, is an egregious fault; because it takes greatly from the beauty of the arch, as well as its significancy. The proper method of skewing all camber arches should be one-third of their height. For instance, if an arch is nine inches high, it should skew three inches; one of twelve inches, four; one of fifteen inches, five; and so of all the numbers between those. Observe, in dividing the arch, that the quantity consists of an odd number: by so doing, you will have proper bond; and the key-bond in the middle of the arches; in which state it must always be, both for strength and beauty. Likewise observe, that arches are all drawn from one centre; the real point of camber arches is got from the above proportion. First, divide the height of the arch in three parts; one is the dimensions for the skewing; a line drawn from that through

may be removed with the aid of a wire brush but never on soft facings. Some cement stains may be difficult to remove by washing due to setting. In such cases a dilute solution (10 per cent) of spirits of salts (hydrochloric acid) may be used to soften the cement stain, but this should only be used in extreme circumstances and with great care. The salts must be well washed down with water when the stain has been removed.

After scrubbing down, a little time should be allowed for the wall to dry off before pointing begins as it is difficult to point a wet wall without soiling the face of the bricks. There is also the possibility that the bond between the pointing mortar and the bedding mortar will break down through 'drying shrinkage'. Ideally a wall should be damp when it is being pointed; then maximum adhesion will be achieved and drying shrinkage kept to a minimum. The advantages of pointing are:

1   The wall can be thoroughly cleaned before finishing.
2   Coloured mortars may be used easily and to advantage.

The disadvantages are:

1   It is a more costly method than jointing.
2   It takes longer.
3   Great care must be taken with the gauging of the mortar, particularly when using pigments or colouring agents.

Mortars for pointing vary in composition and colour to suit particular requirements. Generally speaking the ultimate strength of the pointing mortar for a wall should not exceed the strength of the bricks with which the wall has been built. This should be watched carefully in conservation work that is carried out on old walls constructed with soft facing bricks. For walls in exposed positions and which are built with hard facing bricks one part of cement to two or three parts of well graded sand may be used. Cement and sand mixtures, however, have a drab grey colour which is not particularly pleasing. A small addition of lime will give a lighter colour. It is good practice to point a trial piece of wall with several mixes about three or four weeks before the pointing work commences to allow the mortars to set, thus ensuring that the right coloured mortar is obtained, as there is always a change in colour when the mortar dries out. Types of pointing used in conservation work are:

Flush pointing — the mortar is pressed into the joint and finished flush with the face of the work. Sometimes a piece of sacking, hessian or a soft brush is rubbed lightly over the joints to make them even, but this should be turned or changed frequently to prevent smearing the bricks.

the point at the bottom to the perpendicular of the middle arch, gives the centre: to which all the rest must be drawn.

Of FOUNDATIONS.—*Rules to be observed in laying Foundations.*

If a projected building is to have cellars, or under-ground kitchens, there will commonly be found a sufficient bottom, without any extra process, for a good solid foundation. When this is not the case, the remedies are to dig deeper, or to drive in large stones with the rammer, or by laying in thick pieces of oak, crossing the direction of the wall, and planks of the same timber, wider than the intended wall, and running in the same direction with it. The last are to be spiked firmly to the cross-pieces, to prevent their sliding, the ground having been previously well rammed under them.

The mode of ascertaining if the ground be solid is by the rammer; if, by striking the ground with this tool, it shake, it must be pierced with a borer, such as is used by well-diggers; and, having found how deep the firm ground is below the surface, you must proceed to remove the loose or soft part, taking care to leave it in the form of steps, if it be tapering, that the stones may have a solid bearing, and not be subject to slide, which would be likely to happen if the ground were dug in the form of an inclined plane.

If the ground prove variable, and be hard and soft at different places, the best way is to turn arches from one hard spot to another. Inverted arches have been used for this purpose with great success, by bringing up the piers, which carry the principal weight of the building, to the intended height and thickness, and then turning reversed arches from one pier to another, as shown in *figure* 18, *(Plate* LXXXV.*)* In this case, it is clear that the piers cannot sink without carrying the arches, and consequently the ground on which they lie, with them. This practice is excellent in such cases, and should, therefore, be general, wherever required.

Where the hard ground is to be found under apertures only, build your piers on these places, and turn arches from one to the other. In the construction of the arches, some attention must be paid to the breadth of the insisting pier, whether it will cover the arch or not; for, suppose the middle

89

Tuck pointing — this method of pointing is often encountered in conservation work. Originally a lime putty was commonly used for this work, but it is now considered more advantageous to use a white putty joint. A little fine sand would also make the mix workable without making it too 'fatty'. The joints in the walling should first be filled flush with a pointing mortar to match the bricks or, alternatively, the joints filled and the walls coloured with a wash of yellow or red ochre or copperas. The putty is then mixed and applied to the joints with the aid of a tuck jointer and pointing rule. The top and bottom edges of the bed joint are cut off with the aid of a 'Frenchman'. The thickness of these joints is usually 3–6 mm to suit requirements.

FOUNDATIONS

In Georgian times it was common practice to build houses with cellars which took the kitchens and sculleries and provided additional storage space. Foundations were dug deep enough to reach a suitable load bearing strata and also, to avoid soil expansion and contraction caused by water particularly in clay soils. In older dwellings the provision of cellars ensured that the foundations were usually deep enough, but the walling was generally built direct from the soil. If the soil was considered to be too soft to carry the walling then builders would ram in large stones or even lay thick pieces of oak across the direction of the wall with thin oak planks laid along and spiked to the cross pieces. The brickwork was then build directly off these planks. Such construction would not be acceptable under modern building regulations.

Another form of construction which was used to overcome the problem of transmitting loads over unstable soils (before the advent of concrete as we understand it), was the inverted arch. This system allowed the weight of the building to be evenly distributed over the whole of the foundation. Many walls were provided with a number of brick offsets built directly off the earth. When a cellar is incorporated in a building, it is often necessary to place a vertical damp-proof course either around or within the external walls. In many older structures the cellars are damp because there is no damp-proofing membrane. In such cases it is usually more economical to line the inside of the walls with a vertical damp proof course and then build a protective wall in front. Similarly the floor should be provided with a damp-proof course and covered with a suitable floor covering.

Older buildings were often erected without regard to damp prevention or, if a damp-proof course was introduced into the walling, it has often fallen into decay or become defective in one way or another. In cases where the damp-proof course has to be replaced it should be done in short sections at a time by

of the piers to rest over the middle of the summit of the arches, then the narrower the piers, the more curvature the supporting arch ought to have at the apex. When arches of suspension are used, the intrados ought to be clear, so that the arch may have the full effect: but, as already noticed, it will also be requisite here that the ground on which the piers are erected be uniformly hard; for it is better that it should be uniform, though not so hard as might be wished, than to have it unequally so: because, in the first case, the piers would descend uniformly, and the building remain uninjured; but, in the second, a vertical fracture would take place, and endanger the whole structure.

WALLS, &c.—The foundation being properly prepared, the choice of materials is to be considered. In places much exposed to the weather, the hardest and best bricks must be used, and the softer reserved for in-door work, or for situations less exposed. In slaking lime, use as much water only as will reduce it to a powder, and only about a bushel of lime at a time, covering it over with sand, in order to prevent the gas, or virtue of the lime, from escaping. This is a better mode than slaking the whole at one time, there being less surface exposed to the air.

Before the mortar is used, it should be beaten three or four times over, so as to incorporate the lime and sand, and to reduce all knobs or knots of lime that may have passed the seive. This very much improves the smoothness of the lime, and, by driving air into its pores, will make the mortar stronger: as little water is to be used in this process as possible. Whenever mortar is suffered to stand any time before used, it should be beaten again, so as to give it tenacity, and prevent labour to the bricklayer. In dry hot summer-weather use your mortar soft; in winter, rather stiff.

If laying bricks in dry weather, and the work is required to be firm, wet your bricks by dipping them in water, or by causing water to be thrown over them before they are used, and your mortar should be prepared in the best way. Few workmen are sufficiently aware of the advantage of wetting bricks before they are used; but experience has shown that works in which this practice has been followed have been much stronger than others wherein it has been neglected. It is particularly serviceable where work is carried up thin, and in putting in grates, furnaces, &c.

In the winter season, so soon as frosty and stormy weather set in, cover your wall with straw or boards; the first is best, if well secured; as it protects the top of the wall, in some measure, from frost, which is very prejudicial, particularly when it succeeds much rain; for the rain penetrates to the heart of the wall, and the frost, by converting the water into ice, expands it, and causes the mortar to assume a short and crumbly nature, and altogether destroys its tenacity.

In working up a wall, it is proper not to work more than four or five feet at a time; for, as all walls shrink immediately after building, the part which is first brought up will remain stationary; and, when the adjoining part is raised to the same height, a shrinking or settling will take place, and separate the former from the latter, causing a crack which will become more and more evident, as the work proceeds. In carrying up any particular part, each side should be sloped off, to receive the bond of the adjoining work on the right and left. Nothing but absolute necessity can justify carrying the work higher, in any particular part, than one scaffold; for, wherever it is so done, the workman should be answerable for all the evil that may arise from it.

The distinctions of *Bond* have already been shown, and we shall now detail them more particularly; again referring to *Plate* LXXXV, in which the arrangement of bricks, in depths of different thicknesses, so to form *English Bond*, is shown in *figures* 1, 3, 6, and 7.

The bond of a wall of nine inches is represented by *fig*. 1. In order to prevent two upright or vertical joints from running over each other, at the end of the first stretcher from the corner, place the return corner-stretcher, which is a header, in the face that the stretcher is in below, and occupies half its length; a quarter-brick is placed on its side, forming together $6\frac{3}{4}$ inches, and leave a lap of $2\frac{1}{4}$ inches for the next header, which lies with its middle upon the middle of the header below, and forms a continuation of the bond. The three-quarter brick, or brick-bat, is called a *closer*.

Another way of effecting this is, by laying a three-quarter bat at the corner of the stretching course; for, when the corner-header comes to be laid over it, a lap of $2\frac{1}{4}$ inches will be left at the end of the stretchers below for the next header; which, when laid, its middle will come over the joint below the stretcher, and in this manner form the bond.

In a fourteen-inch or brick-and-half wall, (*fig.* 3,) the stretching course upon one side, is so laid that the middle of the breadth of the bricks, upon the opposite side, falls alternately upon the middle of the stretchers and upon the joints between the stretchers.

In a two-brick wall, (*fig* 6,) every alternate header, in the heading course, is only half a brick thick on both sides, which breaks the joints in the core of the wall.

In a two-brick and a half wall, (*fig.* 7,) the bricks are laid as shown in *figure* 6.

Flemish Bond, for a nine-inch wall, is represented in *figure* 2, wherein two stretchers lie between two headers, the length of the headers and the breadth of the stretchers extending the whole thickness of the wall.

In brick-and-half Flemish bond, (*fig.* 4,) one side being laid as in *figure* 2, and the opposite side, with a half-header, opposite to the middle of the stretcher, and the middle of the stretcher opposite the middle of the end of the header.

Figure 5 exhibits another arrangement of Flemish Bond, wherein the bricks are disposed alike on both sides of the wall, the tail of the headers being placed contiguous to each other, so as to form square spaces in the core of the wall for half-bricks.

The *Face of an upright-wall*, English Bond, is represented by *figure* 19, and that of Flemish Bond, by *figure* 20.

Brick-nogging is a mode of constructing a wall with a row of posts or quarters, disposed at three feet apart, with brick-work filling up the intervals. In this mode the wall is, generally, either of the thickness or breadth of a brick, and the wood-work flush on both sides with the faces of the bricks. Thin pieces of timber, laid horizontally from post to post, are so disposed

cutting out a course of bricks and laying in a length of damp course material. For this work, bituminous felt with a thin layer of lead in the middle is ideal, as the replacement of bricks which were cut away can be carried out straight away. Also the felt may be unrolled as the work proceeds, thus ensuring a minimum number of joins.

Brick nogging is a method of construction which, rarely seen in modern construction, may be found quite frequently in older structures. A wall is constructed with a row of timber studding at approximately one metre centres and the spaces between filled with brickwork usually of half brick thickness. Usually the walling is laid in stretcher bond, but on more decorative work the walling may be built with herring-bone bond laid either vertically or horizontally. The face of the brickwork is flush with the timbers and to provide anchorage to the brickwork hoop iron cramps are fixed to the timber posts.

ARCHES

Openings in walls are necessary to provide access and light but they cause weaknesses. Great care should be taken therefore, to achieve the maximum strength and stability from the surrounding walling. Wooden lintels were commonly used in older buildings. In order to reduce the loading on the lintel a relieving arch was usually introduced above it. The door or window opening

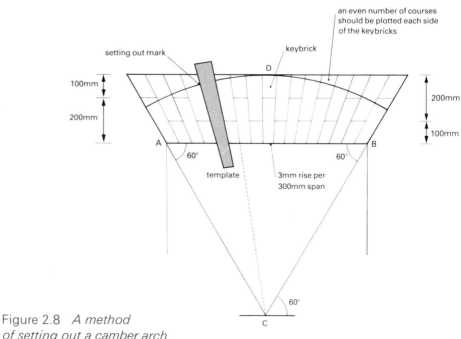

Figure 2.8 *A method of setting out a camber arch*

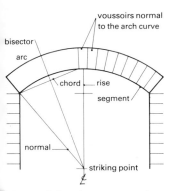

Figure 2.9 *A segmental arch*

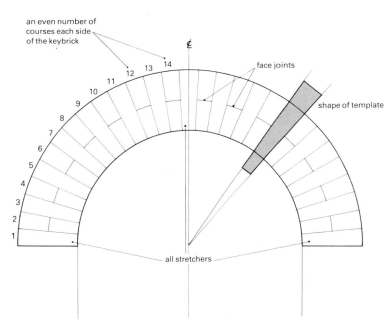

Figure 2.10 *A semi-circular arch*

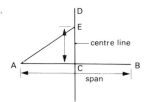

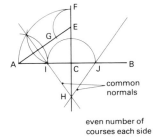

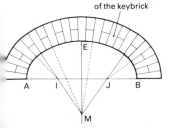

Figure 2.11 *Setting out a three centre arch*

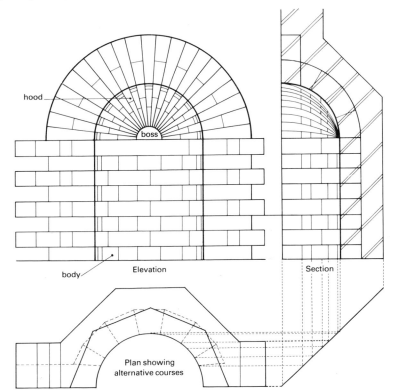

Figure 2.12 *A semi-circular niche*

may also be bridged by means of a brick arch which can be very ornamental and provides a pleasing finish to the opening. Typical arches are as follows:

Camber arch — basically a flat arch, although the voussoirs are set out on an arc (Figure 2.8).

Segmental arch — lines are drawn from each of the springing joints to the height of the rise. These are bisected and where the lines meet is the striking point of the arch curve; all the voussoirs radiate to this point (Figure 2.9).

Semi-circular arch — a simple arch to set out, although it is important to note that in bonded arches there should be an even number of arch courses each side, of the key brick. This is to ensure that the bond of the springer course is the same as for the key course (Figure 2.10).

Three centred or semi-eliptical arch — set out on three arcs and the voussoirs in each segment radiate to the striking point of that segment (Figure 2.11).

GROINS

These are vitually unknown in modern buildings but are often seen in older structures. If repairs are to be carried out to this form of construction it is essential that the work being supported is well pinned up with the aid of shores before work begins. The defective area should then be removed carefully and the space well cleaned and dampened. Formwork or centring is then fixed into place and the groin bricks built over ensuring that as each brick is laid the space between the brick and the work above is made solid and carefully pinned up. Where the groins meet at the apex will require a purpose cut brick which is best obtained by the 'cut and fit' method.

VAULTING

This is a type of construction which is seldom seen these days. An example of this work has been completed in recent years at the Hampshire County Council Offices at Winchester.

CORNICES OR STRING COURSES

These are ornamental courses built into a wall to form an architectural feature. Important points to keep in mind are:

1   Overhanging work must not project so far as to make it unstable.
2   Projecting work should be well tailed down or anchored to the main walling in order to ensure its safety.

as to form the brick-work, between every two posts or quarters, into several compartments in the height of the story; each piece being inserted between two courses of brick, with its edges flush with the faces of the wall.

Figure 13 is that of the head of an aperture, with a part of each jamb, the arch being straight. The manner of drawing the joints are as follow: (see *figure* 17.)

Describe an equilateral triangle upon the width, AB, of the aperture; and, from the vertex, C, or opposite angular point, describe a small circle, with a radius equal to the thickness of a brick. Draw the upper line, DE, forming the extrados, at a distance equal to the height of four bricks from the intrados. Draw the skew-backs, AB, DE, one upon each side; and draw a line parallel to one of the skew-backs touching the small circle, and cutting the extrados line in F, and draw the line CF. Find the point G, in the same manner, and draw GC, and so on to the middle, when the operation will be complete.

By *figure* 14, is represented the head of an aperture with a part of each jamb, the head being an arch formed by two concentric arcs, less than a semi-circle. This kind of arch is called a *Scheme or Segment Arch*. *Figure* 15 is a *semi-circular arch*. *Figure* 16 is a *semi-elliptic arch*, struck from the two centres, A and B, and having the longer axis in a horizontal position.

GROINS.—In *figure* 12 is represented the mode of constructing Groins rising from octagonal piers, and which are very convenient in cellars, where the removal of great weights are required. This is Mr. Tapper's improvement on the common four-sided groin. The improvement consists in raising the angle of the groin from an octagonal pier, instead of a square one, which gives more strength, and, from the corners being removed, renders it more commodious for turning any kind of goods around it: and it is farther to be observed that, in this construction, the angles of the groin are strengthened by carrying the band round the diagonals of equal breadth, and affording better bond to the bricks.

CONSTRUCTION OF BRICK GROINS.—The construction of groins and arches has already been shown in this work, under the head of *Carpentry*, pages

109 to 118. We shall, therefore, only add that the difficulty attending the execution of a brick groin lies in the peculiar mode of appropriating proper bond at the intersecting of the two circles, as they gradually rise to the crown to an exact point. In the meeting or intersecting of these angles, the inner-rib should be perfectly straight, and perpendicular to a diagonal line drawn upon the plan. But no definition, either by lines or description, can be given equal to what may be gained by a little practice. After the centres are set, let the bricklayer apply two or three bricks to an angle, by which he will effectually see how to cut them, as well as the requisites of bond.

The workman must observe, that the manner of turning groins with respect to the sides, is the same as in other arches and centres, except in the angles, which must be traced by applying the bricks. If the arch is to be rubbed and guaged, you must divide each arch into an exact number of parts, and extend the lines till they meet in the groin; by which means you will easily find the curve for the angle, from which you must make your templets; observe, in fixing the centres, that the carpenters raise them something higher at the crown, to allow for settling, which frequently happens, sometimes by the pressure upon the butments, otherwise from the length of the crown.

Be cautious, in building of vaults, that the piers or butments are of sufficient strength: all butments to vaults, whether groined, or only arched, should be one-sixth part of the width of the span; and moreover, if there is any great weight to be sustained, bridgings of timber should be framed, to discharge the weight from the crown of the arch; after a vault or groin is finished, it is highly necessary to pour on a mixture of terras, or lime and water, on the crown; and give it some little time to dry, before you strike the centres, in order to cement the whole together.

CORNICES.—Ornamental brick cornices are represented in *figures* 21 and 22. The first shows the rudiments of the Doric entablature, and the second is a *Dentil Cornice*. Many pleasing dispositions of bricks may thus be made, frequently without cutting, or by chamfering only.

OF A NICHE IN BRICK-WORK.

The formation of niches has already been described under *Carpentry,* pages 134 to 138. The practice of this in Brick-work is the most difficult part of the profession, on account of the very thin size the bricks are obliged to be reduced down to at the inner circle, as they cannot extend beyond the thickness of one brick at the crown or top; it being the usual, as well as much the neatest, method, to make all the courses standing.

The most familiar way to reduce this point to practice, is to draw the front, back, &c., and make a templet of pasteboard, after you have divided the arch for the number of bricks. Observe that, one templet for the standing courses will answer for the front, and one for the side of the brick; and at the top of the straight part, whence the niche takes its spring, remember to make a circle of the diameter of eight or nine inches, and cut this out of pasteboard also, and divide it into the same number of parts as the outward circle; from which you will get the width of your front-templet at the bottom. The reason of this inner circle is to cut off the thin conjunction of points that must all finish in the centre, and which in bricks could never be worked to that nicety; it being impossible to cut bricks correctly nearer than to half an inch thick; within the inner circle the bricks must be lying. It will be necessary to have one templet made convex, to try the faces of bricks to, as well as sitting of them, when they are gauged. The stone you rub the faces of the bricks upon, must be cut at one end in the exact form of the niche, or it will be impossible to face them properly. The level of the flat sides of the bricks is got by dividing the back into the number of parts with the front, and all struck to the centre; from the circle of the front of one brick, set your level, which will answer for the sides of the whole: take care that the bricks hold their full guage at the back; or, when you come to set them, you will have much trouble. Works of this kind, as they require much skill and attention, should bear a handsome price.

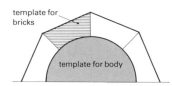

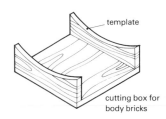

Figure 2.13

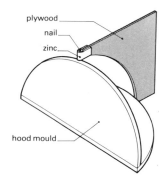

Figure 2.14

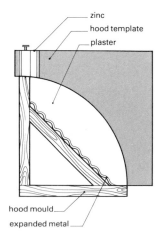

Figure 2.15

NICHES

These have little to do with the general stability of walling as they are simply decorative, but nevertheless must be constructed carefully so that no weakness is caused in the walling. An elevation, vertical section and plan of a semi-circular niche are shown in Figure 2.12. The lower part of the niche is called the body and the upper part is the hood. This type of niche would normally be constructed with very soft bricks, such as red rubbers, so that the shapes can be cut easily. The method for cutting and setting the body is as follows:

1 The plans of the body are set out full size and the bonding for each course drawn.
2 Templates are produced for the brick shapes and secured in a cutting box (Figure 2.13).
3 A full size plywood template is made to the shape of the inside curve of the body.
4 When the bricks have been bedded, squared and sawn they can be bedded in place using the template to check the accuracy of the work, and ensuring that each course is level by being lightly rubbed down with a carborundum stone to take out any irregularities. The bricks can be bedded in a lime putty but white lead mixed with shellac is preferable as this provides a neater and more durable joint.
5 The body is built up to the springing of the hood.

The method for cutting and setting the hood is as follows:

1 The hood must be built on a mould and this can be made by cutting out two templates in the same shape as the inner curve of the hood. The templates should then be fixed together at right angles to each other and strutted together for stability.
2 A plywood template is cut out to the shape of the curve and a piece of zinc or other soft metal is fixed around a nail at one end. This nail is then driven into the vertical template of the mould (Figure 2.14).
3 Some expanded metal is then fixed over the struts; this holds the vertical and horizontal members of the mould together.
4 Plaster is then spread over the expanded metal and built up to the shape of the mould; a perfect shape is obtained with the plywood template which is rotated over the plaster. The plaster mould is then allowed to set (Figure 2.15).
5 The courses are marked off on the front edge of the mould by measuring the distances between the bricks on the intrados. When the distances are

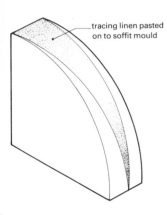

tracing linen pasted on to soffit mould

Figure 2.16

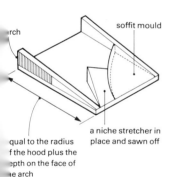

arch

soffit mould

equal to the radius of the hood plus the depth on the face of the arch

a niche stretcher in place and sawn off

Figure 2.17

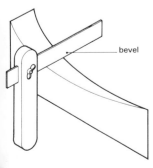

bevel

Figure 2.18

determined the course lines are then projected right over the mould with a flexible straight edge or straight piece of soft metal.

6 Because of the difficulty of cutting the bricks to these fine limits a boss is usually provided at the centre of the hood; this boss will also be set out on the mould.

7 When the course lines are marked, a piece of tracing linen or paper is then placed over any two adjacent lines and the two lines are marked on the linen (Figure 2.16). This should be checked by placing the linen over other pairs of lines on the mould. A piece of timber of sufficient width and length is then cut out to the curve of the mould and the tracing linen is glued on to the centre of this timber. The timber is then reduced to the shape of the tracing linen; this is called a soffit mould.

8 The cutting box is prepared by fixing two lengths of timber to a base board. The shape and length of these timbers will be equal to the distance from the extrados of the hood to its springing as seen in elevation; the width will be equal to one course (Figure 2.17).

9 The soffit mould is fixed into the cutting box, and the positions of the hood courses are marked on to this soffit mould.

10 The bricks which were cut to the same shape as those for the body of the niche are now used for cutting the hood. These are placed in their correct positions in the cutting box and then reduced to the required shape with a bow saw.

11 The correct angle is then applied to the lower and upper edges of the hood voussoirs. This should be marked with a bevel and the angle on the bricks adjusted with a file. This is the final cutting operation (Figure 2.18).

12 The hood mould is now firmly placed in position.

13 The boss is cut to the required shape to fit over the hood mould and is usually hollowed out by a small piece of carborundum. The shape of the hollowed portion of the boss should fit the template which was used to build up the body of the niche.

14 The boss is bedded into place; the hood voussoirs are then carefully bedded around the mould, working from both sides and ensuring that each course coincides with the course marks on the hood mould.

15 When the hood courses have set the final step is to remove the hood mould. Great care must be taken with this operation as the hood mould is heavy and it is very easy to chip the bricks which have been bedded in the niche. The face of the niche is then cleaned with the aid of a fine piece of rounded carborundum stone.

Much skill is needed for this work and great care must be taken at every stage to ensure accuracy. When the work is done well it looks most impressive.

are used for the furnace. In a work of this nature, it is usual to introduce a considerable quantity of old iron hoops, more especially around and over the oven, in order to keep the work together. This precaution is adviseable on all occasions where great heat is required.

In building the oven, the crown is turned with the bricks on end, as shown in the section, *(fig. 4)*; and, instead of centering, the custom is to fill the whole space with sand, clay, or rubbish, which is well trodden down, and fashioned to the shape which it is intended the crown shall be of. When the upper work is finished, the sand is dug out or removed by the mouth of the oven.

Other particulars, interesting to the bricklayer, will be found in the Explanation of Terms, used by Bricklayers and Plasterers, hereafter.

SUBSTANCE OF THE BUILDING ACT, &c.

By the Building-Act, of the 14th of Geo. III., every master-builder, or owner, in the cities of London and Westminster, the Weekly Bills of Mortality, the Parishes of Saint Mary-la-Bonne, Paddington, St. Pancras, and St. Luke's, Chelsea, prior to beginning any building, within the first and seventh rates, must give twenty-four hours notice of his intention to the district-surveyor, descriptive of the edifice to be erected or altered. And the proprietors of houses and grounds must also give three months' notice to pull down old party-walls, party-arches, party fence-walls, or quarter partitions, when decayed, or of insufficient thickness, and to be left with the owner or occupier of such house; and, if empty, such notice to be stuck up on the front door, or front of such house.

The same Act also recites, that every front side or end wall, not being a *party-wall*, shall be deemed an *external wall*.

The thicknesses of party and external walls are described only of the *first, second, third,* and *fourth,* rates of building, the thicknesses of which, together with the prescribed thicknesses of the walls to the backs of the chimnies, in the several party and external walls, are described in *Plates* LXXXVII,

PLATE LXXXII.

PARTY and EXTERNAL WALLS.

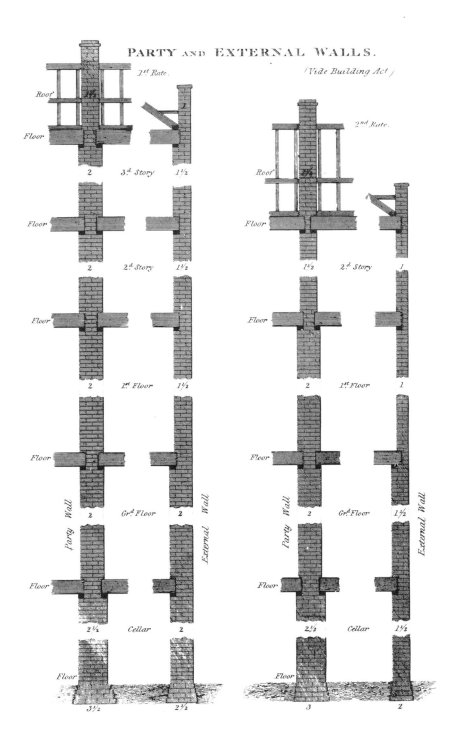

LXXXVIII, and LXXXIX, which will fully elucidate the subject, as regards the construction of party and external walls, with the chimnies therein.

The footings of external walls must have equal projections, except where the adjoining buildings will not admit of it, in which case the builder must be guided by circumstances, and conform, as nearly as possible, to the directions of the Act, under the guidance of the district surveyor.

Walls, and other external inclosures to buildings, of the first, second, third, fourth, and fifth, rates, must be of brick, stone, artificial stone, lead, copper, tin, slate, tile, or iron, or a combination of those articles; but for foundations, wood-planks may be used.

If it should be required to make recesses in external walls, they must be arched, in order that the arches and recesses may each be equal in thickness to one brick: of course recesses cannot be formed in walls which are only one brick thick.

External walls of buildings, of the first, second, third, and fourth, rates, cannot be converted into party-walls, unless they are of the heights and thicknesses above the footings required for party-walls.

Party-walls appertain to such persons who are the owners of first, second, third, or fourth, rate buildings, and who do not intend to have distinct and separate walls on such sides as are contiguous to other buildings. Party-walls must be placed half and half on the ground of each of the owners, without any notice being given, provided it adjoins vacant ground.

Party-walls, or additions thereto, must be carried up at least eighteen inches above the roofs of the adjoining premises, measuring at right angles with the back rafters, and twelve inches above the gutters of the highest buildings against which they may abut, unless the height of the party-walls shall exceed those of the parapets, or blocking courses; in which events, they may be left less than twelve inches above the gutters, at distances of two feet six inches from the fronts of the parapets and blocking courses.

Where it occurs that dormer-windows, or the heads of trap-doors, &c. are fixed upon flats, or roofs, within four feet of party-walls, such party-walls must be carried two feet higher than such dormer or erections previously constructed.

PLATE LXXXVIII

PARTY AND EXTERNAL WALLS.

Vide Building Act.

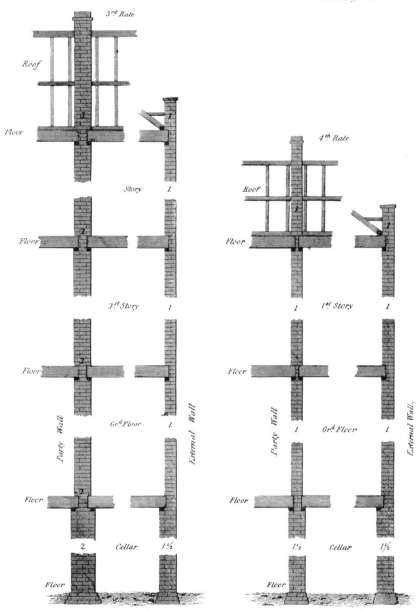

105

PLATE LXXXIX.

BACKS of CHIMNIES in PARTY WALLS.

Back to Back   *(Vide Building Act)*

1st Rate

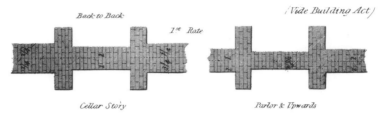

Cellar Story   *Parlor & Upwards*

2d 3d & 4th Rates

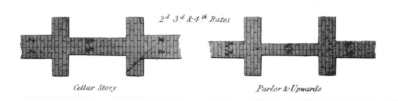

Cellar Story   *Parlor & Upwards*

Not Back to Back   *1st 2d 3d & 4th Rates*

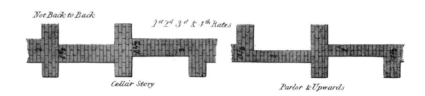

Cellar Story   *Parlor & Upwards*

Note Party Walls may be thinner if against another

1st Rate

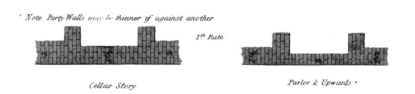

Cellar Story   *Parlor & Upwards ·*

2d 3d & 4th Rates

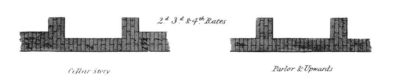

Cellar Story   *Parlor & Upwards*

Recesses must not be made in party-walls, that will reduce any parts thereof to thicknesses less than the Act requires for the highest rates of buildings, to which such walls shall appertain, except for chimney-flues, girders, &c., or for embracing the ends of piers or walls.

Openings must not be made in party-walls, unless to communicate between two or more stacks of warehouses, or between one approved stable-building and another, in which cases, the communications must have iron-doors, not less than a quarter of an inch thick in the panels, fixed in stone frames and sills.

Openings, also, may be made for public passage-ways on the ground-floor for foot passengers, or sufficiently wide for the egress and regress of carriages of every description; as likewise for cattle, provided such passages or carriage-ways are arched over with brick or stone, or brick and stone united, of the thickness of one brick and a half at the least, for first-rate and second-rate buildings, and not less than one brick for the third and fourth rates; and where cellars, or vaults, are required under such passages, or arch-ways, they must be arched over throughout in the same manner, and according to the same proportions before-mentioned. Party-walls, party-arches, or chimney-shafts, old or new, may be cut into, except in the following instances. Where the fronts of buildings are in lines with each other, incisions may be cut, either in the rear or principal fronts, for the purposes of inserting the ends of any new external walls of any intended adjoining building, but such incisions must not be made more than nine inches deep from the outward faces of the external walls, nor beyond the centres of the party-walls. And for the more convenient insertion of bressumers and story-posts, to be fixed on the ground-floors, either in the back or principal front walls, recesses may be cut from the foundations of the new walls to the heights of the bressumers, fourteen inches deep from the outward faces of such walls, and four inches wide in the cellar stories, and two inches wide in the ground stories.

Party-walls may also be cut into for the purposes of tailing-in stone steps or stone landings, or for bearers to wood-stairs, or for laying in stone corbels, for supporting chimney-jambs, girders, purlines, binding or trimming joists, or any other principal timbers.

Perpendicular recesses may also be cut in party-walls, which are not less than one brick and a half thick, for the purposes of inserting walls or piers; but the incisions must not be more than fifteen inches deep; and where two or more incisions are made in the same description of walls, they must not approximate nearer to each other than ten feet.

Incisions may be made in party-walls for any of the preceding purposes, that is, provided they are not likely to injure, remove, or endanger the timbers, chimnies, flues, or internal finishings, of the adjoining buildings. The incisions, indents, cuts, or recesses, before-mentioned, must be made good as soon as possible; and during the time such operations are carrying into effect, the buildings adverted to must be carefully pinned up, where required, with bricks, stone, slate, tile, or iron-bedded, in mortar.

The portions of houses, or other buildings, which are contrived to be built over public passages, or gateways, being divided, and again sub-divided, into rooms and stories, the property of different owners, when built or re-built, must have party-walls and party-arches, at least a brick and a half thick, for first and second-rate buildings, and one brick thick for second and third-rate buildings, between the several rooms or stories belonging to the different proprietors; but the buildings to the Inns of Court are exempt from the latter regulation, it being deemed sufficient to build party-walls where any rooms or chambers communicate with the stair-cases, the walls in which instances are subject to the same regulations as other party-walls.

Where the lower-rate buildings adjoin those of higher rates, the additions intended to be made thereto must be built according to the rules prescribed for the higher rates.

Party-walls, which are built against other buildings, must be of the same thicknesses with the walls of the highest adjoining buildings in the stories next below the roofs; but such party-walls must not be erected, unless they can be done with the greatest safety to the adjoining walls or buildings.

Dwelling-houses, or other buildings, four stories high from the foundations, exclusive of the rooms in the roofs, must have party-walls, according to the third-rate of buildings, although such houses, or other buildings, estimated by the numbers of squares on the ground-floor, are of the fourth-rate. And every dwelling-house, or other building, exceeding four stories in height from the foundations, exclusive of rooms in the roofs, must have party-walls according to the first-rate, although such houses, or other buildings, are not of the first-rate, that is, according to the number of squares on the ground-floor.

Chimnies must not be erected on timbers, unless it be indispensably necessary to pile and plank the foundations.

Chimnies may be built in party-walls back to back; but they must not be less in thicknesses, from the centres of such walls, than are described in the plate of plans elucidating the intention of the Act of Parliament, as regards the construction of chimnies in party and external walls.

The breasts of chimnies in party-walls must not, in any instance, be less than one brick thick in the cellar, and half a brick in every other story, and the divisions or widths, between the flues, must never be less than half a brick thick. The flues in party-walls may be built against each other, but must not approach nearer than two inches to the centres of such walls.

The breasts of chimnies and backs, together with the flues, must, in all cases, be rendered or pargetted, care being taken that timbers are not any where introduced for supporting the breasts, which must be carried by strong brick or stone arches, assisted by wrought-iron bars, as many as are requisite to each opening.

The flues in party-walls against vacant ground, must be lime-whited, or marked in some durable manner, and immediately after any other houses are erected against them, whatever is deemed requisite to be done to the flues must, as soon as possible, be completed.

Brick-flues, or funnels, must not be made on the outside of any building, of the first, second, third, or fourth, rates, next to any street, square, road, or passage, so as to project beyond the general line of the buildings; nor must any funnel, or pipe of iron, copper, or tin, for the conveyance of smoke or steam, be fixed near any public street, or court, &c., to buildings of the first, second, third, or fourth, rate description; nor must any pipes, for the conducting of smoke, be fixed within any of the before-mentioned buildings, nearer than fourteen inches to any timber, or other materials subject to take fire.

Every dwelling-house, which exceeds NINE squares of building on the ground-floor, including internal and external walls, are deemed the first-rate or class of buildings, and subject to be built in manner before-described; and, likewise, according to the thicknesses of the walls, drawn and figured in the sections and plans hereunto referred.

Dwelling-houses, also, which exceed FIVE squares of building, and are not more than NINE, are deemed second-rate houses.

Dwelling-houses, also, which exceed THREE squares and ONE-HALF, and are not more than FIVE squares, are deemed third-rate houses.

Dwelling-houses, also, which shall not exceed THREE and ONE-HALF squares, are deemed fourth-rates.

Fifth, sixth, and seventh, rate buildings, may be built of any dimensions, provided the conditions, stipulated in the Act of Parliament, are adhered to.

DISTRICT-SURVEYORS' FEES.

	£.	s.	d.
For every first-rate building	3	10	0
For every alteration or addition	1	15	0
For every second-rate	3	3	0
For every alteration or addition	1	10	0
For every third-rate	2	10	0
For every alteration or addition	1	5	0
For every fourth-rate	2	2	0
For every alteration or addition	1	1	0
For every fifth-rate	1	10	0
For every alteration or addition	0	15	0
For every sixth-rate	1	1	0
For every alteration or addition	0	10	6
For every seventh-rate	0	10	6
For every alteration or addition	0	5	0

The District-Surveyors are elected by the Magistrates for the Counties of Middlesex and Surrey.

PLATE 1.

FIRST-RATE HOUSE.

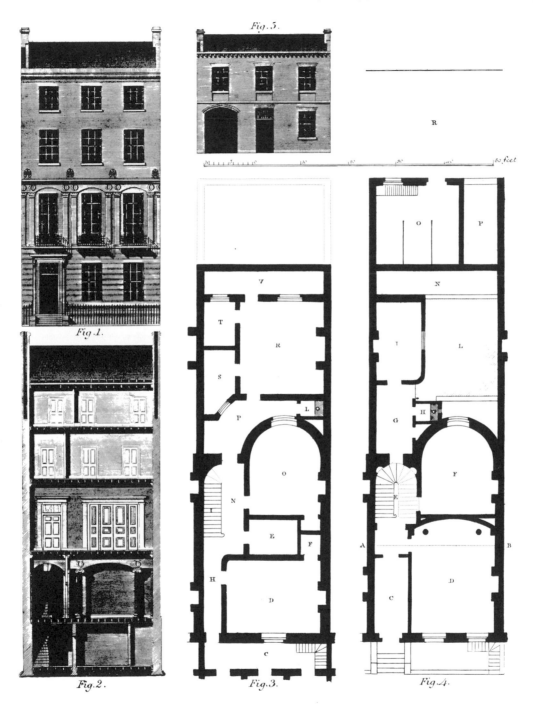

Fig. 5.

R

Fig. 1.

Fig. 2.

Fig. 3.

Fig. 4.

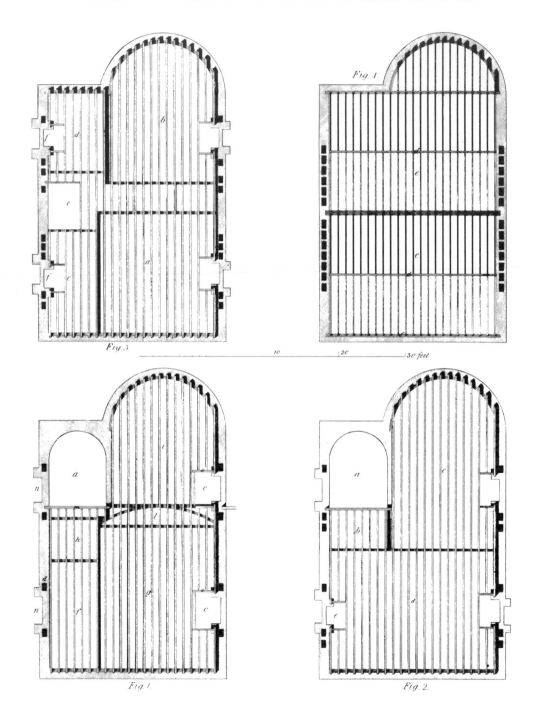

Fig. 4.

Fig. 3.

10   20   30 feet

Fig. 1.

Fig. 2.

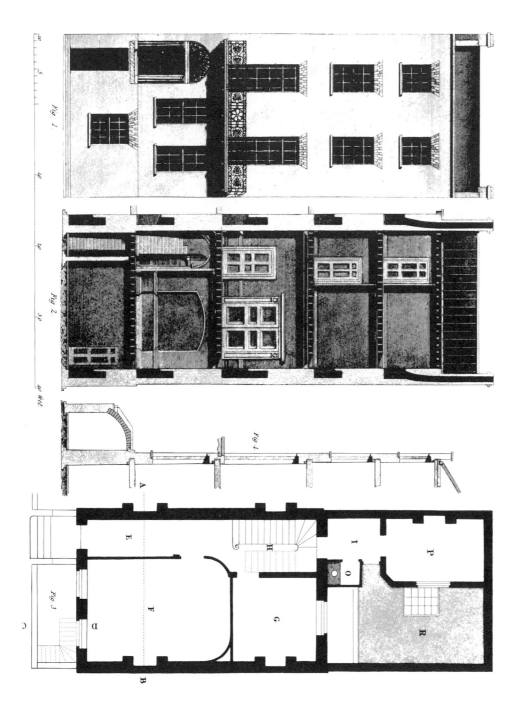

PLATE III.

SECOND RATE HOUSE.

PLATE IV

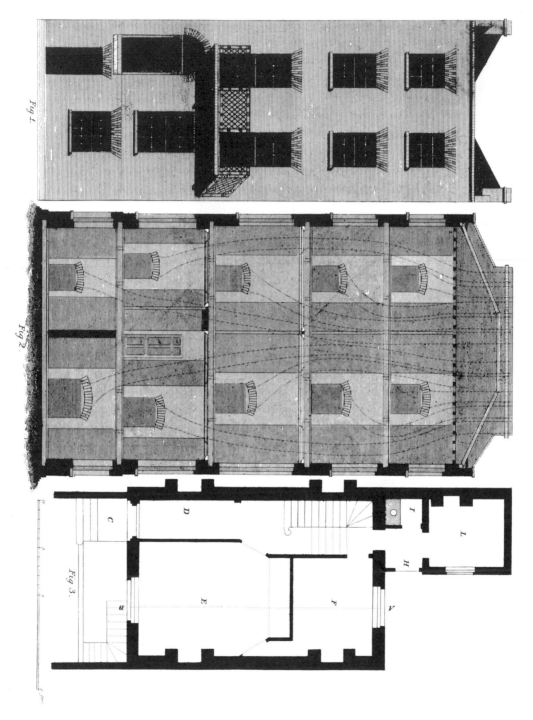

Fig 1.

Fig 2.

Fig 3.

THIRD RATE HOUSE.

PLATE V

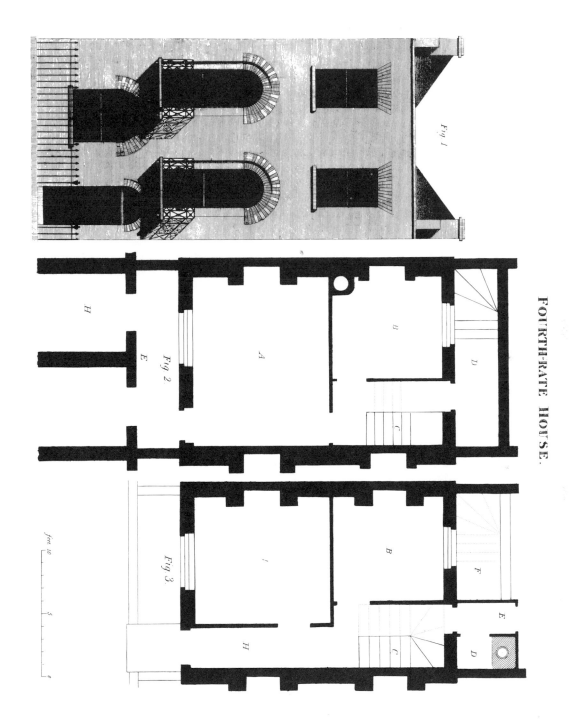

Fig 1

Fig 2

Fig 3

FOURTH-RATE HOUSE.

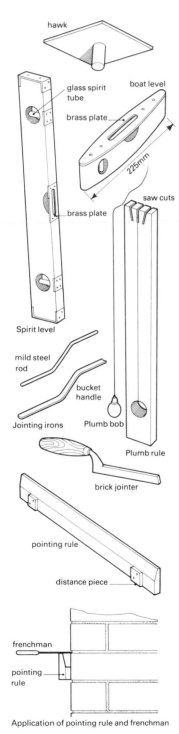

hawk

glass spirit tube

brass plate

boat level

225mm

brass plate

saw cuts

Spirit level

mild steel rod

bucket handle

Jointing irons

Plumb bob

Plumb rule

brick jointer

pointing rule

distance piece

frenchman

pointing rule

Application of pointing rule and frenchman

Figure 2.19

TOOLS

The basic tools used by a bricklayer today include the following (Figure 2.19):
Brick trowels — made in sizes ranging from 225 to 350 mm and although it may be felt that the larger sizes may produce more work, there is no evidence to prove this. It is found that a 250 or 275 mm blade is suitable for most general work. Trowels are available with right-handed blades or left-handed ones for left-handed craftsmen.

Pointing trowels — generally range in size from 75 to 150 mm; the smaller ones are often referred to as dotters, and the larger ones as bed jointers.

Club hammers — 0.90 or 1.135 kg are generally heavy enough for cutting bricks or cutting away holes and chases in brickwork.

The Bolster or Boaster — used in conjunction with the club hammer for cutting bricks and should always be used for this purpose in preference to a trowel.

The brick hammer or comb hammer — older types had heads which consisted of a hammer at one end and a blade at the other. The modern type has, instead of the blade, a slotted end into which a blade or comb is inserted. The comb hammer is slotted at both ends of the head so that a comb may be inserted in one end and a blade in the other. No sharpening of blades is necessary; the worn blade is changed for a new one as the blades and combs can be purchased quite cheaply. These hammers are used for trimming the bricks after they have been cut with a hammer and bolster.

Spirit levels — available in various lengths ranging from about 225 mm to 1.2 m. The shorter lengths are used for adjusting small work or individual bricks whereas the longer levels are used for plumbing the angles of work vertically and levelling the courses horizontally. Levels are available with fixed or adjustable bubble tubes; the latter is preferable because if the level is inaccurate it is a relatively simple matter to readjust the bubble.

The plumb rule — is not used so often today but it is an excellent tool and has the virtue of always being accurate and needing no adjustment. The plumb bob is usually of lead, weighing about 2 kg.

The rule — usually made of boxwood the 600 mm four-fold rule is generally the most convenient as it fits into the pocket quite easily, although some craftsmen prefer the metre rule. An alternative type is a 2 m steel tape which rolls into a small steel container, is ideal for making measurements in confined spaces and is easily carried in the pocket.

116

AN EXPLANATION OF TERMS, AND DESCRIPTION OF TOOLS, USED IN BRICKLAYING AND PLASTERING.

ANGLE FLOAT. See *Float*.

BASS.—A short trough for holding mortar, when tiling the roof: it is hung to the lath.

BASTARD STUCCO. See *Stucco*.

BAY.—A strip or rib of plaster between screeds, for regulating the floating rule. See *Screeds*.

BED OF A BRICK.—The horizontal surface as disposed in a wall.

BEDDING STONE.—A straight piece of marble used to try the rubbed side of a brick.

BRICKLAYER'S TOOLS.—The principal tools used by bricklayers are represented in *plate* XC. The *Brick-trowel, (fig. 1,)* is used for taking up and spreading mortar, and likewise for cutting bricks to any required size: this last use renders it necessary that they should be made of the best steel, well tempered.

The *Hammer* used by bricklayers *(fig. 7,)* is adapted either for driving, or dividing bricks, and for cutting holes in brick-work, &c. To suit it for these different purposes, one end of the head is formed like the common hammer; and the other end is furnished with a kind of axe, similar to that used by carpenters, only much narrower in proportion to its length. The handle is

PLATE XC.

BRICKLAYERS TOOLS.

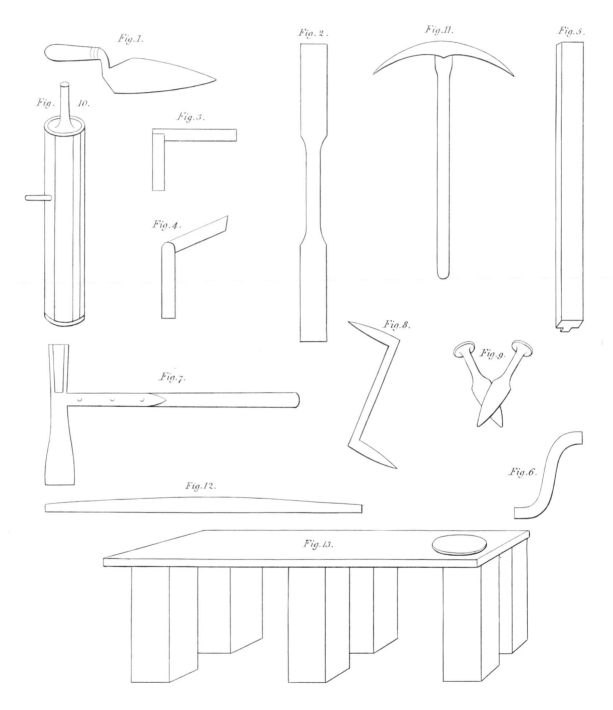

Fig.1. Fig.2. Fig.11. Fig.5.

Fig. 10. Fig.3.

Fig.4.

Fig.8.

Fig.9.

Fig.7.

Fig.6.

Fig.12.

Fig.13.

placed much nearer to the striking than to the cutting part of the head. The hammer employed for dividing and pulling down old brick walls, instead of the axe part, more nearly resembles an adze, but is not so broad in proportion to its length.

The *Plumb Rule* is about four feet in length, and it is furnished with a line and plummet, to direct the workman in carrying up walls vertically. It consists of a well-seasoned board, of moderate thickness and breadth, and about four feet long. Down the middle of one side of this board a straight line is drawn, so that a cord which is fastened to the top, equi-distant from the arris on each side of it, may hang straight therein. To this cord a weight is attached, in order to shew the inclination of the cord more correctly, and a hole is cut in the bottom to admit it. The workman, in order to carry up his wall perpendicularly, applies either of the sides of this rule to the wall, so that the plummet and its cord may face him; and if the cord of the plummet does not coincide with the line on the rule, before the mortar becomes dry, he sets the bricks farther in or out, according to circumstances.

The *Level*, used by bricklayers, is similar to that of the carpenter, described in page 233. Its length varies from six to twelve feet. If to the middle of a long narrow edge of a board of the same thickness, but about double the length of the plumb-rule, one end of the plumb-rule were joined at right angles, as the lower edge or side of the piece thus added to the rule would become the surface placed on walls, to ascertain whether they are horizontal or not, the plumb-line would thus become a level. The correctness of a level is determined by placing it vertically on any flat surface, and lowering or raising the support till the cord of the plummet exactly coincides with the line on the perpendicular rule. When this is done, reverse the ends, and if the same effect takes place, the level is true; but if it does not, the bottom of the board must be shot, till this coincidence takes place. The perpendicular and horizontal parts of the level are not only fastened together by a tenon and mortise, but two braces are likewise added, in a slanting direction, from the horizontal piece nearly to the top of the perpendicular one, in order to give it greater firmness.

The hawk — generally made out of a piece of timber 200 mm square (or a piece of resin-bonded plywood serves the purpose admirably) with a handle fixed underneath and used for carrying the mortar when pointing. Aluminium hawks are also available; these are lightweight and convenient for handling.

Pins — made of steel and purchased in pairs and the line in 'knots'. For general purposes two knots of line are sufficient on one pair of pins.

Brick jointers — from 60 to 125 mm long and used for forming recessed joints.

Pointing rule — light, wooden straightedge usually 1 m long, 50 x 6 mm thick in section, and with two corks or distance pieces fixed on the back to allow the pointing mortar-droppings to fall through.

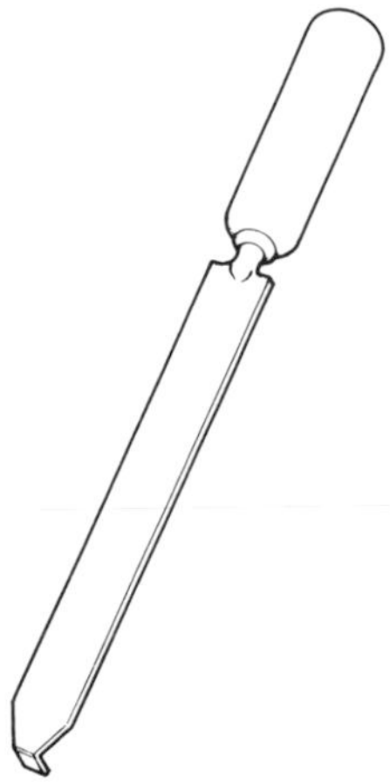

The frenchman — usually made from an old table knife rather than purchased. The end of the knife is heated and with a hammer and chisel is cut back about 25 mm on each side of the end. Then the end is re-heated and bent over about 9 mm from the end (Figure 2.20).

Figure 2.20 *A frenchman ready for use*

Jointing iron — usually made from an old bucket handle or piece of mild steel rod.

The soft brush — for cleaning down the face work when completed.

Closer and bat gauges — easily made and very useful for marking off bats and closers and keeping them all even in size.

Cutting bench — should be of a convenient height and provided with an overhead beam so that the bricks can be held firmly in position by means of struts while they are being sawn. The bench may be of stout timber construction (Figure 2.21).

Rubbing stone — flat piece of York stone 375 to 450 mm square and 50 to 75 mm thick is excellent for this purpose.

Cutting boxes — these have two sides fixed to a base and may be of fixed shape or adjustable (Figure 2.22).

Bow saw — used for sawing the bricks. It has a twisted wire for its cutter or blade, tensioned by means of a tourniquet at the top of the saw. The wire blades may be made by doubling a length of steel (about 20 standard wire gauge [swg]) over a nail and fixing the other end to a breast drill. The drill is then turned to obtain an evenly twisted blade (Figure 2.23).

120

Figure 2.21 *Design for a cutting bench*

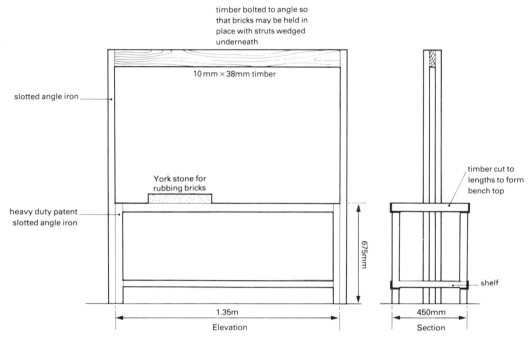

timber bolted to angle so that bricks may be held in place with struts wedged underneath

10 mm × 38mm timber

slotted angle iron

York stone for rubbing bricks

heavy duty patent slotted angle iron

675mm

1.35m

Elevation

timber cut to lengths to form bench top

shelf

450mm

Section

Figure 2.22 *An adjustable cutting box*

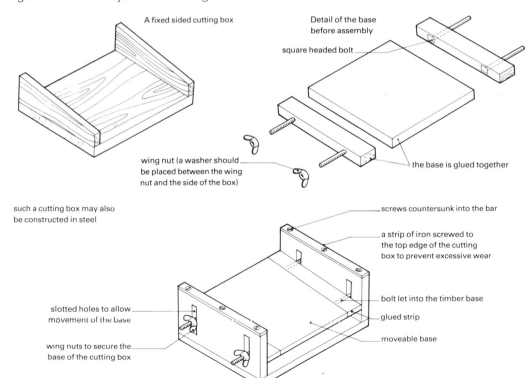

A fixed sided cutting box

Detail of the base before assembly

square headed bolt

wing nut (a washer should be placed between the wing nut and the side of the box)

the base is glued together

such a cutting box may also be constructed in steel

screws countersunk into the bar

a strip of iron screwed to the top edge of the cutting box to prevent excessive wear

slotted holes to allow movement of the base

wing nuts to secure the base of the cutting box

bolt let into the timber base

glued strip

moveable base

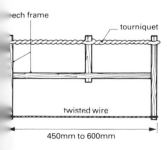

ench frame

tourniquet

twisted wire

450mm to 600mm

Figure 2.23 *A typical bow saw*

121

The *Large Square* is employed for setting out the sides of a building at right-angles.

The *Small Square, (fig.* 3,) is used for trying the bedding of bricks, and squaring the soffits across their breadth.

The *Bevel, (fig.* 4,) is employed in drawing the soffit line on the face of the bricks.

The *Rod* is from five to ten feet in length, and is used for measuring lengths, heights, and breadths, with more facility than could be done by a pocket-rule. The feet are divided by notches, and one of those next to the extremity of the rod is subdivided into inches.

The *Measuring-Tape* is a kind of strong tape, graduated, marked, and coiled up by a little winch into a cylindrical box; and thus it unites the portableness of the pocket-rule, with the greater despatch of the rod.

The *Jointing-Rule (fig.* 5,) is about eight or ten feet long, and about four inches broad. It is used for running the joints of brick-work. When it is designed for the use of two bricklayers, the latter length is employed.

The *Jointer (fig.* 6,) is an iron tool, used along with the jointing-rule, to mark the joints of brick work horizontally and vertically. Its form nearly resembles an ∽, with less flexure in proportion.

The *Raker, (fig.* 8,) is a piece of iron, pointed with steel, with two knees or angles, so as to resemble a Z, if the connecting stroke of the top and bottom were perpendicular instead of slanting; so that the pointed parts are of equal lengths, and stand at contrary sides of the middle part. It is used to pick or rake loose and decayed mortar out of the joints of old walls, that are intended to be re-filled with new mortar, or fresh pointed.

The *Hod* resembles the half of a rectangular box, divided so as to consist of two boards at right angles to each other, and a third board to shut up one end. From the middle of the angular ridge, formed by the meeting of the two sides, projects the handle, which is a pole of about four feet long. That part of the ridge which is between the back or end board, is generally covered with several thicknesses of leather; or with leather stuffed with wool, in order that the angle of the ridge may not cut the shoulder of the labourer.

This utensil is used for carrying bricks or mortar for supplying the brick-layer. When used for mortar, it is customary to strew the internal surface of the hod with clean dry sand, to prevent the mortar from adhering to the wood.

The *Line Pins*, *(fig. 9,)* consist of two iron pins, with a line of about sixty feet, fastened by one of its extremities to each. It is used by being stretched close to the wall, and removed at proper intervals as the work advances, in order to guide the workmen in laying the different courses of bricks exactly straight.

The *Rammer*, used by bricklayers, *(fig. 10,)* is similar to that of paviors, and it is used for ascertaining whether ground is sufficiently strong to bear a foundation. It is also used for giving unstable ground its proper degree of compression, in order to prevent fractures in the walls; which would naturally ensue, if the foundation were laid when the ground is in a loose state.

The *Iron Crow* is a long bar of iron used for breaking through old walls, or raising heavy bodies out of the ground.

The *Pick-axe*, *(fig. 11,)* consists of a long bar of iron, of considerable thickness in the centre, which is furnished with a hole or mortise for receiving a handle. The two arms on the sides of the centre and handle generally diminish or taper considerably towards their extremities, in order that their points may more readily enter the earth in digging; or be inserted between bricks or stones to separate them. The arms, likewise, incline towards the handle, so as to form the segment of a circle. The pick-axe is frequently used in conjunction with the iron crow.

The *Compasses*, used by the bricklayer, are similar to those used by the carpenter and joiner, and are employed for traversing arches.

The *Grinding-Stone* is used for sharpening axes, hammers, &c., and scarcely, perhaps, requires to be mentioned.

The *Scribe* is a pike, or large nail, ground to a sharp point, and used for marking the bricks in the part where they are to be cut.

The *Chopping-block* is made of any chance piece of wood that can be obtained, of about six or eight inches square, when for two men to work thereon; and lengthened in proportion for four or more. It is generally supported, about two feet three inches from the ground, upon two or more fourteen-inch brick piers. It is better to have several blocks when they can be obtained, in preference to allowing many hands to be employed at one; because the vibrations communicated by one workman are liable to inconvenience another.

The Chopping-block is used for reducing bricks to any required form by means of the axe.

The *Banker (fig. 13,)* is a bench, from six to twelve feet in length, according to the number of men it is intended to accommodate; from two to three feet in breadth, and about one inch thick. An old ledged door may easily be converted into a banker, by placing its back edge against a wall, and supporting the front with three, four, or five posts: it is used for rubbing and guaging bricks for arch-work. B, in the figure, represents the rubbing-stone.

The *Camber-slip (fig. 12,)* is a piece of board of any length or breadth, made convex on one or both edges, and generally something less than an inch in thickness: it is made use of as a rule. When only one side or edge is cambered, it rises about one inch in six feet, and is employed for drawing the soffit lines of straight arches: when the other edge is curved, it rises only about one half of the other, *viz.* about half an inch in six feet, and is used for drawing the upper side of the arch, so as to prevent its becoming hollow by the settling of the arch. But some persons prefer having the upper side of the arches straight; and, in this case, the upper edge of the arch is not cambered. When the bricklayer has drawn his arch, he gives the camber-slip to the carpenter, who by it forms the centre to the curve of the soffit. The bricklayer, in order to prevent the necessity of having many camber-slips, should always be provided with one which is sufficiently large for the widest aperture likely to be arched.

The *Mould* is used for forming the face and back of the brick to its proper taper; and, to this end, one edge of the mould is brought close to the bed of the brick previously squared. The mould has a notch for every course of the arch.

The *Templet* is an instrument for taking the length of the *stretcher* and the width of the *header,* in building walls, &c.

The *Tin Saw* is used for cutting, to about the eighth of an inch deep, the soffit lines made, first by the edge of the bevel on the face of the brick, and then by the edge of the square on the bed of the brick. This incision is made in order to form an entrance for the brick-axe, that it may reduce the bricks to the proper form for arches, without splintering or jagging their edges. This saw is likewise used for cutting the false joints of headers and stretchers.

The *Brick-axe* is used for reducing or cutting off the soffits of bricks to the saw-cuttings, and the sides to the lines drawn by the scribe. Much of the labour required for rubbing the bricks may be removed by the axe being managed with dexterity.

The *Rubbing-Stone,* B, (*fig.* 13,) is a rough grained stone, of about twenty inches in diameter, generally fixed at one end of the banker, on a bed of mortar. It is used for smoothing those bricks which have been brought to their proper form by the axe. The headers and stretchers in returns, which are not axed, are likewise dressed upon the rubbing-stone. If the grain of the stone is found not to be sufficiently sharp to reduce the bricks with the necessary expedition, a little sand will tend to remove this deficiency.

The *Bedding-Stone* consists of a marble slab, from eighteen to twenty inches in length, and from eight to ten wide, and of any thickness. It is used to try whether the surface of a brick, which has been already rubbed, be straight, so that it may fit upon the leading skew back, or leading end of the arch.

The *Float-stone* is used for taking out the axe-marks, and smoothing the surfaces of curved work, as the cylindrical backs, and spherical heads of niches. But, for this purpose, the Float-stone must itself be curved in the reverse form, though of a radius equal to that intended for the brick, so that it may coincide, as nearly as possible, with the brick.

CEILING.—The upper side of an apartment, opposite to the floor, generally finished with plastered work. Ceilings are set in two different ways, the best is where the setting coat is composed of plaster and putty, commonly called *gauge*.

CLINKER.—A portion of a brick, used where the distance will not permit a whole one in length.

COARSE STUFF.—See *Lime* and *Hair*.

COAT.—A stratum, or thickness, of plaster-work, done at one time.

COMPO, or *Compos*, used in outside stucco-work, implies the materials with which Roman or any other similar cement is composed: that is, when the component parts are all incorporated. To ascertain their different qualities, the same must be decomposed, or analysed.

COURSE.—A horizontal stratum, layer, or row, of bricks, extending along the whole length of a wall.

DERBY.—A two-handed float.

DIE.—Plaster is said to die when it loses its strength.

DOTS.—Patches of plaster put on to regulate the floating-rule in making screeds and bays.

FINE STUFF, for plastering, is made of lime slaked and sifted through a fine sieve, and mixed with a due quantity of hair, and sometimes a small quantity of fine sand.

FINISHING, in plastering, is the best coat of three-coat work, when done for stucco. The term *setting* is commonly used, when the third coat is made of fine stuff for papering.

FIRST COAT, of two-coat work, in plastering, is denominated *laying* when on lath, and *rendering*, when on brick: in three-coat work upon lath it is denominated *pricking-up;* and upon brick, *roughing-in*.

FLOAT.—An implement used in plastering for forming the second coat of three-coat work to a given form of surface.—An *Angle-Float* is a float made to any internal angle to the planes of both sides of a room. The *Derby* is a two-handed float.

FLOATED LATH and PLASTER, set fair for paper, is three-coat work; the first *pricking-up*, the second *floating*, and the third, or *setting coat* of fine-stuff, understood to be *pricked-up,* as there is no floated work without pricking-up.

FLOATED, RENDERED, and SET.—A common term explained in the previous definitions.

FLOATED WORK, in plastering.—That which is pricked-up, floated and set, or roughed-in.

FLOATING, in plastering.—The second coat of three-coat work.

FLOATING-RULES, used by plasterers, have been already noticed. They are of every size and length.

FLOATING-SCREED, in plastering, differs from cornice-screeds, in this, that the former is a strip of plaster, and the latter wooden rules for running the cornice. See *Screed.*

GAUGE, in plastering.—A mixture of fine-stuff and plaster, or of coarse-stuff and plaster, used in finishing the best ceilings, and for mouldings, and sometimes for setting walls.

HAWKE.—A board, with a handle projecting perpendicularly from the underside, for holding plaster.

LATHS.—Small slips of wood nailed to rafters, for hanging the tiles or slates upon. For laths used in plastering, see page 372.

Double Fir Laths are laths three-eighths of an inch thick, single laths being a bare quarter, or less than a quarter of an inch.

LATH, FLOATED and SET FAIR.—These words bear the same meaning as lath pricked-up, and floated and set, to which the reader is referred.

LATH, LAYED and SET, in plastering, is two-coat work; only the first coat, called *laying,* is put on without scratching, unless it be with the points of a broom. This is generally coloured on walls, and whited on ceilings.

LATH, PLASTERED, SET, and COLOURED, is the same with lath, layed, set, and coloured, to which the reader is also referred.

LATH, PRICKED-UP, FLOATED and SET, for PAPER, is three-coat work; the first is *pricking-up,* the second *floating,* and the third the *finishing* of fine-stuff.

LAYING, in plastering.—The first coat on lath of two-coat plaster, or *set-work.* It is not scratched with the scratcher; but its surface is roughed by sweeping it with a broom; it differs only from *rendering* on its application. *Rendering* is applied to the first-coat work upon brick; whereas *laying* is the first of two-coat work upon lath.

LAYING ON TROWELS.—The trowels used for laying on plaster.

LIME and HAIR, in plastering.—A mixture of lime and hair used in first-coating and in floating: it is otherwise denominated *coarse-stuff*. In floating, more hair is used than in first-coating.

MITERING ANGLES.—Making good the internal and external angles of mouldings.

MORTAR.—A preparation of lime and sand mixed with water, and used as a cement, as already explained in pages 329, 371, &c.

MOULDINGS, in plastering. When not very large, mouldings are first run with coarse gauge to the mould, then with fine-stuff, then with putty and plaster, and, lastly, run off, or finished, with raw putty. When mouldings are large, coarse-stuff is first put on, then it is filled with tile-heads or brick-bats, and run off successively with coarse gauge, fine-stuff gauge, putty gauge, and finished with raw putty. In running cornices, there must always be screeds upon the ceiling, whether the ceiling is floated or not.

PARGETING.—A term derived from *parget,* or the plaster-stone, and used for the plastering of walls; sometimes for the plaster itself.

PLASTER.—The material with which ornaments are cast, and with which the fine-stuff of gauge for mouldings and other parts are mixed.

PRICKING-UP, in plastering.—The first-coating of three-coat work upon laths. The material used is coarse stuff, sometimes, in London, mixed up with drift road sand, scrapings, or Thames sand, and its surface is always scratched with an instrument used for that purpose.

PUGGING.—The materials composed of bricks and mortar, &c. introduced between the joists of floors, in order to prevent the communication of sound, or to deaden it in the interval from one story to another.

PUTTY.—A very fine cement, made of lime only.

RENDERED and FLOATED, in plastering, is three-coat work, more commonly called *floated, rendered,* and *set.*

RENDERED, FLOATED, and SET, for paper, should be termed *roughed-in.* Floated and set, for paper, is three-coat work; the first, lime and hair upon brick-work; the second, the same stuff, with a little more hair, floated with a long rule; the last, fine stuff, mixed with white hair.

RENDERED and SET.—The same as set-work. See *Set-work.*

ROUGH-CAST.—The overlaying of walls with mortar, without smoothing it with any tool whatever. This has been already noticed. See page 380.

ROUGHING-IN, in plastering.—The first coat of three-coat work.

ROUGH-RENDERING, in plastering, means one coat rough.

ROUGH-STUCCO. See *Stucco.*

SAIL-OVER.—A term denoting the over-hanging of one or more courses of bricks beyond the naked of the wall.

SECOND COAT, in plastering.—Either the finishing coat, as in layed and set, or in rendered and set; or it is the floating, when the plaster is roughed-in, floated, and set, for paper.

SCREEDS.—Wooden rules for running mouldings, and also the extreme guides upon the margins of walls and ceilings for floating.

SET-FAIR.—A term in plastering, used after roughing-in and floated, or pricked-up, and floated work.

SETTING.—The quality that any kind of stuff has to harden in a short time.

SETTING-COAT, on ceilings or walls, in the *best* work, is gauge, or a mixture of putty and plaster; but in common work it consists of fine-stuff.

SET-WORK, in plastering.—Two-coat work upon lath.

SKEW-BACK.—The sloping abutment for the arched head of a window.

STOPPING.—Making good apertures and cracks in the plaster.

STUCCO, or FINISHING.—The third coat of three-coat plaster. Rough Stucco is that which is finished with stucco, floated, and brushed.

BASTARD STUCCO.—Three-coat plaster, the first generally *roughing-in,* or rendering; the second *floating,* as in *trowelled-stucco;* but the finishing coat contains a little hair besides the sand. It is not *hand-floated,* and the troweling is done with less labour than what is denominated *trowelled-stucco.*

THIRD COAT, in plastering.—The *stucco* for paint, or *setting* for paper.

THREE-COAT WORK, in plastering, is that which consists of pricking-up, or roughing-in, floating, and a finishing coat.

TOOLS, BRICKLAYERS'. See *Bricklayers' Tools*, pages 384, &c.

TOOLS, PLASTERERS. See pages 370, 371, &c.

TOOTHINGS.--Bricks projecting at the end of a part of a wall, to bond a part of the said wall, not yet carried up.

TRAVERSING THE SCREEDS FOR CORNICES, is putting on gauge-stuff on the ceiling screeds, for regulating the running mould of the cornice above.

TROWELLED-STUCCO, for paint.—The same as roughed-in for brick-work.

TWO-COAT WORK, in plastering, is either layed and set, or rendered and set. See those articles.

WATER TABLE.—The bricks projecting below the naked of a wall to rest the upper part firmly upon.

WORK.—The coating of plaster layed and set, and applied to brick-work where there are two coats only.

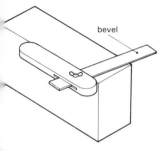

Figure 2.24 *Transferring the angle that the skewback makes with the soffit from the full size drawing*

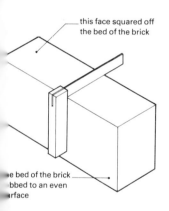

Figure 2.25 *'Squaring' the brick*

Flat and half-round files and rasps – particularly useful to give a final polish to the bricks after they have been sawn. They are also useful for filing out the grooves in the beds of the voussoirs to provide joggle joints.

A fine carborundum stone – another tool for rubbing-down the voussoirs and for cleaning and polishing the arch when it is in position and completed.

Setting out board – essential for setting out the arch full size, from which the templates may be accurately obtained. 6 mm plywood is a very good material for the templates and a carpenter's saw and plane should be available for shaping them.

Short straight-edges – about 375 or 450 mm in length and used for traversing the templates. Trammel heads are used for setting out curves, in the same way as a pair of compasses. They are used in pairs and are connected by a length of batten.

Dividers – necessary when plotting the voussoirs on the full-size drawing. The most useful type for this work has a screw-locking device to prevent stretching apart when in use.

Bevel – with a screw-locking arrangement is used for plotting and transferring angles (Figure 2.24).

A square – necessary for squaring the voussoirs across their widths (Figure 2.25), for example at the soffit.

A pencil – an ordinary drawing type or an oval carpenter's type is suitable. (An indelible pencil must never be used for this work.)

3. Carpentry

Giles Munby

TIMBER

There has been considerable development in the building industry since
Nicholson wrote his *Practical Builder*. The need for economy led to the
development of stress grading for timber, based on Navier's 'theory of bending'
which was developed for steel in the mid nineteenth century, which means that
the size of timber to be used can be worked out scientifically. The use of
oversize timber, however, is often the main reason for much timber in buildings
still being structurally sound despite having its section reduced by insect attack.
Oak shows this especially well. The sapwood, being prone to insect attack, may
have been entirely eaten away over the years, whereas the heartwood, forming
the larger part of the section, may be almost untouched.

The use of oversize timber and increasing demands on oak for tanning and
shipbuilding meant that Britain's supplies quickly dwindled. From the sixteenth
century onwards softwood, fir and pine were imported from the Baltic, and later
from the United States of America. This was often timber of very high quality,
available in long lengths and large sections and approaching the strength of oak
These softwoods and oak are almost the only timbers used structurally in British
building and from the eighteenth century may be found alongside each other.
For example, principal rafters and purlins in a roof might be oak while the
common rafters would be softwood. This use is as much a tradition as anything
as the strengths of good quality heartwood fir, pine and oak are almost the
same.

The increase in building in the towns and cities from the mid nineteenth
century led to the rapid depletion of stocks of good quality timber from the
Baltic. By this time, in all but the grandest buildings, imported softwood had
replaced oak as the structural timber mainly on account of cost and availability.
Ingenious ways were developed to increase the strength of the softwoods that
were available. One way was a form of pre-stressing where grooves were run
diagonally from the centre of the top of the beam to the bottom edge of the
ends. This was repeated on another beam which was bolted to the first. A
hardwood strip was then inserted and compressed by wedges thus
strengthening the beam. Trussed partitions often incorporated these for their
sills.

American and Canadian timber began to appear in Britain in large quantities
in the nineteenth century. This was mainly Douglas fir and pitch pine, used
increasingly both structurally and decoratively. These became the Victorian
church timbers and were also used in large buildings such as warehouses where
their strength and availability in long lengths made them popular.

The use of timber in building has continued to the present day and new
methods of growing have had to be devised. Varieties of quick growing trees ar

CHAPTER II.

CARPENTRY.

CARPENTRY is the art of applying timber in the construction of buildings.

The CUTTING OF THE TIMBERS, and adapting them to their various situations, so that one of the sides of every timber may be arranged according to some given surface, as indicated in the designs of the architect, requires profound skill in geometrical construction.

For this purpose it is necessary, not only to be expert in the common problems, generally given in a course of practical geometry, but to have a thorough knowledge of the sections of solids and their coverings. Of these subjects, the first has already been explained in the series of Problems given in the geometrical part of this Work, and we are now about to treat on the other; that is, the METHOD of COVERING them.

As no line can be formed on the edge of a single piece of timber, so as to arrange with a given surface, nor in the intersection of two surfaces, (by workmen called a *groin*,) without a complete understanding of both, the reader is required not to pass them until the opérations are perfectly familiar to his mind. For the more effectually rivetting the principles upon the mind of the student, it is requested that he should *model* them as he proceeds, and apply the sections and coverings found on the paper to the real sections and surfaces, by bending them around the solid.

The SURFACES, which timbers are required to form, are those of *cylinders, cylindroids, cones, cuneoids, spheres, ellipsoids*, &c., either entire, or as terminated by cylinders, cylindroids, cones, and cuneoids.

being used but their speed of growth is affecting the quality of timber now on the market. This quick growth and short life means that sections of any size have a much larger proportion of sapwood than previously as they are smaller in girth when felled. This makes them less strong and also more susceptible to attack by insects and rot. Treatment against these defects depends almost entirely on economics and the conscience of the contractor or developer. In conservation work, where new timber is being put in with old, treatment against rot and insects should be carried out as a matter of course.

The development of strong waterproof glues has had a great effect on timberwork since Nicholson's time. Some now form a stronger joint than the wood around them, although *in situ* work does not necessarily provide ideal conditions for their use as dampness or cold may hamper setting. They can also be used to fill gaps, not as an excuse for poor workmanship but for example in cases where a beam has cracked after being put under greater stress than was intended. It may not be possible, due to subsequent movement in the timber itself, to pull either side of the crack together completely and so a glue which will fill the gap is very useful. Other repairs such as patching over mortices or replacing tenons which have rotted away are made considerably stronger by using glue. Providing the surfaces to be glued are of sound timber and clean, a very strong repair can be made without the need for unsightly permanent bolting or metal plates, although some form of initial cramping would be necessary.

The development of glues has made lamination possible; lengths of timber can be glued together to form almost any shape. This is particularly useful in curved work, where the strips can be bent round a template and then all glued together, thus keeping the shape when the glue has set. Strips about 25 mm wide are used for this, and the joints staggered to avoid lines of weakness. This process can be used to build up a variety of curved members; for example, purlins and ribs of a dome. As the shape is already formed by the template, the only waste is the cleaning up after the glue has set. By using short lengths as the lamina, considerable savings in timber can also be made. Curved work from the solid leaves large offcuts and there is also the risk of weakness at the ends of the curve where short grain might occur if the curvature is large.

TIMBER DECAY

There have been great advances in the understanding of timber decay (wet and dry rot) and insect attack, all of which can now be eradicated permanently. Dry rot (*Merulius lacrymans*) is the most virulent and can spread very rapidly in the damp conditions on which it thrives, where moisture content of the timber is between 20 and 25 per cent and the temperature between 7 °C and 27 °C. It spreads very quickly where the air is still and this is why it so often occurs in cellars or behind boarding or panelling. Remedies have to be ruthless and involve cutting out and burning all affected timber and treating thoroughly the remaining timber.

Brickwork and stonework will also have to be treated as the spores can be lying dormant. This can be done by spraying with a fungicidal liquid but it may sometimes be necessary to drill holes and inject liquid into them. The cause must also be found and put right. This is not always easy because the spores spread so far from their original source and timber and plaster may have to be stripped out to find it. (Treatment of timber against fungal decay or infestation is done with water borne copper/chrome/arsenic compositions in accordance with BS 4072 (1966). The treatment described covers the impregnation of new timbers by the full-cell vacuum and pressure impregnation process or the Lowry empty-cell pressure impregnation process. The approved compositions can also be used for brush application and injection.

Once it has been found, the cause of dampness must be investigated. Often it will be rising damp from a cellar which has rotted the ends of the floor timbers, or it may be a leaking roof wetting the rafters or ceiling joists. Once found and remedied, and ventilation provided, a careful watch should be kept for recurrence.

Cellar fungus (*Coniophora cerebella*) is the most common of the wet rots. It usually occurs where there is actual leakage onto timber, as it cannot live where the moisture content is less than 25 per cent. While it will destroy the timber on which it is growing, it is not as virulent as dry rot. Treatment involves burning the affected timber and treating the surrounding area, after remedying the cause of the outbreak.

Attack by insects, while not as dangerous as that by fungus, should also be treated. In timber where only the sapwood has been attacked it may well be that there is still sufficient strength in the heartwood to carry the load. The four main types of beetle — death watch, furniture, house longhorn and powder post — can be eradicated by the same means, as all ingest the timber in which their grubs burrow. Liberal brushing or spraying of the surfaces of the timber, and the injection of any holes or cracks, including the insect's own flight holes, with insecticide, will discourage the beetles from laying any more eggs and those grubs that are still in the timber should not survive to burrow out as beetles. New timber and timber removed for repair is better treated by soaking. Damp and the lack of ventilation produce situations conducive to attack by beetles and so their cause should be found and remedied. Timber under metallic coverings, especially guttering, is particularly vulnerable to decay through damp penetration and condensation and this is often the cause of moisture spreading through to roof timbers making them prone to beetle attack.

GEOMETRY

Nicholson's geometry in his carpentry chapter covers almost every conceivable shape and form and he is correct in emphasizing the need for 'complete understanding'. Many readers must have wondered at the wording of the problems, even after having their minds prepared by the introduction. The style, however, seems to have appealed to several later authors on the same subject, who have done little more than alter the lettering of the examples before putting them in their own books. Despite the dryness of the descriptions, the geometry is very correct and thorough, with only double curvature being a notable omission. No mention either is made of this under 'Niches' in circular walls, although Nicholson does excuse himself by limiting his description to the forming of the ribs. Having got that far, it presumably became the carpenter's problem to finish it off.

GROINS AND ARCHES

Groins and arches in brick or stone have to have some form of support while they are being constructed; this support is known as centering.

The design of centering will depend on the span, weight and thickness of the arch or vault to be constructed. The load on centering increases towards the crown, as the voussoirs are laid on. Those near the springing line bear almost entirely on the jambs while those near the crown bear on the centering itself. It is therefore important to construct it strongly enough to prevent any sagging as this would distort the arch or vault. It is essential to provide for the centering to be eased after the structure has been completed. This is normally done by incorporating folding wedges under the props as these can be tapped free gently to prevent too great a shock being transmitted through the arch or vault as it takes its own support. These wedges, or jacks in the case of heavy work, are also useful to level the centering as it is being set up.

While the centering itself must be a rigid structure it is also important that the props are held firmly to avoid any movement as the centering is loaded, and they should also be placed on a firm base to prevent any subsidence. A heavy timber sill is usually placed on the ground to carry the props.

The covering of centering is known as lagging and the type used depends on the material of the structure. Rough brick and stone arches need only open lagging, where there may be a gap of up to 50 mm between each cross piece. Gauged brick arches with their shaped bricks and small joints will require close lagging to form a true smooth surface on which to build. Timber strips may be used for both open and close lagging and for small structures requiring the

The FORMATION of ARCHES, GROINS, NICHES, ANGLE-BRACKETS, LUNETTES, ROOFS, &c. depend entirely upon their *Sections,* or upon their *Covering,* or upon both.

This branch of carpentry, from its being subjected to geometrical rules, and described in schemes or diagrams upon a floor, sufficiently large for all the parts of the operation, has been called DESCRIPTIVE CARPENTRY.

In order to prepare the reader's mind for this subject, it will be necessary to point out the figures of the sections, as taken in certain positions.

ALL THE SECTIONS OF A CYLINDER, parallel to its base, are *circles.* All the sections of a cylinder, parallel to its axis, are *parallelograms.* And, if the axis of the cylinder be perpendicular to its base, all these parallelograms will be *rectangles.* If a cylinder be entirely cut through the curved surface, and if the section is not a circle, it is an *ellipse.*

ALL THE SECTIONS OF A CONE, parallel to its base, are *circles:* all the sections of a cone, passing through its vertex, are *triangles:* all the sections of a cone, which pass entirely through the curved surface, and which are not circles, are *ellipses:* all the sections of a cone, which are parallel to one of its sides, are denominated *parabolas;* and all the sections of a cone, which are parallel to any line within the solid, passing through the vertex, are denominated *hyperbolas.*

ALL THE SECTIONS OF A SPHERE or GLOBE, made plane, are *circles.*

The solid formed by a SEMI-ELLIPSE, revolving upon one of its axes, is termed an *ellipsoid.*

ALL THE SECTIONS OF AN ELLIPSOID are similar figures: those sections, perpendicular to the fixed axis, are circles; and those parallel thereto are similar to the generating figure

PLATE VII.

COVERINGS of SOLIDS.

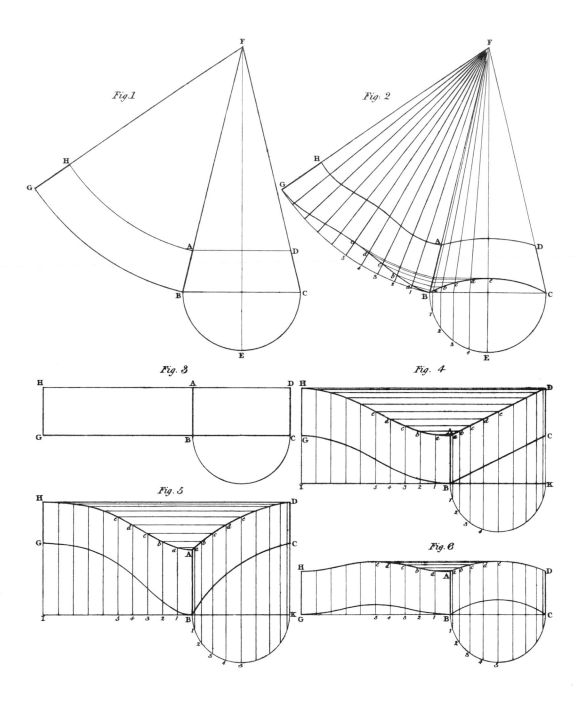

OF THE COVERINGS OF SOLIDS.

PROBLEM 1.

To find the covering of the frustum of a right cone.

Let ABCD (*fig.* 1, *pl.* VII,) be the generating section of the frustum. On BC describe the semi-circle BEC, and produce the sides BA and CD, of the generating section ABCD, to meet each other in F. From the centre F, with the radius FA, describe the arc AH ; and, from the same centre, F, with the radius FB, describe the arc BG; divide the arc, BEC, of the semi-circle, into any number of equal parts ; the more, the greater truth will result from the operation ; repeat the chord of one of these equal arcs upon the arc BG, as often as the arc BEC contains equal parts ; then, through G, the extremity of the last part, draw GF, cutting the arc AH at H ; then will ABGH be the covering required.

PROBLEM 2.

To find the covering of the frustum of a right cone, when cut by two concentric cylindric surfaces, perpendicular to the generating section.

Let ABCD (*fig.* 2, *pl.* VII,) be the given section, and AD, BC, the line on which the cylindric surface stands. Find the arc BG, as before, in *problem* 1, and mark the points, 1, 2, 3, &c. of division, both in the arc BG, and in the semi-circumference ; from the points 1, 2, 3, &c. draw lines to F ; also from the points 1, 2, 3, &c. in the semi-circumference, draw lines perpendicular to BC ; so that each line thus drawn may meet or cut it. From the points of division in BC, draw more lines to F, cutting the arc BC in *a, b, c,* &c. From the points *a, b, c,* &c. draw lines parallel to BC, to cut the side BA : from the centre F, through each point of section in BA, describe an arc, cutting the lines drawn from each of the points 1, 2, 3, &c., in BG, at *a, b, c,* &c. ; then will B*e*G be the curve, which will cover the line BC on the plan, or BC will be the seat of the line B*e*G.

In the same manner AH, the original of the line AD, will be found ; and, consequently, B*e*GHA will form the covering over the given seat, ABCD, as required to be done.

139

PROBLEM 3.

To find the covering of a right cylinder.

Let ABCD (*fig*. 3, *pl*. VII,) be the seat or generating section. Produce the sides DA and CB to H and G, and on BC describe a semi-circle, and make the straight line BG equal to the semi-circumference : draw GH parallel to AB, and AH parallel to BG ; then will ABGH be the covering required.

PROBLEM 4.

To find the covering of a right cylinder contained between two parallel planes, perpendicular to the generating section (*fig*. 4, *pl*. VII).

Through the point B draw IK, perpendicular to AB, and produce DC to K ; on BK describe a semi-circle, and make BI equal to the length of the arc of the semi-circle, by dividing it into equal parts, and extending them on the line BI. Through the points of section, 1, 2, 3, &c., in the line BI, draw lines, 1*a*, 2*b*, 3*c*, &c., parallel to BA, and through the points 1, 2, 3, &c., in the arc of the semi-circle, draw the other lines 1*a*, 2*b*, 3*c*, &c., parallel to BA, cutting AD in *a, b, c*, &c. Draw *aa, bb, cc*, &c., parallel to BK ; then, through the points, *a, b, c*, &c., draw the curve AH, and AH will be the edge of the covering over AD.

In the same manner the other opposite edge BG will be found, and the whole covering will therefore be ABGH.

PROBLEM 5.

ABCD (*fig*. 5, *pl*. VII,) being the seat of the covering of a semi-cylindric surface, contained between the surfaces of two other concentric cylinders, of which the axis is perpendicular to the given seat ; it is required to find the covering.

Through B draw IK, perpendicular to AB ; and produce DC to K. On BK describe a semi-circle, and divide its circumference into equal parts, at the points 1, 2, 3, &c. ; the more of these the truer will be the operation ; and repeat the chord on the straight line BI, as often as the arc contains equal parts, and mark the points 1, 2, 3, &c., of division. Through the points

1, 2, 3, &c., in the arc of the semi-circle, draw the lines 1*a*, 2*b*, 3*c*, &c., parallel to BA; and, through the points 1, 2, 3, &c., in BI, draw lines 1*a*, 2*b*, 3*c*, &c., parallel to BA. Draw *aa, bb, cc,* &c., parallel to KI, and through all the points *a, b, c,* &c., draw the curve line AH, which is one of the edges of the covering.

In the same manner the other edge BG will be found; and, consequently, the whole covering ABGH.

PROBLEM 6.

To find the covering of that portion of a semi-cylinder contained between two concentric surfaces of two other cylinders, the axis of these cylinders being perpendicular to ABCD (*fig*. 6, *pl*. VII).

Join BC, and, in this case, BC will be perpendicular to AB. Produce CB to G; and, on BC, describe a semi-circle. Divide the arc of the semi-circle into any number of equal parts, and extend the chords upon the straight line BG, marking the points of section both in the semi-circle and in the straight line BG. Through the points, 1, 2, 3, &c., in the arc of the semi-circle, draw lines 1*a*, 2*b*, 3*c*, &c., parallel to AB; and through the points 1, 2, 3, &c., in BG, draw the lines 1*a*′, 2*b*′, 3*c*′, &c., parallel to AB; also draw *aa*′, *bb*′, *cc*′, &c., parallel to BG, and, through the points *a, b, c,* &c, draw a curve, which will form one of the edges of the soffet; the opposite edge is formed in the same manner.

GROINS AND ARCHES.

GROINS are the intersections of the surfaces of two arches crossing each other.

CONSTRUCTION OF GROINED ARCHES.

GROINED ARCHES may be either formed of wood, and lathed over for plaster, or be constructed of brick or stone.

When constructed of brick or stone, they require to be supported upon wooden frames, boarded over, so as to form the convex surface, which each

latter, plywood can be used although it may not be viable in large structures where the spans might be too great to be covered by plywood without the addition of more ribs.

The construction of centering for a small arch, for example over a window or door, is fairly simple. The ribs may be cut out of 25 mm board, or ply or blockboard may be used. Blocks are nailed in to keep the ribs the correct distance apart and laggings are nailed to the top as required. Some form of bearing must be provided for the props. Usually this is a piece of timber lined under the ribs to give equal support to the centering. When constructing centering 25 mm should be allowed at each end, and in the width, for clearance of mason's lines.

Where the arch is too large for solid ribs, they may be formed from planking or rippings from a sheet of ply, cut to the correct curvature and pieced together in a manner similar to lamination. Joints should be staggered to avoid points of weakness, and bracing may be necessary to transmit the load down to a tie.

Centering for vaulting, while constructed on the same principles as arch centering, has to be of heavier construction because of the greater weights involved. Trussing and framing will almost certainly be necessary – a square metre of brickwork weighs nearly 250 g. Jointing may be fairly crude, making use of bolts, connections and metal straps, but it is important that the members are held rigid. In barrel vaulting, ribs should all be made from the same pattern to ensure that there is equal loading on the structure when it is completed and the centering has been removed.

The setting out of ribs for centering vaults and groins should be done with great care as the required shape of the soffit will have to be formed in the centering. The number and position of ribs will have to be decided upon and their shape and radii worked out. Allowance must be made for the thickness of the lagging before the ribs are cut. Where close lagging is required it may be necessary to clean the arrises to provide a smooth surface for the brickwork. Similarly the edges of the ribs should be bevelled to the slope of the vaulting to allow the laggings to sit firmly on the ribs without settlement.

Where repairs are necessary to arches and groins, centering will be used to carry the weight of the arch while repairs are carried out; this is known as shoring. As shores will be required to take some of the weight of the building above the arch as well as that of the arch itself, they should be more strongly constructed than equivalent centering.

NAKED FLOORING

In both single and double flooring, jointing of members is necessary to prevent the movement of timbers in relation to each other, as this may reduce the

vault is required to have, in order to sustain the cross arches during the time of turning them. This construction is called a CENTRE, and is removed when the work is finished. The framing consists of equidistant ribs, fixed in parallel planes, perpendicular to the axis of each body; so that, when the under sides of the boards are laid on the upper edges of the ribs, and fixed, the upper sides of the boards will form the surface required to build upon.

In the construction of the centering for groins, one portion of the centre must be completely formed to the surface of its corresponding vault, without any regard to the cross-arches, so that the upper sides of the boards will form a complete cylindric or cylindroidic surface. The ribs of the cross-vaults are then set at the same equal distances as that now described; and parts of ribs are fixed on the top of the boarding at the same distances, and boarded in, so as to intersect the other, and form the entire surface of the groin required.

Groins constructed of wood, in place of brick or stone, and lathed under the ribs, and the lath covered with plaster, are called *plaster-groins.*

PLASTER-GROINS are always constructed with diagonal ribs intersecting each other, then other ribs are fixed perpendicular to each axis, in vertical planes, at equal distances, with short portions of ribs upon the diagonal ribs; so that, when lathed over, the lath may be equally stiff to sustain the plaster.

When the axis and the surface of a semi-cylinder cuts those of another of greater diameter, the hollow surface of the lesser cylinder, as terminated by the greater cylinder, is called a *cylindro-cylindric arch*, and, vulgarly, a *Welsh groin.*

CYLINDRO-CYLINDRIC ARCHES, or *Welsh groins*, are constructed either of brick, stone, or wood. If constructed of brick or stone, they require to have centres, which are formed in the same manner as those for groins; and, if constructed of wood, lath, and plaster, the ribs must be formed to the surfaces.

In the construction of groins, and of cylindro-cylindric arches, the ribs that are shorter than the whole width are termed *jack-ribs.*

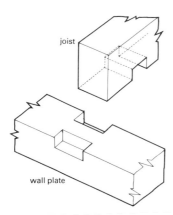

Figure 3.1   *The cogged joint*

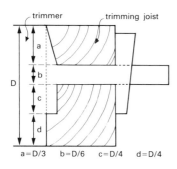

a=D/3   b=D/6   c=D/4   d=D/4

Figure 3.2   *The tusk tenon, showing proportions*

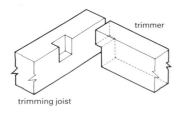

Figure 3.3   *The housed joint*

bearing and lead to eventual collapse of the floor. Secure jointing would also mean that walls were tied together at a point between the roof and the ground, and would therefore help to compensate the outward thrust of the roof. This is a principle that seems to have almost disappeared in all but the best quality buildings today, due partly to the small size of many buildings and the increased use of a steel framework to tie buildings together.

In single floors the most suitable joint between joists and wall plates is cogging (Figure 3.1), as this resists any kind of horizontal movement. Housing or notching may also be used, although they are obviously not as secure as the cogged joint. An added advantage of using these joints is that slight discrepancies in levels can be taken up by adjusting the depth of the timber removed.

Where openings occur in the floor, such as stairwells or fireplaces, it will be necessary to trim round the opening. As the trimmer will have to take the ends of the trimmed joists, it will need to be of heavier construction than normal, and be securely jointed into the trimming joists. The traditional joint used here is the tusk tenon which gives a good bearing, any horizontal movement being prevented by a wedge between the tenon. For maximum strength, care must be taken over the proportions of the joint; they should be prepared as shown in Figure 3.2. Today it is more common to use the housed joint (Figure 3.3) which is then nailed, and this may be given more horizontal strength by dovetailing one side of the housing.

In double or triple flooring, using timber as the binders, joints for the joists are similar to those used in single floors. However, it may be necessary for the joists to stop on the binders to avoid using long lengths of timber. In this case the joists may still be cogged, but they may also be tenoned in, bringing them flush with the top of the binder.

As a greater understanding of the proportion of beams was gained, it was realized that much of the centre of the beam was not structurally essential to the strength of the binder itself, as can be seen in the 'I' section of the rolled steel joists used today. By the early sixteenth century the haunched tenon, as shown in Figure 3.4 had been developed, where the binder is not weakened and the joist retains its strength by having maximum bearing provided by the tenon at the bottom of the joist and the splayed haunch running up to the top. Horizontal movement can be prevented by dowelling the joint through the tenon.

It is usual today to use RSJs as binders for double floors (see Figure 3.5) with bearers bolted to the beam to carry the joists, the ends notched over the flange. Ceiling joists can be fitted in the same way, although it is unnecessary to use a bearer as well.

In old buildings floor joists that need attention will be indicated by sagging or

144

semi-circle which is the section of the annular vault, into the same number of equal parts. Draw lines through the points of division in each arc, perpendicular to the base or diameter, to meet the said diameter. Through the points of section in the diameter of the annular vault, and from the point of concourse of the two sides of the radiating vault, describe arcs. From the same point of concourse, and through the points of section of the diameter of the semi-circle, which is the section of the radiating vault, draw lines from the point of concourse of the two sides of the radiating vault. Then, through the intersection of these lines, and the arcs drawn from the points of section in the diameter of the semi-circle, which is the section of the annular vault, trace a curve, which will be the seat of the groin. The method of fixing the timber is exhibited at the other end of the figure. The ribs of both the annular vault and the radiating vault are all fixed in right sections of these vaults, as must appear evident from what has been shown.

NAKED FLOORING.

FLOORS are those partitions in houses that divide one story from another.

FLOORS are executed in various ways : some are supported by single pieces of timber, upon which boards for walking upon are nailed. Floors of this simple construction are called *single-joisted floors*, or *single floors ;* the pieces of timber, which support the boards, being called *joists*. It is, however, customary to call every piece of timber, under the boarding of a floor, used either for supporting the boards or ceiling, by the name of *joists*, excepting large beams of timber into which the smaller timbers are framed.

When the supporting timbers of a floor are formed by one row laid upon another, the upper row are called *bridging joists*, and the lower row are called *binding joists*. Sometimes a row of timbers is fixed into the binding joists, either by mortises and tenons, or by placing them underneath, and nailing them up to the binding-joists : these timbers are called *ceiling-joists,* and are used for the purpose of lathing upon, in order to sustain the plaster-ceiling.

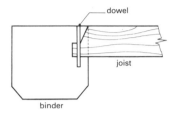

Figure 3.4   *The haunched tenon*

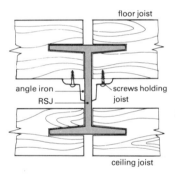

Figure 3.5   *Method of jointing joists to an RSJ*

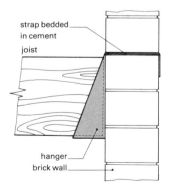

Figure 3.6   *Metal joist hanger*

vibration. Sagging can occur for a number of reasons. It may be that a support underneath has been removed, and the section of the joists is too small for the present span. Here it may be possible to put a beam underneath to take the load, although this will probably show in the room below. Alternatively, the boarding above may be stripped, and new joists run alongside the old ones. It may be possible to jack the floor straight, in which case the old joists can be bolted to the new ones, which will help to keep the floor level. Where the ceiling is decorative plaster this may not be possible but the floor above can be levelled by fixing the boards down to the new joists.

Where sagging has occurred because of overloading, through the building of a partition for example, it may be possible to straighten out the sag but often this may be more trouble than it is worth. Defects in the joists themselves will also cause sagging. On inspection, it may be found that the ends have rotted away in the walls and that some repair is necessary to make them sound again. There are a number of ways in which this can be done. The wall can be corbelled out to take the shortened joist, or a bearer, either steel angle or timber, can be fixed underneath. With both these methods, it is possible that the repairs will be seen from below, although they may be lost in a cornice. If this is unsatisfactory, metal joist hangers may be used built into the walls, with the end of the joist carried in the cradle (Figure 3.6). Where it is an exposed joist or binder that has rotted, repairs may be made by splicing on a new end, or using flitch plates. It would also be possible to use resins, all of which will be dealt with under the heading 'Lengthening timber'.

Joists and binders may also be weakened by insect attack. Here the decayed timber must be well impregnated to BS 4072, all the frass removed and the joint strengthened. Strengthening is often done either by running another timber alongside the decayed one or total replacement if the attack has weakened it too much. Where the joist or binder is decorative, it may be possible to use a steel plate let into the joist and bolted. The repeated notching of joists for piping and electrical cables can also result in weak joists and in this case the same remedies will apply.

When laying floorboards, care should be taken to ensure that they are of the same moisture content as the building in which they are to be laid. If they have a greater content, shrinkage will occur, showing the joints and in extreme cases, releasing the tongues in tongued and grooved boarding. Where the building is damper than the boards, the swelling that this will cause may result in buckling and unless the damp can be remedied, it will be necessary to relay the floor. Often, a local fault such as a dripping radiator or pipe can cause this and the boards should shrink sufficiently to be nailed down again when they dry out, although this may spoil the effect of a secret nailed floor.

In forming the naked flooring, over rooms of very large dimensions, it is found necessary to introduce large strong timbers, in order to shorten the bearing of the binding-joists; such strong timbers are called *girders*, and are made with mortises, in order to receive the tenons at the ends of the binding-joists, which, by this mean, are greatly stiffened, being much shorter.

The *bridging-joists* are frequently notched down on the binding-joists, in order to render the whole work more steady.

Figure 1, *pl.* X, is the plan of a naked floor; *b, b, b,* &c. are the binding-joists; *a, a, a,* &c. are the bridging-joists; *d,* a timber close upon the stair-case. This piece of timber is called a *trimmer:* its use is to receive and secure the ends of the joists, *e, e, e,* &c. upon the landing.

C, C, C, &c. are *wall-plates,* upon which the ends of the binding-joists rest.

In the construction of floors, great care must be taken that no timber come near to a chimney; therefore, the ends of the timbers, as here shown, have no connection with the fire-place, nor with the flues.

The flues, in this plan, are indicated by their being shadowed darker than the other parts of the plan.

Figure 2, *pl.* X, is the plan of naked flooring with a girder.

Figure 3, shows the manner of framing joists into a girder, with the form of the mortise and tenon. No. 1, is the part of a joist framed into the girder; and No. 2 is a joist out of the mortise.

Figure 4, shows the connection of binding-joists, bridging-joists, and ceiling-joists; as, also, the manner of fixing the binding-joists upon the wall-plates, which manner is called *cocking,* or *cogging.* The long dark parts represent the mortises, into which one end of the ceiling-joists are fixed. These long mortises are called *pulley-mortises,* or *chase-mortises.* The ceiling-joists are introduced into common mortises at one end, and the other end of them are let into these long mortises obliquely, and slide along until they are perpendicular.

Figure 5, shows how the bridging-joist is let down upon the binding-joist, and how the ceiling-joists are fitted into the binding-joists.

PLATE X

NAKED FLOORING

AND LENGTHENING OF BEAMS

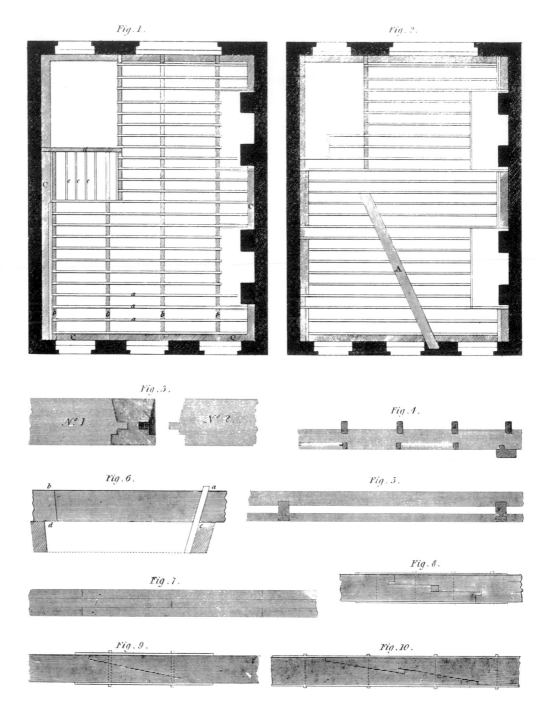

Fig. 1.

Fig. 2.

Fig. 3.

Fig. 4.

Fig. 6.

Fig. 5.

Fig. 7.

Fig. 8.

Fig. 9.

Fig. 10.

TUMBLING IN A JOIST, is to frame a joist between two timbers, of which the sides, which ought to be vertical or square to the upper edges, are oblique to these edges.

Figure 6, shows the method of fitting in a joist between the sloping sides of two others. The first thing done is, to turn the upper edge of the joist upon the top of the two pieces into which it is to be fitted, and brought over its proper place. The next thing is to turn the joist on its under edge, so as to lie over its place ; then apply a rule, or straight edge, upon the side of the one piece where the shoulder of the joist is intended to come ; then slide the joist until the line drawn come to the straight edge of the rule so applied ; then draw a line by the edge of the rule. Do the same at the other end, and the two lines thus drawn will mark the shoulder of the tenon at each end.

LENGTHENING TIMBERS.

TIMBERS may be lengthened in various ways, either by making the piece of timber in two or more thicknesses ; or by securing one piece to another, with a piece on each side, in order to cover the joint ; and by spiking or bolting each piece on both sides of the joint. Sometimes the pieces that are applied on the sides are made of wood ; in this case, it is called *fishing the beam :* such modes are used in ships, when their masts, beams, or yards, are broken, in order to mend them. Other modes of continuing the length of timbers or beams is, by splicing them with a long bevel-joint, ending in a sharp edge at the end of each piece. Sometimes the sharp edge of the end of each piece is cut off, so as to form an obtuse angle at the top. Sometimes the splice is so formed as that the two surfaces which come into contact are reciprocally indented into each other, which will add greatly to their security, when firmly bolted together. Every kind of scarf should have a strong iron-strap upon each opposite side, extending in length considerably beyond each joint.

149

Where the boards to be used are of the same moisture content as the building, or old boards are to be relaid, cramping will be necessary to ensure that the joints are tight. There are various mechanical cramps available, the best of which have a quick release arrangement, whereby the cramps tighten themselves onto the joists as the boards are cramped, and special shoes are available to enable cramping to be done close to a wall. Ideally, there should be a cramp every third or fourth joist cramping up to six boards at a time, although this will obviously not be possible with secret nailing, where each board will have to be cramped and nailed individually. If no cramps are available the boards may be wedged tight with folding wedges either off the opposite wall or from a batten screwed to the joists. When cramping up boards care should be taken to ensure that the boards are being kept straight and not bowing with uneven pressure.

LENGTHENING TIMBERS

Modern methods of jointing timber to increase length are basically similar to those described by Nicholson, although they will be used less in new buildings, where steel has tended to take the place of timber for large spans. However, in restoration work lengthening timber is still important. It may be necessary to join new timber to gain length to be in keeping with the rest of the building, and in the repairing of existing timber, where it will often be necessary to join comparatively short lengths together to retain as much as possible of the original.

The position of the timbers to be lengthened and their role in the structure will govern the type of joint used. Where timber is in compression, such as a post or a strut, the main problem is to prevent the timber buckling under its load. The usual joint here is the scarfed compression joint (Figure 3.7) which can be bolted to keep the two parts together. The ends can also be tenoned into each other to prevent any lateral movement, but great care must be taken to ensure that each half of the joint is taking an equal load. Where bolts might be regarded as unsightly, the timber can be counterbored for the head and nut, allowing clearance for a box spanner, and the holes pelleted up afterwards in matching timber.

Where beams or ties are to be lengthened, the jointing is usually more complicated as both tensional and compressional stresses are involved. In most cases, the bottom of the beam will be in tension, while the top will be in compression. In a normal beam, unsupported except at the ends, with evenly distributed loading, the maximum bending moment falls in the centre, diminishing to zero at the ends, and so it follows that any joint used to lengthen a beam should be as near the end as possible. Where a beam is supported at

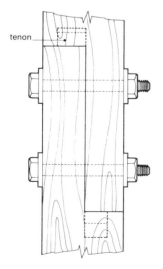

tenon

Figure 3.7 *The scarfed compression joint*

150

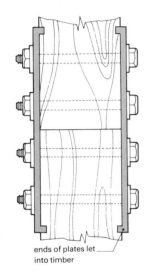

ends of plates let
into timber

Figure 3.8   *The fished
joint*

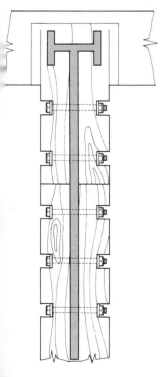

Figure 3.9   *The flitch
plate*

various points along its length, there will be points between the centre of each individual span and the point where the beam is supported where the bending moment will be nil and the jointing should be as near these points as possible. At these points, as there is no bending moment, theoretically the joint would only be required to resist movement at the ends of the beams and therefore need not have to withstand vertical load. However, in practice it will be better to give the joint some strength as subsequent movement of the building may throw stresses on the beams, which the repair was not designed to take.

The usual joints for lengthening such members are either fished or scarfed joints, or a combination of the two. In fished joints (Figure 3.8), the lengths are butted together, the joint being made by wood or metal plates bolted through the timber. These fishplates should have the same strength as the timber they are joining, and their length should be roughly three times the depth of the beam. Thus timber fish plates used to join two 200 × 100 mm timbers would each be 200 × 50 mm and 600 mm long. If steel were used, the comparative strengths would have to be calculated and the steel chosen accordingly. Normally the strength of the bolts used to hold the plates is not allowed for, although they can add to the joint's resistance to sheer, especially if the bolts are a tight fit in the holes. It is better to use several small diameter bolts rather than a few larger ones as these give a greater surface area of timber on which the load is taken. The bolts and steel plates should be galvanized and painted a neutral colour to blend in with the timber as much as possible or pelleted. Where oak is being lengthened, it will be better to use bolts made from materials other than untreated steel, such as phospher bronze, delta metal, gunmetal or stainless steel, as the tannic acid in the oak will corrode plain steel.

Resistance to sheer may also be increased by keying the plates to the beam; with timber plates, wooden keys are run between the plate and the beam, and with steel plates, the ends are bent inwards and let into the beam. Where new timber is being used, it is important that the bolts are tightened as the timber dries out. The fished joint can be made *in situ* without much difficulty and has the advantage over the scarfed joint in that no timber is lost in the joint itself. However, it is usually unsightly and although metal plates look less bulky than wooden ones, should be regarded as a last resort for lengthening timber where the join will be seen. The comprative ease with which the joint can be made may influence its use in situations where removal of existing work to use another form of jointing would be too disruptive.

Over short lengths where, for instance, the end of a beam has rotted in a wall, a steel flitch plate may be used (Figure 3.9). In this method, a steel plate carries the load on the beam to the wall and the outside timber covering need not be structural, serving only to hide the steelwork. The advantage of this method over

151

fishplating is that the outsides of the beams are not covered and therefore any detail or moulding will not be lost and can be continued on the facing timber. As with fishplating, bolts should be a tight fit in their holes, and the heads and nuts can again be counterbored and pelleted. Flitching can be done fairly easily with the timbers *in situ*, especially with the increased use of portable circular saws, which, unlike a hand saw, do not require clearance of the underside of the beam.

Where jointing is to be done without plating, the scarfed joint may be used. Originally, the timbers were tenoned together using pegs to hold the joint, but with the development of ironwork, bolts tended to be used instead and the joint reinforced with steel plates. The development of glues to the point where they can form a bond stronger than the timber itself has meant that plating is no longer necessary to give the joint sufficient strength and to prevent the bolts being pulled through the wood. Provided the joint is well made, gluing and bolting, using washers rather than plates, should give the strength and a neater repair. The wedges used to drive the joint together also form a key which prevents movement in the joint under tension. As with the scarfed compression joint, it is important that the joint should be well made so that pressure is equal on both ends of the splay.

The splayed scarf joint most used today is that shown in *Fig. 10, Plate X* (page 148) although it would be normal to undercut the ends of the splays as this will not only give better resistance to sheer but will also provide a larger gluing area. By being cut on a splay, it forms a stronger joint than that shown in Figure 3.8 where, when loaded, there is a point of weakness where the end of one length of timber is tongued into the other. When under tension, there will be a tendency for the timber to split along the grain back from the tongue. This particular joint might be strengthened by being splayed from the end of the tongue to the bottom of the joint, so that the load would be taken over the whole area rather than just the tongue.

When using the splayed scarf joint, it is usual to have the bearing end of the timber carrying the rest of the beam. However in restoration work, where it is often the ends of the beams that are being replaced, it may be desirable to reverse the joint, as length is lost in the timbers when the joint is cut. By doing this, more of the decoration can be preserved without altering the strength of the joint too drastically. Where the beam is to be lengthened in position, the reversed joint will also be easier to cut and is therefore likely to be better made, while the loose end, being easier to manage, can be cut elsewhere and then fitted to the joint on the beam.

Other forms of lengthening will depend on the timber in question. Rafters are usually jointed over a purlin with the rafter being cut on a splay and the new

Figure 7, *pl.* X, shows the manner of building a beam in three thicknesses; which, being strapped with iron across every joint, and bolted, will be exceedingly strong and firm.

Figure 8, exhibits the method of joining timbers by two *tables* and a *key*.

Figure 9, the method of lengthening timber by a plain scarf, being cut only with an obtuse angle at the ends.

Figure 10, the same kind of scarf, with two tables and a key.

Timbers that are scarfed and strapped ought to be so applied, that the sides which are strapped should be the horizontal sides; for, if otherwise applied, they will be liable to split at the bolting.

But, if the surfaces of the joints are to be placed in a vertical position, there ought to be two straps upon the top and two upon the bottom; each strap being brought close to the vertical face. By this method it will be much stronger than when set in the other position, or with the joint of the scarf horizontal.

OF NICHES.

NICHES are ornamental recesses formed in walls, in order to enshrine some ornament, as a statue, or elegant vase. They are often constructed in thick walls, in order to save materials in masonry, or brick-work.

Niches are sometimes constructed of ribs of timber, and lathed and coated over with plaster, which forms the surface to be exhibited.

The plans or bases of niches are always some symmetrical figure; as a rectangle, a segment of a circle, or one of an ellipse.

All the sections of niches, parallel to the base, are similar figures; and all the sections parallel to the base, to a certain distance, are equal. Niches sometimes terminate upwards in a plane surface, and sometimes in an ellipsoidal surface; but most frequently in the portion of a spherical surface: so that, as the faces of walls are generally perpendicular to the horizon, the aperture in the face is either a rectangle, or a rectangle terminating in the

part being cut to fit it, giving maximum bearing for each. Joists, where unseen, may be lengthened by having a new length run alongside and bolted to the old. This will form an inelegant, although structurally sound repair.

Alternative methods of repairing timber include the use of resins and glass fibre. When used structurally, holes are bored in the timber and spiralled glass fibre rods inserted. This forms the key for the resin to bond to and the joint between the timber and the resin is extremely strong, with the strength of the glass fibre approaching that of steel. The resin used is in liquid form and therefore has considerable penetration into the timber. This means that all holes must be plugged and latex rubber wrapped round the beam which is peeled off once the resin has set. This method can be used to advantage where other methods of repairing would involve considerable work both in the removal and replacement of surrounding work. However, the use of glass fibre and resin has been criticized on the grounds that the fibre will restrain the movement of the timber and therefore set up new stresses that may weaken the beam further. Although glass fibre has been used with success in structural repairs it may be too early to say whether it is an entirely satisfactory substitute for timber repairs.

NICHES

The simplest form of niche discussed by Nicholson is one with a rectangular plan, with its elevation as the segment of a circle. The setting out of such a niche is relatively simple, as the curvature of the ribs will follow that of the front elevation and all the ribs will be identical. As in most curved work, the elevation should be drawn out full size, although for niches, where each side is formed by separate ribs, only one side need be shown, as the other will be a mirror image. Templates can be made from the drawings and the springing line plotted. The ribs themselves can be cut from a sheet material, preferably blockboard, and it may be possible to cut the whole sweep from one sheet. Alternatively, the ribs may be formed from two layers of boarding, each piece cut to the required radius and nailed together with each joint staggered to give strength to the rib. The ribs should be left 100 mm to 150 mm longer than the springing line, as this will enable the ribs to be fixed to the studs, and will help to ensure that the curve runs regularly into the uprights. Where the outer rib is exposed, the construction will need to be of better quality and probably rebated to take boarding or plaster. In the case of the latter, a cover mould will be necessary to make the joint between timber and plaster, thus concealing any movement that may occur between the two. In this case, it should be noted that the inner surface of the sweep will be of a different radius to the ribs, being smaller by the thickness of the covering of the niche.

segment of a circle, or in the segment of an ellipse. Two of the sides of the rectangle are perpendicular to the horizon.

Niches are always constructed in a symmetrical form; *viz.* if a vertical plane be supposed to pass through the middle point of the breadth, perpendicular to the surface of the wall, it will divide the niche into two equal and similar parts; or, if any two points be taken in the breadth, equidistant from the sides of the niche, and if two vertical planes be supposed to pass through these points, perpendicular to the surface of the wall, the sections of the niche will be equal and similar.

Niches are placed either equi-distantly, in a straight wall, or round a cylindrical wall, dividing the circumference into equal parts: sometimes they are placed in an elliptic wall. In the latter case, however, they ought not to divide the circumference into equal parts, but to be at an equal distance from each extremity of the major axis. Niches are frequently constructed in polygonal rooms; a niche being placed in the middle of each side of the prismatic cavity. The opposite sides of such rooms are always equal and similar rectangles. The plans are either hexagonal or octagonal; but, most frequently, of the latter form.

THE PRINCIPLES of FORMING the RIBS, for the heads of spherical niches, are drawn from the following considerations:

All the sections of a sphere, made by a plane, are circles; therefore the edges of the ribs to be lathed ought to be portions of circles.

The ribs of niches may be placed either in vertical planes, or in horizontal planes; and, indeed, in any manner, so as to form the spherical surface as required: it will be most convenient, however, to dispose the ribs either in vertical planes, or in planes parallel to the horizon, as the case may require.

One of the most easy considerations for the ribs of a niche, when placed in vertical planes, is to suppose them to pass through a common line of intersection; and, if this line passes through the axis of the sphere, the ribs will be all equal portions of the circumference of a great circle of the sphere; and will, in consequence, be very easily executed. In this case, the square edges of

The number and spacing of the ribs will be governed by the size of the niche to be formed. Laths may be fixed across the backs of the ribs to hold them parallel and in the same plane and these will also give greater rigidity to the structure while the covering is being fixed. In smaller niches, the ribs can be nailed to the sides of the studs from which they spring, ensuring that the springing lines marked on the studs and ribs coincide. In larger niches, a plate is normally fixed to the top of the studs, the upper face of which forms the springing line. The ribs can then be trenched into this plate, and glued and nailed together.

In niches with a curved plan (*Plates XII* and *XIII*, pages 158, 159) it is normal practice to have the centre lines of the ribs radiating out from the centre of curvature of the plan. In this way, the inner face of the ribs will be at the correct angle to take the required covering and will not need backing off, thus saving materials and time. The setting out is basically as before — full size drawings are made and templates cut from these for the ribs, head, and where necessary the curb, with the true shapes developed from the plan. Where the plan is semi-circular, the ribs can be set out at the same length, as the centre of curvature will fall on the outer face of the head. In niches where the plan is a smaller segment of a circle, this would prove very wasteful of timber and the length of the ribs can be obtained by plotting the points where the face of the niche cuts the projected centre lines of the ribs.

The construction of the ribs is again as previously described, with the choice between solid timber or sheet material governed by the size of the niche. A curb is often used to increase the strength, being similar to the plate in rectangular plan niches. Again, the studs and ribs are trenched into it. In a similar way, the rib lying on the axis of symmetry of the niche is usually trenched into the head. The other ribs, meeting the inner face of the head at an angle, will need to be bevelled before fixing by nailing or screwing to the head. These bevels can be obtained from the drawings and therefore marked on before the ribs are sent out on site.

The construction of niches of different curvature follow the same principles as those with semi-circular plans and provided the shape of the ribs is developed, the method of setting out and construction are the same.

BRACKETING FOR COVES AND CORNICES

Nicholson's use of profiled bracketing to take plaster coves and cornices is still common practice, although the laths nailed to each bracket have now been replaced by expanded metal (BS1369 (1947) metal lathing (steel) for plastering). The laths were often sapwood oak, thus prone to attack by worm

the ribs will range, or form the surface of the niche. This position of the ribs is therefore very convenient for forming them, as it not only requires less time to execute them, but much less wood will be required.

There is another position of vertical ribs, which is frequently convenient; that is, by placing the ribs in equi-distant planes, perpendicular to the surface of the wall; and, consequently, when the surface of the wall is a plane, the planes of the ribs will be all parallel.

Figure 1, in *pl.* XII, exhibits the plan and elevation of a niche; the ribs are disposed in vertical planes, which intersect in the centre of the sphere. The plan, No. 1, is the segment of a circle; and, in consequence of this, the back ribs are of different lengths, and will therefore meet the front rib in different places, as shown in the elevation, No. 2. For, if the plan had been a semi-circle, all the back ribs would have necessarily met the front rib in the middle of its circumference. Numbers 3, 4, 5, 6, (*fig.* 1,) exhibit the ribs, as cut to their proper lengths, according to the plan, No. 1. Thus, let it be required to find the rib standing upon the plan BCED, of which the sides BD and CE are equi-distant from the line that passes through the centre A. In No. 6 draw the straight line *ad*, in which make *ac*, *ab*, *ad*, equal to AC, AB, AD, No. 1: in No. 6, from the point *a*, as a centre, describe an arc of a circle; from the points *b*, *c*, draw two straight lines, perpendicular to *ad*, cutting the arc; then the portion of the arc, intercepted between the point *d* and the perpendicular drawn from the point *b*, is the *arris line* next to the front, and the part intercepted between the point *d* and the perpendicular is the arc forming the arris line next to the back; so that the extremities of the perpendiculars drawn from *b* and *c*, give the extremities of the joint against or upon the front rib.

As to the form of the back edges of the ribs, they may be curved or formed in straight portions. In this manner all the other ribs will be formed; as is evident from the preceding explanation.

Figure 2, *pl.* XII, exhibits the plan and elevation of a niche, with the method of describing the ribs when they are disposed in parallel planes. No. 1 is the *plan*, No. 2 the *elevation*, and Nos. 3 and 4 the method of

157

PLATE XII.

NICHES.

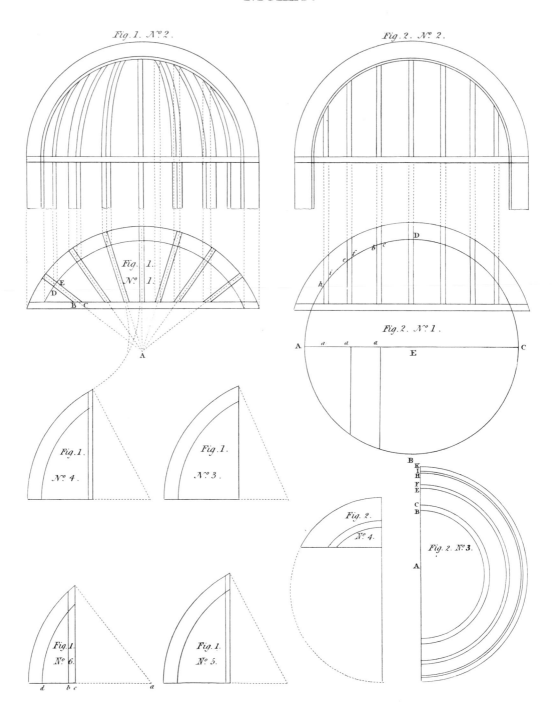

Fig. 1. Nº 2.

Fig. 2. Nº 2.

Fig. 1. Nº 1.

Fig. 2. Nº 1.

Fig. 1. Nº 4.

Fig. 1. Nº 3.

Fig. 1. Nº 6.

Fig. 1. Nº 5.

Fig. 2. Nº 4.

Fig. 2. Nº 3.

PLATE XIII.

NICHES.

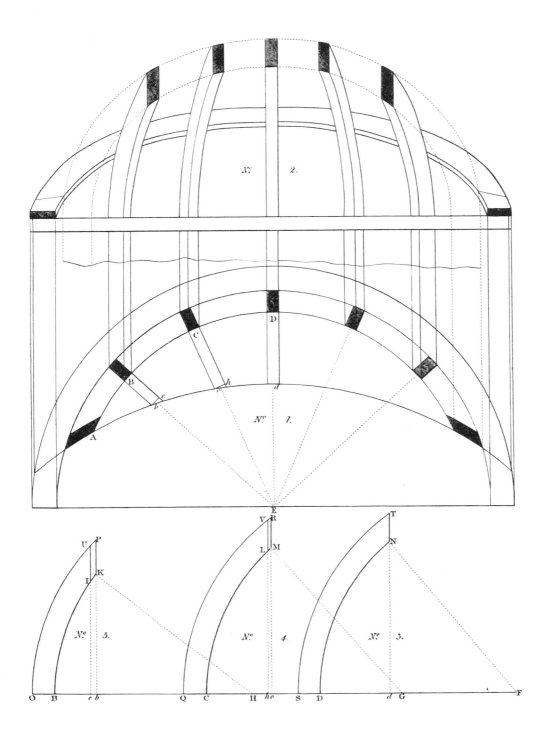

drawing the ribs. The lengths of the bases of the ribs, in Nos. 3 and 4, are taken from the plan No. 1; as AK, AI, AH, AF, AE, AC, AB, are respectively equal to ED, *ac, ab, af, ae, ai, ah,* in the base No. 1. The two distances which approach near to each other show the quantity of bevelling. With these distances, from the centre A, No. 3, describe as many semi-circles as there are points; then the double lines will represent the quantity of bevelling, or the distance from the square edge. No. 4 shows one of the ribs alone by itself.

To DRAW THE RIBS OF A SPHERICAL NICHE, in a circular wall. *Plate* XIII, *Nos.* 1, 2, 3, 4, 5.

Let No. 1 be the plan of the niche, and that of the wall A*bcd*, &c. the base line of the circular wall; ABCD the base line of the spherical niche; and A, B, C, D, &c. the bases of the ribs, of which the sides are all supposed to stand in a vertical plane; and a plane, passing through the middle of the thickness of each rib, parallel to the sides of that rib, is supposed to pass through the centre of the sphere; and, therefore, the bases of these planes will pass through the point E, which is the projection of the centre of the sphere, on the horizontal plane, where the cylindrical and spherical surfaces meet each other; and this we may suppose to be the plane of the paper.

Now, since all sections of the sphere are circles, all the edges of the ribs of the niche will be circular; but, because all the circles pass through the centre of the sphere, the edges of the ribs of the niche must be all segments of great circles of the sphere; and, therefore, they must all be described with one radius, which is equal to that of the arc A, B, C, D, &c., and, consequently, with the radius EA, EB, EC, ED, &c., as at No. 3, No. 4, No. 5, &c.; therefore, from F, G, H, as centres, describe the arcs DN, CM, BK; and draw FD, GC, HB. Produce FD to S, GC to Q, and HB to O. In the radius FD, No. 3, make F*d* equal to E*d*, No. 1, and draw *d*T perpendicular to FD, cutting the arc DN at N: then DN will be the under edge of the rib which stands upon *d*D, its plan. In No. 4, upon the radius CG, make C*h*, C*c*, equal to the plan of each side of the rib which stands upon C, No. 1; and, in No. 4, draw *c*R, *h*V, cutting the arc CM at L and M.

In like manner, in No. 5, make B*e*, B*b*, each equal to the side of the rib B, in the plan, No. 1; and, in No. 4, draw *b*P, *e*U, perpendicular to BH, cutting the arc BK in I and K. Then the backs of these ribs may either be the arcs ST, QR, OP, or may have any outline whatever; but, for the convenience of what will be presently shown, in the fixing of the ribs, it will be proper to make them all circular arcs of one radius, which will make them sufficiently strong. Then IPKU is the representation of the top of the rib, which top coincides with the face of the wall, and, consequently, the distance between the lines LV, MR, is the quantity which this rib, now under description, must be bevelled. In like manner, IKPU is the representation of the upper end of the rib which stands upon its plan B, and where it falls in the surface of the wall.

The back of the ribs being made circular, and of one radius, they will all coincide with another spherical surface: if, therefore, the back ribs are fixed at their bases, the inner edges will be brought to the spherical surface, by fixing a rib, whose inner concavity has the same radius as the backs of the ribs, upon the backs of these ribs; so that the plane, passing through the middle of its thickness, parallel to its sides, may pass through the centre of the sphere. In other respects, the plane of this fixing rib may have any other position whatever, besides what has now been described.

BRACKETING FOR COVES AND CORNICES.

Cove-bracketing is the finish of the top of the faces of a room, adjacent to the cornice, and consists, generally, of the concave surface of a cylinder; though it may be, occasionally, that of a cylindroid; and the latter surface will, in many cases, have the appearance of greater ease than the surface of a cylinder.

All the vertical sections of coved ceilings, perpendicular to the wall, are equal and similar figures, alike situated to the surface of the wall, and equidistant from the floor.

The CORNICE of a room has the same properties; that is, its vertical sections, perpendicular to the surface of the wall, an equal and similar figures: and their corresponding parts are equi-distant from the wall, and also from the floor.

As the coves and cornices of rooms are generally executed in plaster, when they are large, in order to save the materials, the plaster is supported upon lath, which is fastened to wooden brackets, and these again to bond-timbers, or plugs in the wall: for this purpose the brackets are equi-distantly placed, and are about three-quarters of an inch within the line of the cornice; and, in order to support the lath at the mitres, brackets are also fixed in the angles.

In *fig*. 1, *pl*. XIV, ABCD is the plan of the faces of the walls of a room. The plan of the bracketing is here disposed internally, and the angle brackets are placed at B and C.

In *fig*. 2, ABCD is the plan of part of one side and the chimney-breast; and here, on account of the projection, we have one internal angle and one external angle. We may here observe, that the angle bracket of the external angle is parallel to that of the internal angle.

Figure 3 exhibits a bracket upon a re-entering obtuse angle.

In *fig*. 4, ABCDEF, is part of the section of a room; CD is the ceiling line; CB and DE are the sections of the coves; BA and EF are portions of the wall-lines.

Figure 5 shows the construction of a cove-bracket at a right angle. Let AC be the projection of the cove, and let A*a* be part of the wall-line: make A*a* equal to AC, and join *a*C; on the base AC describe the bracket AB, which is here the quadrant of a circle. In the arc AB take any number of points, *d, e, f,* &c., and from these points draw lines parallel to A*a*; that is, perpendicular to AC, cutting both AC and *a*C in as many points; from the points of section in *a*C draw lines perpendicular to *a*C, and make the lengths of the perpendiculars respectively equal to those contained between the base AC and the curve AB; and, through the points of extension, draw a curve; and the curve, thus drawn, will form the cove in the angle, as required to be done.

PLATE. XIV.

BRACKETING FOR CORNICES AND COVES.

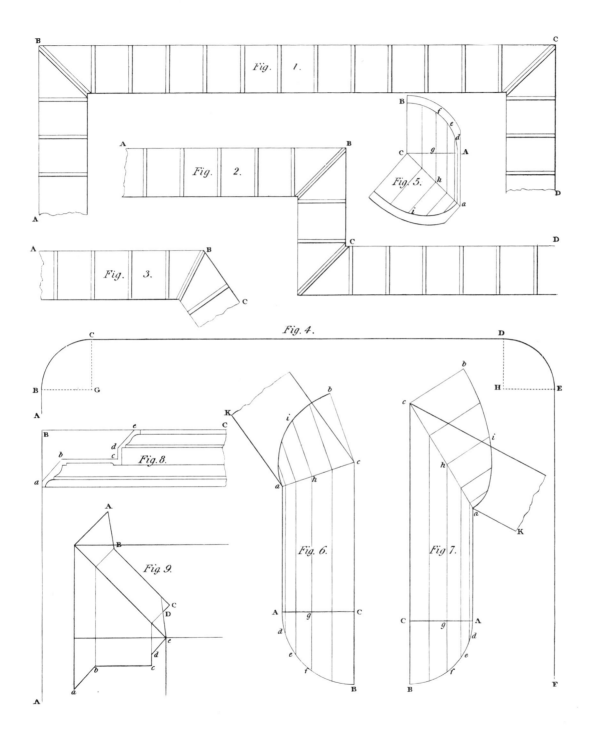

Fig. 1.

Fig. 2.

Fig. 3.

Fig. 4.

Fig. 5.

Fig. 6.

Fig. 7.

Fig. 8.

Fig. 9.

163

which might then spread to adjacent timber, and the tannic acid in the oak reacted with the iron nails holding the laths which tended to rust them away in a comparatively short time. Lack of ventilation in the space behind the cornice also made these laths prone to dry rot, especially on external walls where penetrating damp might increase their moisture content.

The use of expanded metal lathing and the coating of rendering now applied has meant that the profiles of the brackets need follow only roughly the shape of the cornice or cove, although excessive use of plaster should obviously be avoided. The brackets should be set out and cut in the workshop before being sent on site, particulary if they are to be curved, when a band saw could be used for shaping. Brackets more than approximately 150 mm wide can be made of plywood or blockboard, which gives greater strength than solid timber, and should not be less than 12 mm thick to avoid splitting when the expanded metal is nailed to them. The angles should be treated as Nicholson describes although it should be unnecessary to have two brackets in each corner as each run of metal could be fixed on top of the other run, the extra thickness being taken up in the rendering. The brackets should then be treated against worm and rot, preferably by submersion, although brushing and spraying should suffice.

The method of fixing is determined by the way the joists run or whether grounds are provided. On walls with grounds for plastering or panelling where the joists run parallel, the grounds should be made to run through far enough to take the sides of the brackets. This will allow the brackets to be screwed to the sides of the grounds and, if the cornice is not too large, should provide ample support. Where extra strength and rigidity is needed hangers from the joists could be fixed to the top edge of the brackets. On walls which carry joists, the brackets should be screwed through the sides of the joists as well as the grounds. Where there are no grounds it may be necessary to fix a batten along the wall to carry the brackets, as well as fixing to the joists, either by screwing direct or again by the use of hangers. These brackets should be notched over the batten, giving a firm fixing at the back. In all methods a line would be fixed across the room parallel to the ceiling to ensure that the brackets run true for plastering, an allowance being made for the thickness of render and plaster required.

BOARDING CIRCULAR ROOFS

Circular roofs can be boarded both horizontally or vertically, as described by Nicholson. The framework of the dome, however, makes horizontal boarding a more obvious choice, as the boards will run in the opposite direction to the ribs and therefore it will not be necessary to use noggins. Horizontal boarding will

Figure 6, exhibits the construction of a bracket for an external obtuse angle, A*a*K being the wall-line.

Figure 7, exhibits the construction of a bracket for an external acute angle.

Figure 8, exhibits the section of a large cornice, where the lines within the mouldings form the bracket required.

Figure 9, shows the construction of the angle-bracket for a cornice in a right angle.

To form the bracket in the obtuse or acute angle, take any point *f* (*figures* 6 and 7,) in the given cove, and draw F*h* parallel to A*a*, cutting the base AC of the given bracket in *g*, and the base *ac* of the angle-bracket in *h*: draw *hi* perpendicular to *ac*, and make *hi* equal to *gf*; then will *i* be a point in the curve. In the same manner we may obtain as many points as we please.

This description also applies to the construction of an angle-bracket of a cornice; the only thing to observe with regard to this is, to make all the constructive lines pass through the angular points in the edge of the common bracket.

In the construction of angle-brackets, it will be the best method to get them out in two halves, and so range each half to its corresponding side of the room; and, when they are ranged, we have only to nail them together.

METHODS OF BOARDING CIRCULAR ROOFS.

With regard to the boarding of roofs for slates, there are two principles; first, it is evident that, if a round solid be cut by two planes, each parallel to the base, the portion of the surface of the solid, between these planes, will nearly coincide with a conic surface, contained between sections perpendicular to the axis of the cone, of the same diameter each as those made by cutting the round solid; therefore the whole of the round solid may be looked upon as so many conic frustums, lying upon one another; therefore, to cover all the conic frustums is to cover the round solid.

be suitable for most coverings, one exception being lead, when the boards should be laid either vertically or diagonally thus preventing water from being trapped by any subsequent curling of the boards.

Nicholson's principles for developing boarding can still be used (*Plates XV* and *XVI*, pages 167 and 173). The roof should be set out full size, usually on a floor, and from this the required shapes of the boards can be developed as Nicholson describes. When developing boards for a dome, it is important that the width of available timber is taken into account and the boards developed accordingly. It must be remembered that boards near the top of the roof will need to be cut to a much tighter curve than those lower down. Because of this, it is likely that shorter lengths will be most economical and practical, as the use of longer or wider boards will lead to weakness on the short grain, as well as increased waste.

The total length of boarding required to cover each developed shape should be calculated from the circumference of the roof at the bottom point of each zone. From this, the number of boards of a given length can be found governed by the curvature required. A template for each individual shape is then cut, checked for accuracy and then all other boards required to be the same shape can be cut on a bandsaw, allowing for subsequent machining of tongues and grooves. This process will be done on the spindle moulder, using a ring fence and working off the original template. This machining will not only ensure that the boards will fit accurately together, by removing any irregularities that may have occurred in the sawing, but the tongues and grooves will also help to hold the boards flat to the ribs and prevent any curling that may either lift the tiles or rub the lead.

Where once the use of oak boarding was common practice, softwood is almost exclusively used today. There will be considerable waste in cutting the boards to the required shape and thus softwood will be less expensive. Where boarding is to be covered in lead, oak should definitely not be used, even for repairs to an existing roof (except where covered as described later). The tannic acid in the oak reacts with the lead and can eventually eat it away, leaving only a thin skin covering a layer of white powder. Where repairs are necessary to an oak boarded roof, unseen boarding should be replaced by softwood. Where the boarding can be seen, a separate skin of softwood boarding should be laid on battens raised through the oak boarding into the ribs. This gap will increase ventilation to the boarding, and will therefore lessen the chances of fungus or insect attack.

All new timber used in circular roofs should be treated, preferably under pressure, before fixing. Tanalized timber can be used, as this not only resists attack by insects and fungus, but is also fire resistant. All insect attacks in timber

PLATE XV

METHODS FOR COVERING CIRCULAR ROOFS.

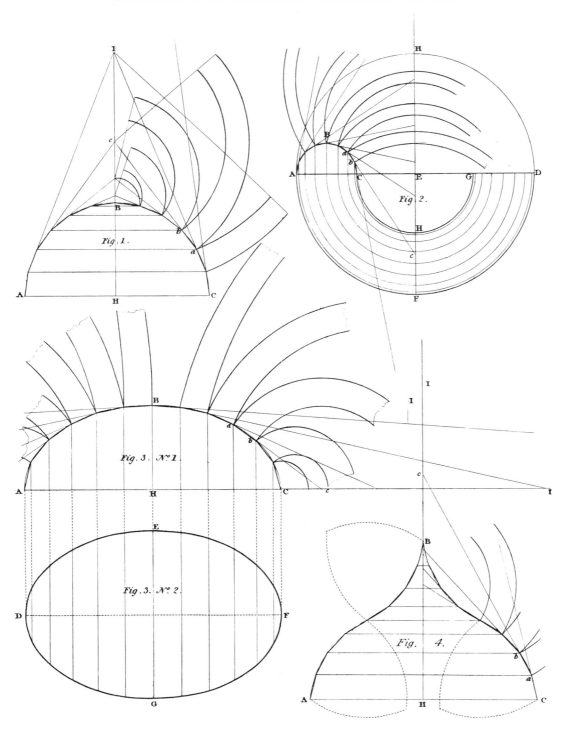

Fig. 1.

Fig. 2.

Fig. 3. Nº 1.

Fig. 3. Nº 2.

Fig. 4.

The other method of covering a round solid is to suppose the base divided into equal parts, and the solid to be cut by planes passing through the points of division, and through the fixed axis; then the surface of the body will be divided into as many equal and similar parts; so that, if any one of these portions of the solid be covered, the cover will, of course, fit any other portion thus divided; and, as all the horizontal sections of each portion of the solid is the sector of a circle, the chords of all the sectors will be parallel to each other; therefore the curved surface will be nearly prismatic. This, therefore, affords another method of forming the boarding.

The first of these methods is called the *horizontal method,* and the second the *vertical method,* of covering a dome.

In *fig.* 1, *pl.* XV, let ABC be a vertical section of a circular dome, through its axis; and let it be required to cover this dome horizontally; bisect the base, AC, in the point H, and draw HI perpendicular to AC, cutting the semi-circumference in B. Divide the arc BC into such a number of equal parts that each part may be less than the breadth of a board; that is to say, allowing the boards to be of a certain length, each part may be of the proper width, allowing for waste: Then if, between the points of division, we suppose the small arcs to be straight lines, as they will differ very little from them, and if horizontal lines be drawn through the points of division, to meet the opposite side of the circumference, the trapezoids will be the sections of so many frustums of a cone, and the straight line HI will be the common axis for every one of these frustums.

Now, therefore, to describe any board, which shall correspond to the surface of which one of the parts, *ab*, is the section, produce *ab* to meet HI in *c*; then, with the radii *cb, ca,* describe two arcs; then radiating the end to the centre, the lines thus drawn will form the board required.

In the same manner any other board may be found; as is evident from the principle described.

To FIND THE FORMS of the BOARDS for covering an ANNULAR VAULT (*pl.* XV, *fig.* 2).

Let AD be the outer diameter of the annulus, CG the inner, E the centre, and AC the thickness of the ring.

On AC describe the semi-circle ABC: then, if ABC be supposed to be set or turned perpendicular to the plane of the paper, it will represent half the section of the ring. From E, with the radius EA, describe the semi-circle AFD; and, from the same centre, E, with the radius EC, describe the semi-circle CHG; then AFD is the outer circumference, and CHG the inner circumference; and, consequently, AFDGHCA, is the section of the ring, perpendicular to the fixed axis; and the section ABC of the solid itself is perpendicular to the section AFDGHC.

To find the form of any board; divide the circumference ABC of the semi-circle into such a number of equal parts as the boards or planks out of which they are to be cut will admit.

Let ab be the distance between two adjacent points; through the centre E draw HI, perpendicular to AD; and through the points a and b, draw the straight line ac, meeting HI in the point c: from c, with the radius ca, describe an arc; and from the same centre, c, with the radius cb, describe another arc, and enclose the space by a radiating line at each end; and the figure bounded by the two arcs, and the radiating lines, will be the form of the board required.

In the same manner the form of every remaining board may be found.

It is obvious that, as common boards are not more than nine or ten inches in breadth, the boards formed for the covering cannot be very long; or otherwise they must be very narrow, which will produce much waste.

To COVER an ELLIPSOIDAL DOME, the major axis of the generating ellipse being the fixed axis (*pl.* XV, *fig.* 3).

Let ABC be the section through the fixed axis, or generating ellipse, which will also be the vertical section of such a solid.

Produce the fixed axis AC to I, and divide the curve ABC into such a number of equal parts that each may be equal to the proper width of a board. Then, as before, draw a straight line through two adjacent points a and b, to meet the line AI in c; then, with the radii ca and cb, describe arcs, and terminate the board at its proper length.

No. 2, (*fig.* 3,) is an horizontal section of the dome, exhibiting the plan of the boarding.

Figure 4 is a section of a circular roof.   The principle of covering it with boards bent horizontally, is exactly the same as in the preceding examples.

It is now necessary only to explain ONE GENERAL PRINCIPLE, which extends to the whole of these round solids.   The planes which contain the conic frustums are all perpendicular to the fixed axis, which is represented by HC, in all the figures.   Produce *ab*, to meet the fixed axis HI in *c*; then, with the radius *ca*, describe an arc ; and, with the radius *cb*, describe another arc, which two arcs will form the edges of the boards; the ends are formed by radiating lines.   Now, which ever figure we inspect, we shall find this rule to apply.

As the boards approach nearer to the revolving axis, they may be made either wider or longer; but, as the boards approach nearer to the fixed axis, the waste of stuff will be greater, and, consequently, the boards must be shorter.

When the boards come very near to the bottom of the dome, the centres for describing the edges of the boards will be too remote for the length of a rod to be used as a radius.   In this case we must have recourse to the following method.   Let ABC, (*fig.* 1, *pl.* XVI,) be the section of the dome, as before, and let *e* be the point in the middle of the breadth of a board : draw *ed* parallel to AC, the base of the section, cutting the axis of the dome in *g*, and join A*e*, cutting the axis in *f*.   Then, by *problem* 10, *page* 64, describe the segment of a circle, through the three points *d, f, e*, and this will give the curve of the edge of the board, as required.

Figure 1, No. 2, exhibits the manner of using the instrument.   Thus, suppose we make DE equal to *de*, No. 1 : Bisect DE in G, and draw GF, perpendicular to DE, and make GF equal to *gf*, No. 1.   Draw FH parallel to DE, and make FH equal to FE, and join EH ; then cut a piece of board into the form of the triangle HFE ; then let HFE be that triangle ; then move the vertex F from F to E, keeping the leg FE upon the point E ; and the leg F, and the angular point F of the piece, so cut, will describe the curve, or perhaps as much of it as may be wanted.

It must be here observed that the line described is the middle of the board ; but, if the breadth of the board is properly set off at each end, on each side of the middle, we shall be able to describe the arc with the same triangle ; or, if the concave edge of the board is hollowed out, the convex edge will be found by gauging the board off to its breadth.

As all the conic sections approach nearer and nearer to circles, as they are taken nearer to the vertex ; a parabola, whose abscissa is small, compared to its double ordinate, will have its curvature nearly uniform, and will, consequently, coincide very nearly with the segment of a circle ; and, as this curve is easily described, we shall here employ it instead of a circular arc, as in Nos. 3 and 4.

Draw the chord DE, as before, and bisect it in G. Draw GF perpendicular to DE, and make GF equal to gf, in No. 1: so far the construction of the diagrams, Nos. 3 and 4, are the same ; but, in what follows, they are different : we shall, therefore, take each of them separately, and first No. 3.

Divide each half, DG, GE, into the same number of equal parts ; and, through the points of division, draw lines perpendicular to DE ; also, from the points D and E, at the extremities, draw perpendiculars ; and make each of these perpendiculars equal to GF ; then divide each into as many equal parts as DG or GE is divided into, and, through the points of division, draw lines to F, intersecting the perpendiculars ; and, through the points of intersection, draw a curve, on each side of the middle point F, and this will be the form of the edge of the board, nearly.

In No. 4, make FH equal to gf, No. 1, and join DH and HE. Then divide DH and HE, each into the same number of equal parts ; then, through the corresponding points of division, draw straight lines, and the intersection of all the lines will form the curve sufficiently near for the purpose. The lines thus drawn being tangents to the parabolic curve.

The arc of a circle may, however, be accurately drawn through points, by the following method :

Let DE, (*fig.* 1, No. 5,) be the chord of the segment, and GF the versed sine. Through F draw HF, parallel to DE ; join DF, and draw DH perpendicular to DF. Divide DG and HF each into the same number of equal parts, as five, in this example ; draw DI perpendicular to DG, meeting HF in in I ; and divide DI into the same number of parts as DG : *viz.* five. Join the points of division in DG to those in HF, and also through the points of division in DI draw straight lines to the point F, cutting the former straight lines, drawn through the points of division in the lines DG and HF : then trace a curve from the point D, and through the points of intersection to F, and we shall have one half of the circular arc. The other half is found in the same manner, as is obvious from inspection of the figure.

THE PRECEDING METHOD of covering round solids requires all the boards to be of different curvatures, and continually quicker as they approach nearer to the crown ; but, by the following method of covering a dome, with the joints in vertical planes, when the form of one of the moulds is obtained, this form will serve for moulding the whole solid. The waste of stuff in this case is not less than in the other.

The method which we are about to explain is not only useful in the formation of the boards of a DOME, but in the covering of NICHES.

In *figures* 2, 3, 4, (*pl.* XVI,) No. 1 is the plan, and No. 2 the elevation ; the contour of the latter being a vertical section passing through the axis. *Figure* 2 represents a dome, whose contour is a semi-circle ; *figure* 3 represents a segmental dome; *figure* 4 represents a round body, of which the vertical section is an *ogee,* or curve of contrary flexure.

Through the centre of the plan, G, draw the diameter, AC ; and the diameter BD, at right angles to AC ; and produce BD to E. Let BD, *figures* 2 and 3, be the base of a semi-section of the dome : on BD apply the semi-section CFD ; and as the dome, represented by *figure* 2, is semi-circular, the point F will coincide with the point A in the circumference of the plan. In *figures* 2 and 3 divide the curve FD, of the rib, into any number of equal parts, and extend the curve DF upon the straight line DE, from D to E; that is, make the straight line DE equal in length to the curve DF. Through the points of division, in the curve DA, draw lines perpendicular to DG, cutting it at the points *a, b, c* : then, extending the parts of the arc between the points of division upon the line DE, from D to 1, from 1 to 2, from 2 to 3, &c. : make

PLATE XVI.

COVERINGS OF CIRCULAR ROOFS.

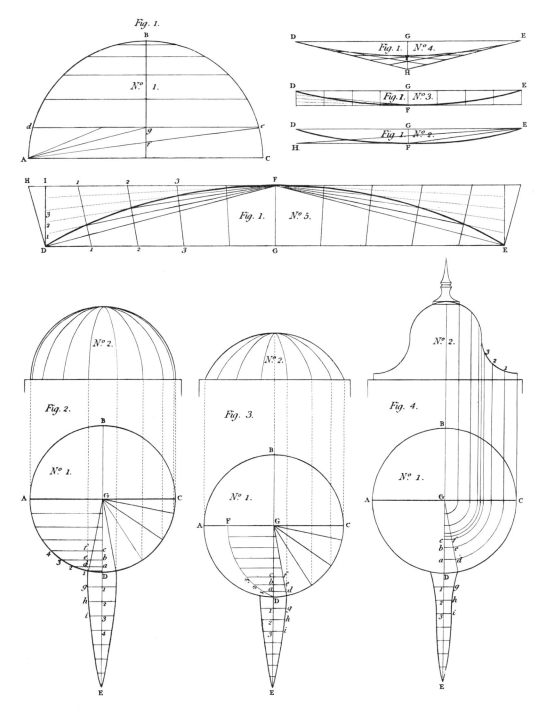

D*d* equal to half the breadth of a board, and join *d*G; produce the lines 1*a*, 2*b*, 3*c*, &c., drawn through the curve DF, to meet the line *d*G, in the points *d, e, f*, &c. Through the points 1, 2, 3, &c., in DE, draw perpendiculars 1*g*, 2*h*, 3*i*, &c.: make 1*g*, 2*h*, 3*i*, &c., respectively equal to *ad, be, cf*, &c.; and, through the points *d, g, h, i*, &c., E, draw a curve, which will form one edge of the board. The other edge, being similar, we have only to describe a curve equal and similar, so as to have all its ordinates respectively equal from the same straight line DE.

In *fig.* 4, the form of the mould for the boards is found in a similar manner, except that the curve DE is one side of the elevation, No. 2: Lines are drawn from the points of division in DE perpendicular to the diameter AC, which is parallel to the base of No. 2; and the points of division are transferred from the radius GC, to the radius GD, which is the base of the section. The remaining part of the process is the same as in *figures* 1 and 2.

In *figure* 2, the curved edge of the board is a symmetrical figure of the sines; the curves of the mould, *fig.* 3, is a smaller portion of the figure of the same curve: and, in *fig.* 4, the mould is a curve of contrary flexure; and if the curve DE be composed of two arcs of circles, the curve of the edges of the mould for the boards will still be compounded of the figure of the sines set on contrary sides; and, if the curve DE be compounded of two elliptic segments, the edges of the mould for the formation of the boards will still be of the same species of curve: *viz.* the figure of the sines.

This figure occurs very frequently in the geometry of building.

COVERINGS OF POLYGONAL ROOFS.

The plans of these roofs are here supposed to be regular polygons, and all the sections parallel to the base, similar to the base, and, consequently, similar to one another. They are made of prismatic solids, meeting each other in planes perpendicular to the plane of the base; and these mitre-planes meet each other in one common axis, which passes through the centre of each polygon.

In *pl.* XVII, *fig.* 1, the plan is denoted by the letters ABCDEFA. Then the centre of the polygon being the point I, draw the lines AI, BI, CI, &c. Bisect any of the sides, as AB, in the point L, and draw LI; then LI is perpendicular to AB.

Produce the line IL to M, and let ILN be the section applied upon IL. In the curve LN take any number of points 1, 2, 3, at equal distances, and transfer these distances to the line LM, so that LM may be equal to the arc LN. Through the points 1, 2, 3, &c. in LM, draw lines 1*g*, 2*h*, 3*i*, &c. parallel to AB; and through the points 1, 2, 3, &c., in the arc LN, draw lines 1*d*, 2*e*, 3*f*, &c., also parallel to AB, cutting LI at the points *a, b, c,* &c., and BI at the points *d, e, f,* &c.: Make 1*g*, equal to *ad*, 2*h* equal to *be*, 3*i* equal to *cf*, &c. Through the points *g, h, i,* &c., draw a curve, which will be the edge of the joint over the mitre.

To find the angle-rib, through the points *d, e, f,* &c., draw *dk, el, fm,* &c. perpendicular to BI. Make *dk, el, fm,* &c., respectively equal to *a*1, *b*2, *c*3, &c. Through the points *k, l, m,* &c., draw a curve, which will be the edge of the angle-rib, as required.

Figure 2 shows the manner of describing a polygon, to any given number of sides. Thus suppose, upon the side AB, it were required to describe a *heptagon.* Produce BA to K, and, with the radius AB, describe a semi-circle, BGK, of which the diameter is BK; divide the arc BK into seven equal parts, and through the second division, G, draw AG; then BA and AG are two adjacent sides of the heptagon. Bisect each of the sides AG and AB by a perpendicular, meeting each other at I. Then I is the centre of a circle that will contain either of the sides AB or AG seven times. The equal chords, being inscribed in the remaining part of the circle, will complete the polygon as required. In this manner we may describe a polygon of any given number of sides whatever; by producing the given side, and describing a semi-circle on that side, and the part produced, and dividing the arc into as many equal parts as the polygon is to contain sides; then, drawing a line from the centre, through the second point of division, will form two adjacent sides of that polygon. The remaining part of the process is to be completed as before.

PLATE XVII.

POLYGONAL ROOFS.

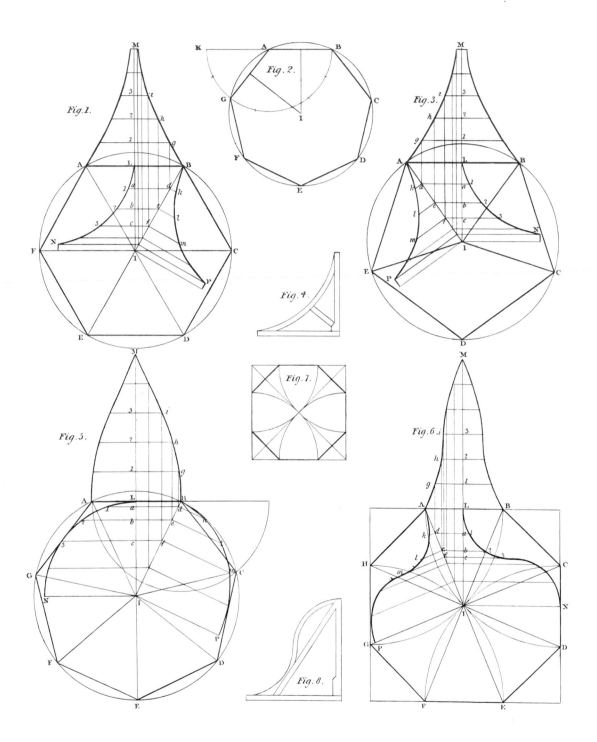

Fig. 1.

Fig. 2.

Fig. 3.

Fig. 4.

Fig. 5.

Fig. 7.

Fig. 6.

Fig. 8.

Figure 3, (*pl.* XVII,) shows the manner of finding the covering of a roof, when the plan is a regular pentagon.

Figure 4, exhibits the method of framing the ribs for such sorts of roofs.

Figure 5, shows the manner of describing the covering and ribs of a domical roof.

Figure 6, shows the manner of describing the covering and ribs of a roof whose vertical section is a figure of contrary curvature.

Figure 7, shows the method of describing a regular octagon from a given square. Thus, draw the diagonals; then, with half the diagonal, as a radius, and from each of the four angular points of the square, describe a quadrant or arc; join the two adjacent points of intersection, in each two adjacent sides of the square, and you have the octagon required.

Figure 8, exhibits the manner of forming one of the ribs for the ogee roof, or that of contrary curvature.

The method of finding the coverings and ribs of *figures* 3, 5, and 6, is the very same as that described in *figure* 1.

Such forms of roofs most frequently occur in temples or garden-buildings.

POLYGONAL ROOFS and CIRCULAR DOMES are of the same nature; as a dome cannot be covered upon any other principle than that of a polygon having a finite number of sides.

PENDENTIVE BRACKETING.

PENDENTIVE BRACKETING occurs when certain portions of a concave surface are carried from the sides of a rectangular or polygonal room to a level ceiling or cornice. The parts thus introduced, between the walls and the ceiling, are called PENDENTIVES.

Pendentives are either spherical, spheroidal, or conical. The figure in the walls, from which they spring, depends entirely upon the following principles:

should be well treated as described earlier, and the rotten timber replaced as necessary. Where lead or any other sheet metal is to be used, special care should be taken to ensure that the timber is treated against fungus and insects, as boarding under these coverings is particularly prone to dry rot because of the lack of air space between the two.

The thermal expansion and contraction of lead can be considerable, and despite laying it in small sheets to offset this, movement over sharp edges will eventually wear it away. It is therefore important to ensure that any ridges left on the joints between the boards are dressed off with a plane, and that any arrises that the lead has to be dressed over are well rounded. For the same reason the nails used to fix the boards should be well punched in and angled when being hammered, as this will help to hold the boards down. The upper surface of the boarding should be covered with either a layer of reinforced building paper or inodorous bitumen felt.

PENDENTIVE BRACKETING

The methods that Nicholson describes for setting out pendentives are normal practice today (*Plate XIX*, page 182). As is usual with work of this nature, the plan of the room is drawn out full size on sheets of plywood or chipboard laid on a floor. The diagonals are then drawn in, to form the centre lines of the longest ribs and from this the centres of the intermediate ribs can be plotted, being governed by the type of finish required. The elevation is then projected from the plan to give the true shape of the wall rib, whose radius will be half the width of the room, although the exact width will depend on how the ribs are to finish in relation to the walls of the room.

Where a hemispherical dome is being brought onto a square base, the ribs will all be of the same curvature, that of a circle whose diameter is the length of the diagonal of the room. The lengths of individual ribs can then be established by working off the known length of the diagonal ribs as Nicholson describes. When developed, this will give the exact lengths of the ribs from where they spring from the wall rib to where they meet the curb at the centre of the dome. This line can then be bisected and the curve drawn in by projecting the bisected line back a sufficient distance to allow the radius to pass through the end points of the ribs. The cuts for the ends of the ribs will also be shown by this method of development; should jointing be required into the wall ribs, extra length must be added. It should be noted that all the lines drawn form the inside surface of the ribs, so when drawing the ribs themselves, the radius for the outer face should be increased as required.

It is well known that, if a sphere be cut by a plane, the section will be a *circle ;* and, if a hemisphere be cut by a plane perpendicular to its base, the section will be a *semi-circle.* If a right cone be cut by a plane, perpendicular to its base, the section will be an *hyperbola ;* and, generally, if any conoid, formed by the revolution of a conic section about its axis, be cut by a plane perpendicular to its base, the section will always be similar to the section of the solid passing through the axis ; and every two sections of a conoid, cut by a plane perpendicular to the base, at an equal distance from the axis, are equal and similar figures. Therefore if, on the base of a hemisphere, we inscribe a square within the containing circle, and cut the solid by planes perpendicular to the base, through each of the four sides of the square, the four sections will represent the four portions of each wall, and the arcs will represent the springing lines for the spherical surfaces.

On *pl.* XVIII, *fig.* 1, No. 1 is the plan of a room, with the ribs which form the pendentive ceiling ; the semi-circles on the sides are supposed to turn up perpendicular to the plan *bnmo,* which will form the terminations of the four walls ; No. 2 is the elevation.

Numbers 3, 4, 5, 6, and 7, exhibit the ribs for one eighth part of the whole ; and, as these ribs are all in planes passing through the axis, they are all great circles of a sphere, of which the diagonals of the square is a diameter ; therefore, though the ribs are shorter in the middle of each side, and increased towards the angles, they are all described with the same radius, which is half the diagonal of that square. The whole of the scheme may be formed in paste-board. Thus, in *figure* 2, let ABCD be the plan ; on each of the sides, AB, BC, CD, DA, describe a semi-circle ; then let each semi-circle be turned round its respective diameter until its plane becomes perpendicular to the plane ABCD ; then the sides, thus turned up, will represent the sections of the sphere, and ABCD the base of the solid ; then the surface extending between the semi-circular arcs is entirely spherical.

In *figure* 3, the pendentives are supposed to be placed on a conic surface, and the sides of the square not perpendicular, but equally inclined on every side, approaching nearer together as they ascend.

179

PLATE XVIII.

PENDENTIVE BRACKETING.

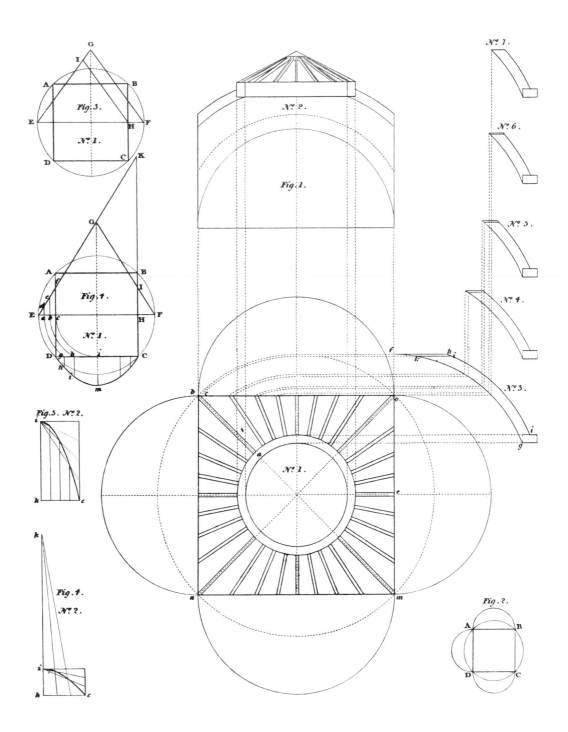

Thus, let ABCD be the plan, and the circumscribing circle the base of the cone, and EGF a section of the cone through its axis. Then, if the inclination of each of these four planes be the angle EHI, making HI parallel to FG, then the conic section is a parabola, and may be drawn as shown at *fig*. 3, No. 2, and as described in the Practical Geometry of this Work.

Figure 4, (*pl.* XVIII,) shows the method of describing the springing lines, when the sides are perpendicular to the plane ABCD. From the centre of the square, and through the angular points, describe the circle ABCD, and draw the diameter EF, parallel to any one of the sides, cutting AD and BC in *c* and H. In E*c* take any number of points, *a, b*, &c., and draw *ad, be, cf*, perpendicular to EF, cutting the side EG, of the section of the cone, in the points *d, e, f*, &c. From the centre of the plan describe the arcs *ci, bh, ag*, cutting the side DC in *g* and *h*, and the arc *ci* touching it in *i*. Perpendicular to DC, draw *im, kl, gh*, and make *im, kl, gh*, respectively equal to *cf, be, ad*. Then, upon the given base, DC, describe the symmetrical figure, D*mc*, which will form the springing line, in order to set the ribs upon the wall.

As this figure is an hyperbola, it may be described, independently of tracing it from the plan, thus: In *fig*. 4, No. 1, draw HK perpendicular to EF, cutting the side GF of the cone in I, and meeting the other side EG, produced in K, and IK will be the axis, IH the abscissa, and HC or HB the ordinate: then describe an hyperbola, *fig*. 4, No. 2, which has its axis, abscissa, and ordinate, respectively equal to IK, IH, HB, or HC.

Figure 1, (*pl.* XIX,) is the elevation of conical pendentives. In order to form the conic surface, the figure of an hyperbola must be described upon each side of the room. The figure in the plate exhibits two sides of the room. In this diagram *aglib* represents the springing line on one side of the room, and *bhc* that on the other side; the former agreeable to the straight line AB on the plan, No. 1, and the latter agreeable to the straight line BC on that plan.

Figure 2 is a section and angular elevation of spherical pendentives; the plan being exhibited by No. 1.

PLATE XIX

PENDENTIVES.

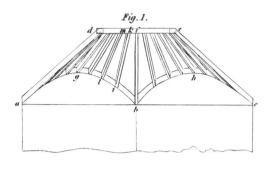

Fig.1.

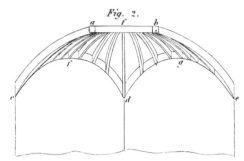

Fig. 2.

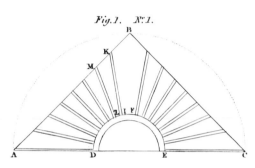

Fig.1. N:1.

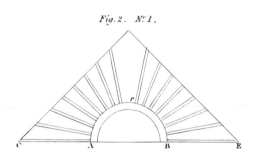

Fig.2. N:1,

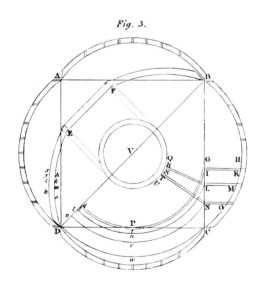

Fig. 3.

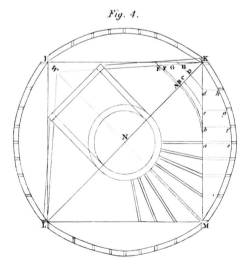

Fig. 4.

Figure 3 shows the method of drawing the springing lines on the walls; the plan and the rib over the diagonal of the plan being given agreeably to the elevation, *fig.* 2. Here the plan is the square ABCD, and the rib over the diagonal of the square is DEFB.

From the centre V, with a radius equal to half the side of the square, describe the arc *g*PG, which will touch the two sides DC, CB, of the square, at P and G, which are each in the middle of these sides; and let the arc, thus described, cut the line BD at *g*. Draw *g*x, perpendicular to DB, cutting the curve DE at *h*.

Let QG, RI, SL, TN, UC, be the seats of the ribs for one-eighth part of the whole; and since these are similar to those in every other eighth part, their formation will be sufficient for the whole of the ribs; since there will be four ribs, for every one of those in the eighth part, exactly alike, so that each rib becomes a mould for three more. The plans QG, RI, SL TN, UC, divide any arc described from the centre, V, into four equal parts, and terminate upon the side BC of the square, in the points G, I, L, N. Draw GH, IK, LM, NO, perpendicular to BC; also draw *iy, lz, n&*, perpendicular to DB, cutting the under edge DE of the rib over the diagonal in the points *k, m, o*. Make GH, IK, LM, NO, each respectively equal to *gh, ik, lm, no*; then the curve HKMOC being drawn, will be half the springing line over BC; the other half, being made similar, will be the whole of the springing line. This springing line will serve as a mould for drawing the springing lines upon each of the four walls. As all the ribs are portions of a circle of the same radius, that is, they will have the same curvature as the edge DE of the rib which stands upon the diagonal; the portion of each rib will be D*h*, D*k*, D*m*, D*o*, cut by the lines *hx, ky, mz, o&*.

Figure 4 shows the springing lines for each wall, agreeably to the plan and elevation, *fig.* 1. The method is exactly the same as that described for *fig.* 3; and thus any farther description will not be necessary.

The construction of the ribs will normally be of laminated timber, as it would be unusual to have pendentives so small that they could be cut from the solid. Lengths of boarding of 19 mm to 25 mm breadth are cut, glued and pressed to make up the correct lengths and width. It is important to stagger any joints that occur, thus avoiding weak points. When the glue has gone off, the ribs can be cut on a bandsaw and planed to size using a template taken from the elevation. If required, the underside edges can be moulded at the same time. The end cuts can then be marked, allowing for housing if required, and the rib sent out for fixing.

When on site, it is important that the springing lines are correctly plotted. These are usually given as a height above a datum line, taken from a fixed point. The wall ribs should then be fixed, either by plugging and screwing for a light structure, or by using rawl bolts if much weight is to be carried. If the room has been built perfectly square with upright walls, and the setting out of the pendentives has been accurate, fixing should only be a matter of cutting the joints on the ribs to the marked lines and assembling the structure with the joints glued and fixed according to the finish. However, problems caused by poor setting out of the pendentives or the room may be encountered and for this reason it is probably better to leave the joints uncut until fixing. If an existing room is having pendentives made for it, irregularities must be carefully noted, and the ribs made accordingly, although if a room is to be plastered or panelled, the grounds can be built out to make the room square.

PURLINS IN CIRCULAR ROOFS

The necessity for purlins in a circular roof will be determined, as in pitched roofs, by the design and span to be covered. Normally spans of up to 4.5 m will not need purlins, as the ribs can be made strong enough to take the roof loading and should also be manageable during construction. In greater diameters, however, purlins may be used, as the section of the ribs necessary would be impractical in both handling and cost. When used, purlins will not only add to the strength of the roof, but will also serve to take the ends of the jack ribs.

As in pitched roofs, the purlins are jointed into the ribs of the roof (*Plate XX*, page 186) as this increases the overall strength and, where solid timber is used, will lessen the tendency for the timber to split along the short grain. In modern practice, much timber in circular roofs is laminated, which adds considerably to the strength, so that purlins of a lighter section can be used than was previously possible using solid timber, saving both in cost and the deadload of the roof. The strength of a laminated beam can be calculated with much greater accuracy than a solid beam, as each individual section can be tested.

PURLINS IN CIRCULAR ROOFS.

IN *plate* XX, *figures* 1 and 2, are the orthographical projections of a conical and domical roof; No. 1 being the plan, and No. 2 the elevation.

The first thing to be done is, to draw the contour both of the plan and elevation. In the one extreme rafter let *gfeh* be the section of the purlin. Round the angular points *g*, *f*, *e*, *h*, describe the square *abcd*: then will *fb*, *fc*, *bg*, *ce*, *ag*, *de*, *ha*, *hd*, be the parts that are to be gauged off, after having been squared to the circular plan.

In church-building, it frequently happens that the windows are either carried entirely across the gallery-floors, or their heads considerably above the ceilings of those floors; in either case, the light is so much intercepted, that it is necessary to hollow out the ceiling, in order to obtain a sufficient quantity of light. This may be done in a very elegant manner, when the head of the window is circular. For, if we conceive an oblique cylinder, forming the head of the window, in the segment of the circle, which is the base of the cylinder to be inserted, and to displace a portion of the ceiling, that portion of the ceiling must therefore be a cylindric surface, and the hollow required to be formed. Now, it is evident that, if ribs are formed to curves of the same circle as the head of the window, and set in vertical planes, or parallel to the surfaces of the windows, and properly ranged, they will form the cylindric surface required.

Let the segment ABC, *fig.* 3, (No. 1, *pl.* XX,) be the head of the window, and let the chord AC be the ceiling-line. Divide the arc into two equal parts, AB, BC, and divide AB into any number of equal parts; as here into five. Through the points of division, draw lines parallel to AC. In No. 2, suppose GH to be the length intended for the curb. Suppose now that planes, parallel to the axis of the cylinder, in No. 1, pass through the chord AC, and through the points 1, 2, 3, 4, all parallel to each other, and to be cut by the plane of the ceiling; the sections of these planes with the ceiling will divide

PLATE XX.

PURLINS IN CIRCULAR ROOFS.

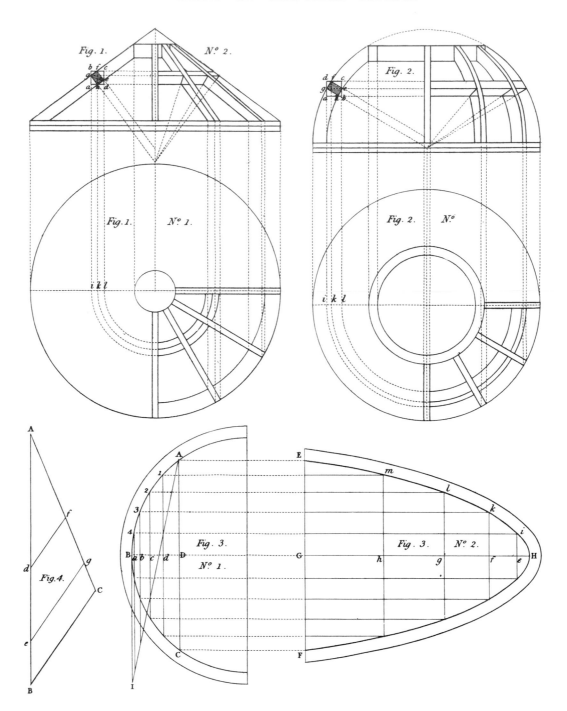

PLATE XXI.

DOMES.

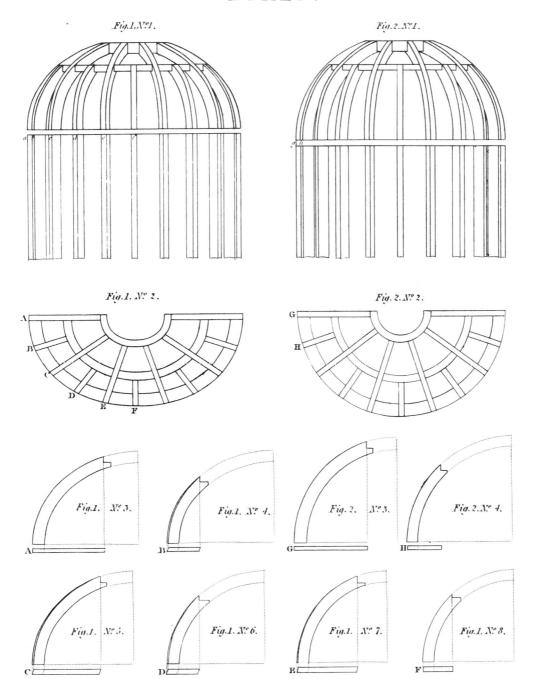

Fig.1.N°1.

Fig.2.N°1.

Fig.1. N° 2.

Fig.2. N° 2.

Fig.1. N° 3.

Fig.1. N° 4.

Fig.2. N° 3.

Fig.2. N° 4.

Fig.1. N° 5.

Fig.1. N° 6.

Fig.1. N° 7.

Fig.1. N° 8.

the ceiling into parts, which will have the same ratio as the parts B*a*, *ab*, *bc*, *cd*, *d*D. Hence, if we take GH, No. 2, as a radius, and in No. 1, from A, describe an arc at I, cutting the line BI parallel to AC ; then the lines passing through the points A, 1, 2, 3, 4, parallel to AC, will divide AI in the same proportion as the planes, parallel to the axis, will divide the ceiling line ; therefore mark out the divisions, thus cut in the line AI, upon GH, No. 2, and let *e*, *f*, *g*, *h*, be these divisions. Through the points *e*, *f*, *g*, *h*, G, draw the perpendiculars *ei*, *fk*, *gl*, *hm*, GE. Make *ai*, *fk*, *gl*, *hm*, No. 2, respectively equal to *a*4, *b*3, *c*2, *d*1, DA, No. 1 ; then make the figure symmetrical upon the base FE ; then the curve EHF is the inside of the curb. As to the outside of the curb, it may be of any form whatever. The segment, whose chord is AC, is the form of the rib to be set upon EF, and the segment which has 2*n* for its base, No. 1, stands upon *lo*, No. 2, &c.

As to the divisions of the line GH, they may be found as in *fig.* 4.

Figure 1, *pl.* XXI, is a design for an ellipsoidal dome, the plan being elliptic, and one of the vertical sections circular. The ribs are constructed without trusses. In order to divide them as equally as possible, a purlin is introduced, to support the upper ends of the jack-ribs. As this dome is supposed to rise from an elliptic well-hole, the timbers are carried below the base, from *a*, *b*, *c*, *d*, *e*, *f*. No. 1 is the elevation, No. 2 the plan, showing the upper face of the wall-plate, purlin, and curb. Nos. 3, 5, 7, are the entire ribs, to be placed upon A, C, E, in the plan ; and 4, 6, 8, are the jack-ribs, to be placed upon B, D, F, on the plan. The upper ends of all the ribs terminate upon the curb, or upon the purlin, with a *sally*, or *bird's mouth*, which is the usual method of fitting them.

Figure 2, *pl.* XXI, is a design for an hemispherical dome, constructed in the same manner as the elliptic dome, *fig.* 1.

In large roofs, constructed of a domic form, without trussing, the ribs may be made in two or more thicknesses, in such a manner that the common abutment of every two pieces, in the same ring, may fall as distant as possible from the abutment of any other two pieces, in a different ring. The number of purlins must depend upon the diameter of the dome.

To find the form of the boards for an ellipsoidal dome, the plan being an ellipse, and the vertical section upon the axis-minor a semi-circle; so that the joints of the boards may be in planes passing through the axis-major of the plan.

Let ABCD, No. 1, *pl.* XXII, be the plan of the dome, AC the axis-major, and DB the axis-minor; E the centre. From E, with the distance ED, or EB, describe the semi-circle BFD. Divide the arc into such a number of equal parts, that one of them may be equal to the breadth of a board, and let the points of division be at 1, 2, 3, 4, &c. Draw the lines 1*a*, 2*b*, 3*c*, 4*d*, perpendicular to BD, cutting BD at the points *a, b, c, d*. Then, upon AC, as an axis-major, and upon E*a*, E*b*, E*c*, E*d*, as so many axes-minor, describe the semi-ellipses, A*a*C, A*b*C, A*c*C, A*d*C, which will represent the joints of the boards upon one side of the dome. Now, since all the sections of this dome, through the line AC, are identical figures, the vertical section, upon the line AC, will be identical to the half plan ABC, or ADC. Divide, therefore, BA into any number of equal parts, by the points of division *e, f, g, h, i, k, l*; the more, the truer the operation. Draw the straight lines *em, fn, go, hp, iq, kr, ls,* perpendicular to AC, cutting AC at the points *m, n, o, p, q, r, s*, and the semi-ellipse A*d*C, in the points *t, u, v, w, x, y, z*. On the straight line, GH, No. 2, set off the equal parts, E*m, mn, no*, &c., from each side of the centre E, each equal to one of the equal parts B*e, ef, fg*, &c., in the semi-elliptic curve, ABC, in the plan No. 1. Through the points *m, n, o, p*, &c., No. 2, draw *tt, uu, vv*, &c., perpendicular to GH. Make *mt, mt*, each equal to *mt* in the plan No. 1; and *nu, nu*, No. 2, each equal to *nu* in the plan No. 1; then, through all the points *t, u, v*, &c., draw a curve on each side of the line AC, to reach from A to C, and each curve will be the edge of a board.

No. 3 shows the longitudinal elevation; *viz.* on the line AC of the plan.

No. 4 exhibits the transverse elevation, the contour being identical to that of the section on the line AB.

PLATE XXII.

ROOFS.

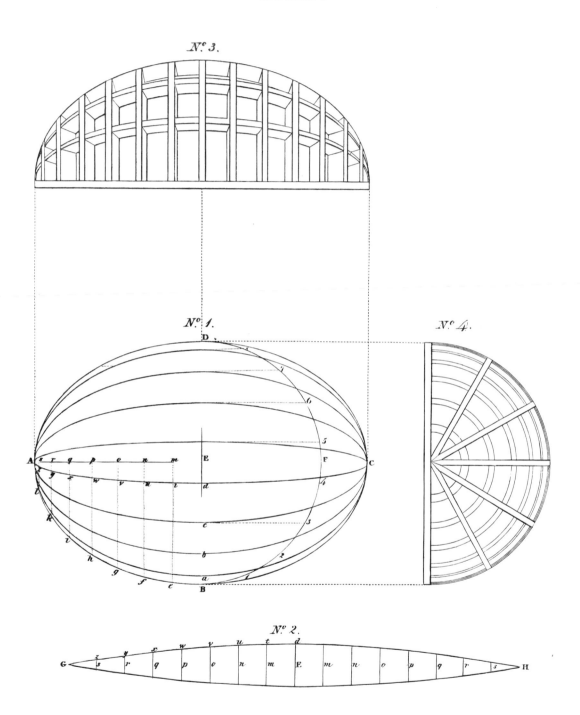

Nº 3.

Nº 1.

Nº 4.

Nº 2.

It is normal practice to set the whole roof out full size, as the shape of the purlins has to be developed. When cut from solid timber, templates are made (normally from plywood) and used to ensure accurate cutting and machining. A bandsaw can be used for the cutting and a spindle moulder or possibly a thicknesser will plane up the purlin after sawing. When laminae are used, the process is much simpler. The required number of boards are planed, thicknessed and placed in a jig, after spreading with glue. The jig is usually made from blockboard and laths similar to the centering for an arch. The laminae are then cramped and when set the only machining necessary will be planing the top and bottom faces to bring the purlins to the required size.

The purlins are normally tenoned into the ribs, thus resisting vertical thrust and generally bracing the whole structure. Stub tenons are usually the best form of joint, as the mortice required is smaller and there is less chance of the rib being weakened unduly and fracturing under load. Where the jack ribs meet the purlins, they may either be 'birdsmouthed' or notched into the purlins.

DESIGNS FOR PARTITIONS

The design of a trussed partition should enable it to carry one or more sets of floor joists without needing any form of support other than the walls on which it bears. The load carried is transmitted through a series of diagonal braces to the ends of the beams supported by the walls. The strength of these partitions depends on their rigidity so any subsequent weakening or removal of one or more members may lead to movement of the whole framework. This would result in cracked plaster, sagging floors and ceilings and, as the partitions tend to support the walls, movement of the framing may disturb these too.

The rigidity of the partition lies in the triangulation provided. Originally joints had to be well made, with those in tension being held by metal straps rather than dowels, dovetailed tenons or halvings. A later development was the replacement of vertical members with long metal bolts with studwork to take the plaster.

Several types of partition are found, depending on size, the number of door openings required and on whether the sill may show as a beam in the ceiling below. Partitions in which no openings were originally provided are particularly vulnerable to any subsequent alteration as this is likely to involve the removal of a brace and possibly the cutting of a sill to form an opening, thus destroying the rigidity of the framework. Repairs in such cases may involve the redesigning of the partition around the doorway and to do this it may be necessary to remove the partition completely. A missing brace could be replaced *in situ* using false tenons on the new timber, or possibly incorporating a steel tie. One of the main

DESIGNS FOR PARTITIONS.

PARTITIONS, in Carpentry, are the ribs of timber used for sustaining the lath and plaster.

It is evident that all single pieces of timber, when supported only at each extremity, will descend more and more towards the middle, and will obtain a curvature; but, if supported from any fixed points, will prevent that deflexion from the straight line.

Figure 1, *pl.* XXIII, is a design for a TRUSS PARTITION, with a door in the middle. In order to keep the timbers from descending, two braces are introduced, one on each side of the door-way, and the weight is discharged at each extremity of the sill. The two struts, which support the middle of these braces, are supported at the lower extremities on the bottom of the door-posts. Now the door-posts cannot descend, without pressing down the braces, and the braces cannot descend without forcing down the extreme post; but, as each end of the foot-beam, or sill, is supported, the extreme posts cannot descend; therefore the two braces cannot descend, and the posts on each side of the door-way cannot descend; consequently, the timbers will keep straight. But the weight of the quarters will still have a tendency to bind the braces: in order to prevent this effectually, the parabolic arch is here introduced.

Figure 2, *pl.* XXIII, is a design for a partition with two door-ways, one of them being a folding door. Here the braces on each side of the large opening not being each supported at each extremity of the sill, and as the space is not interrupted by openings, a complete truss is introduced above the two apertures, particularly as there is sufficient height for the action of the braces.

PLATE XXIII.

DESIGNS FOR PARTITIONS.

Fig. 1.

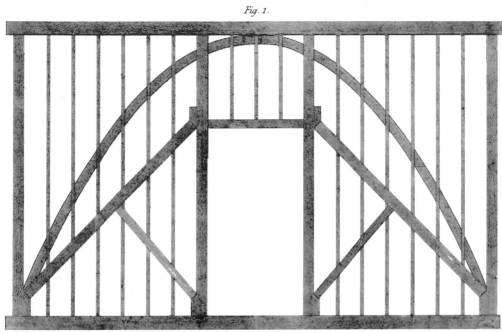

Fig. 2.

problems will be the straightening of the partition; if it has not moved too far it may be better to leave it and to pack the floors level with firring strips.

Where the ends of the beams have rotted a number of repairs may be effective. It may be possible to corbel the wall out under sound timber, as this would be hidden in the partition itself. This may not be practical if the sill member forms part of the ceiling of a room below. In this situation splicing a new piece of timber or using a flitch plate would be a better solution. When the cause of the rot in the timber has been dealt with, new timber should be laid on a concrete pad, allowing for ventilation and movement. All timber should be treated against worm and rot before replacement.

4. Joinery

Harry Munn and David Wallis

Joinery is the skill of uniting and framing wood for the internal and external finishings of buildings. Items of joinery are manufactured in workshops in factory conditions and should not be confused with carpentry, which is a site operation — a carpenter fixes what a joiner constructs. (In some parts of the country the site operative is also called a joiner and the joiner who works in the shop is the 'bench joiner'.) The work, in all but the smallest shops, is covered by two trades, the wood machinist and the bench joiner.

Modern woodworking machinery works with great accuracy and speed; much of the hard hand graft formerly involved in bench joinery has been taken away, leaving the joiner to fit and assemble the machined components. For the very best finish the final surface is always treated by hand. The cutters of all machines work with a circular movement and leave ripples and circular scratches on the surface and across joints. These have to be removed in preparation for stained and polished work and also in finishing better quality work for painting.

TIMBER

The timber employed in joinery is usually the architect's choice, preferably after consultation with the joinery manufacturer. Sources of timber are worldwide and very careful investigation is required of the untried timbers coming on to the market, especially before using them for exterior work. If the natural durability and working properties of any timber are not known, then the joiner should consult the specialist research laboratories or the handbooks that are now available.

Two basic types of timber are used in joinery: hardwoods and softwoods. Hardwoods are from deciduous trees which shed their leaves in the autumn and it does not follow that they are harder timbers to work or have a greater strength or resistance to rot and decay. Softwoods are cone-bearing, needle-leaved trees, which normally grow in the temperate zones of the world. They are valuable for general joinery but do not carry the range of colour or character of hardwoods. Timber can be purchased from the merchant cut in one of a number of ways depending on the specification. In the mid-nineteen seventies the measurement of dimension and volume was changed from the Imperial to the Metric system for most items. Some specialist homegrown supplies and North American lumber are still advised and invoiced in Imperial measurements, although this will change in a few years. Most timbers, both hardwoods and softwoods, are purchased as square edged, usually described as SE material. Many hardwoods are still imported in log form to be converted into boards in this country, though this practice is likely to diminish gradually as exporting countries increasingly

195

Log sawn through and through

outside boards tend to cup due to greater shrinkage on tangential face of boards

area of heart gives strong grain and greatest stress due to wandering heart

log sawn through and through with one square edge

Figure 4.1   *Log sawn 'through and through' and (bottom) with 'one square edge'*

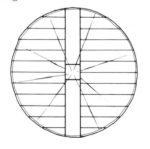

Figure 4.2   *Log sawn 'wainscot'*

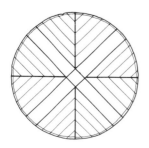

Figure 4.3   *Log sawn 'fully quartered'*

prefer to ship timber sawn to boards, because of its relatively higher price.

Most logs are separated into three grades A, B, and C, before conversion; A being the superior of the three, and the very best selected and retained to cut veneers. Logs are cut 'through and through', or T & T (*see* Figure 4.1) to give the maximum yield, with the very wide boards being cut down the middle — 'with one square edge'. Logs are also cut 'to wainscot' (Figure 4.2) which is especially valuable in oak and chestnut as it exposes the medullary ray figure. Logs cut fully quartered give the most stable material but the most expensive, because of the waste in conversion (Figure 4.3). Log-sawn hardwood is favoured, since it gives a better consistency of texture, colour and grain for high quality work. Each log can be converted to the various thicknesses to meet the cutting sheet requirements of the job.

The internal heating of buildings to today's high levels causes problems with timber shrinkage and rot, especially in old buildings. Both hardwoods and softwoods can be purchased kiln-dried, an artificial process which reduces the moisture content of timber. In a building to be centrally heated and air conditioned, it should be possible to ascertain the normal room temperature and relative humidity at which the mechanical equipment is designed to operate. Then an accurate moisture content can be determined to correspond to those conditions (known as the equilibrium moisture content) and timber may be ordered kilned to that figure. For example, the National Gallery in London has a normal room temperature of 20°C and relative humidity of 55 per cent and the corresponding equilibrium moisture content requires timber kiln-dried to 12 per cent to remain in perfect condition.

Buildings with heating only and no air conditioning will have a relative internal humidity which fluctuates widely according to the seasons and weather conditions. As a result, over-dry timber can expand during periods of high humidity and give greater problems than simply shrinkage of wet timber.

Bio-deterioration in buildings gives the greatest problems with the decay occurring in external joinery, chiefly in softwoods. Modern science has discovered many preservatives, both water and spirit based, that are applied either on the surface, or internally by pressure, to give protection from both fungicidal attack and water rot. Fungus cannot attack timber that has a moisture content below 20 per cent and so it is most important in the design of external joinery to eliminate ledges, level surfaces or long, horizontal shoulder joints that will hold water. Most old buildings are correctly detailed in these respects, so no new problem should arise in restoration work.

Timber for external joinery should be treated with a spirit based preservative applied by pressure and vacuum. This method has the advantage that the timber has the same moisture content after treatment as before, whereas wood treated

CHAPTER III.

JOINERY.*

JOINERY is the art of uniting and framing wood, for the internal and external finishing of buildings. In Joinery, therefore, it is requisite that all the parts shall be much more nicely adjusted to each other than in carpentry, and all the surfaces which are to be exhibited to the eye shall be made perfectly smooth.

The wood employed in Joinery is denominated STUFF; and of this there are BOARDS, PLANKS, and BATTENS; thus distinguished according to their breadths. BATTENS are from two to seven inches wide; BOARDS, from seven to nine inches; and PLANKS, from nine inches to any indefinite breadth.

The OPERATIONS of JOINERY consist in making surfaces of various forms; also of GROOVING, REBATING, MOULDING, MORTISING, and TENONING.

SURFACES, in Joinery, may be either plane or curved; but they are most frequently plane. Every kind of surface is first formed in the rough, and then finished by means of tools, which will be described hereafter.

GROOVING and REBATING consist in taking or abstracting a part which is every where of a rectangular section. A REBATE is formed close to the edge of the stuff; and a GROOVE, at some distance from the edge.

A MORTISE is a cavity formed within the surface, for the purpose of receiving the end of a piece of timber, to be joined at a given angle. The end, which must be very nicely fitted into the mortise, in order to make the two

with a water based solvent would need air-drying over some weeks or rekilning, which often leads to distortion.

Timber can also be treated with a fire retardant, which is either applied dissolved in water under pressure or by brush treatment. Both systems give problems with quality joinery. The pressure treatments so stain the timber that the value of natural colours of hardwood is lost and cannot be regained by bleaching or planing. The surface applied protective materials give a poor finish upon which the polisher cannot match the polishing standards of normal work. The more recent introduction of an intumescent smoke/fire strip meets many of the fire regulations and is a more practical solution for the joiner to apply. This material, measuring 9 x 3 mm is designed to protect the inevitable gap between the frame and the fire door against the passage of smoke and flame by expanding with heat and sealing the joints.

Much research is now undertaken to find materials and processes to help the joiner meet the complex variety of building, fire and other regulations which now apply even to old buildings and cause many problems in restoration. Any person dealing with timber products must become familiar with the relevant British Standards Institute specifications: BS 589 for softwoods and BS 881 for hardwoods. Details include botanical species, standard names, commercial names, sources of supply, weight, etc. Other BS publications of interest to joiners cover adhesives and wood preservatives.

Many stable timber-based sheet materials are now available, such as plywood laminboard, blockboard, chipboard and hardboard. Solid timbers glued up in a number of widths are liable to distortion when used in old buildings when they are subjected to modern heating systems, and the selection of an appropriate sheet material can overcome the problem if the visible surfaces can be formed acceptably. Some of the sheet materials are used as baseboards for veneering, laminboard being regarded as of the very best quality. Plasterboard or asbestos board can be sandwiched between the layers of timber in sheet materials to meet fire requirements and such materials may find their place in work of restoration and conservation to help meet current regulations. Modern adhesive allow for metals to be bonded to wood, and wood to wood after preservative treatment involving the addition of water resistant waxes. Bonding is now a ver specialist subject and requires careful study to ensure that the most effective an efficient glued joints are employed for the work being restored.

DOORS

Doors provide security and access to buildings from the outside, and give privacy, protection and a means of escape to the occupants; these basic

pieces as strong as possible, is called a TENON. As the sides of the mortise are generally perpendicular to the sides of the stuff, and at some distance from the sides of the piece in which the mortise is, a tenon is generally stopped by projecting sides, which are closely fitted upon the side of the piece of wood in which the mortise is made; and the parallel faces of both are made flush, and so closely united, as to appear almost like one single piece. The surface of the piece which has the tenon, and which comes in contact with the surface of the piece in which the mortise is made, is called the *shoulder* of the tenon.

FRAMES are joined together, so as generally to form externally a rectangle, and internally one, two, or more, rectangular openings: these openings are closed with thin boards, fitted into grooves round the edges, called PANELS. In ornamental work, the edges of the frame next to the panels, the two extreme vertical pieces of the frame, are denominated the STILES; all the cross-pieces are denominated RAILS; and vertical pieces, that separate the panels, MOUNTINGS.

PLANKS are joined together by planing the edges straight and square, and rubbing them together with hot glue until the glue has been almost forced out of the joint; then the ends and the proper faces being brought to their places, the rubbing is stopped, and, when the glue is quite dry, the two boards thus fixed will be almost as strong as one entire board.

MOULDINGS have several names, according to their forms, connexion, situation, or size. When the edge of a thin slip of wood is semi-circular, it is said to be *rounded*.

Figure 1, *plate* XXX, represents the section of a piece rounded on the edge.

When a semi-cylinder is formed on the edge of a piece of wood, within both surfaces, so that the diameter may be parallel to one side, this semi-cylinder is called a BEAD; and the recess, between the surface of the cylinder and the solid wood upon the side, which is parallel to its diameter, is denominated a QUIRK; and the whole part thus formed is called a BEAD and QUIRK.

Figure 2, *plate* XXX, is the section of a piece of wood, where a bead and quirk is run on the edge.

BEAD and DOUBLE QUIRK is when a three-quarter cylinder is run on the edge, so that the surface of the cylinder may touch each adjoining face.

Figure 3 exhibits the section of a *bead* and *double quirk*.

A TORUS-MOULDING consists of a semi-cylinder, and two rectangular surfaces, one perpendicular to the diameter, and the other in the diameter produced.

Figure 4 is a *torus moulding :* the small rectangular surface in the plane of the diameter is denominated a FILLET.

Figure 5 exhibits the section of a DOUBLE TORUS.

A FLUTE is the concave surface of the section of a cylinder or cylindroid, depressed within the surface of a piece of wood.

Figure 6 exhibits the section of a piece of wood with three *flutes*.

When a piece of wood is formed into two or more semi-cylinders, touching each other, the semi-cylinders are called REEDS, and the piece of wood is said to be *reeded*.

Figure 7 exhibits the section of a piece of wood with four *reeds* wrought upon it.

Figure 8 is the section of a moulding denominated a QUARTER ROUND. It consists of the fourth part of the convex surface of a cylinder.

Figure 9 is the section of a moulding denominated a CAVETTO, consisting of the fourth part of the concave surface of a cylinder.

Figure 10 is the section of a CYMA-RECTA, consisting of a quarter round and cavetto, joined together by one common tangent plane ; each part being the quarter of the surface of a cylinder, the one concave, and the other convex.

To draw this curve, join the extremities a and c of the moulding : bisect ac in the point b, and draw de parallel to the longitudinal direction of the moulding ; make ad and ce perpendicular to de ; from d, with the radius da, describe the arc ab ; from e, with the radius ce, describe the arc bc ; and abc is the moulding required.

PLATE. XXX.

MOULDINGS.

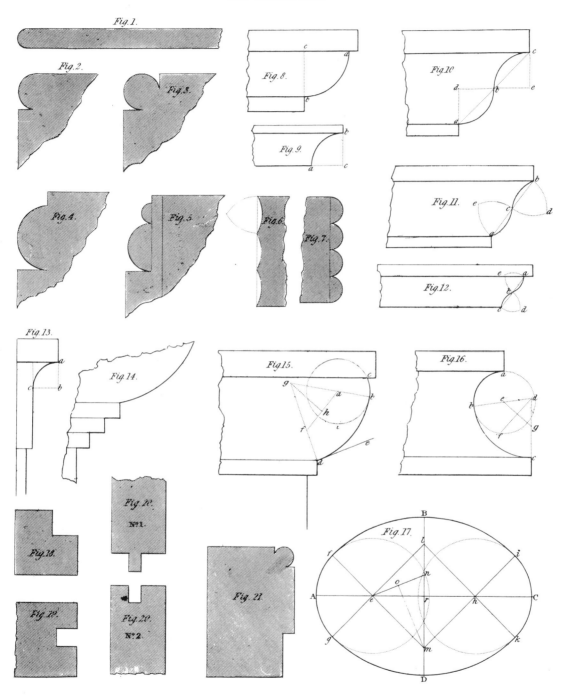

Figure 11 is also the section of a *cyma-recta,* of which the concave and convex parts are equal portions of a cylinder, but each portion less than the quarter.

To draw this curve, join the extremities *a* and *b,* and bisect *ab* in *c* : from *a,* with the radius *ac,* describe an arc *ce* ; and from *b,* with the radius *bc,* describe an arc, *cd* ; from *c,* with the radius *ca,* describe an arc, *ae,* as also the arc *bd.* With the same radius, from the centre *e,* describe the arc *ac* ; and with the same radius, from the centre *d,* describe the arc *cb* ; then *acb* is the the curve, which is the section of the surface of the moulding.

Figure 12 is the section of a moulding of the OGEE kind, called a CYMA-REVERSA : this moulding is of the same form as the cyma-recta, except that, in the cyma-recta, the concave portion of the moulding is the most remote from the eye ; whereas, in the cyma-reversa, the convex part is the most remote from the eye.

Figure 13 is the section of a moulding called a SCAPE, which is composed of the quarter of the circumference of a cylinder, and a plane surface, which is a tangent to the cylindric surface, in the line of their meeting.

Figure 14, part of the section of an *ovolo* with three *fillets,* which, when circular, or encompassing a column, are called ANNULETS.

Figure 15 is the section of a moulding denominated a QUIRKED OVOLO. The method of drawing it is thus : Suppose it were required to touch the line *de* at the point *d* : draw *dg* perpendicular to *de* ; describe the circle *bci* ; make *df* equal to the radius of the circle *bci,* and join *af.* Bisect *af* by a perpendicular, *gh,* meeting *af* in *h* ; then, with the radius *dg,* describe the arc *db* : *dbc* will then be the ovolo required.

Figure 16 is the section of a concave moulding called a SCOTIA. To form this moulding, describe the circle *dabf,* and draw *cd* perpendicular to the fillet. Make *cg* equal to the radius of the circle to be described, and let *e* be the centre of that circle : join *ge,* and bisect *ge* by the perpendicular *df* : from *d,* with the radius *dc,* describe the arc *cb,* and *cba* will be the scotia required.

Figure 17 exhibits the METHOD OF DRAWING AN OVAL, to any length and breadth required. Draw the greater axis AC, and let *r* be the centre ;

through r draw BD, perpendicular to AC. Make rA and rC each equal to the semi-greater axis, and rB and rD each equal to the semi-lesser axis. Take half the difference of the two semi-axes from the lesser semi-axis, and, with the remaining part, as a radius, from the centre e, describe the arc gAf. Make Bn equal to Ae, and join en. Bisect en by the perpendicular om, meeting BD at m: join me, and produce me to f. Make rl equal to rm, and join le, and produce le to g. Make rh equal to re; join lh, and produce lh to k; also, join mh, and produce mh to i. With the centre m, and the radius mf, describe the arc fBi; and, from the centre l, with the radius lg, describe the arc gDk; lastly, from the centre h, and with the radius hk, describe the arc kCi, which will complete the oval required.

Figure 18 represents the section of a piece of wood which is said to be rebated. *Figure* 19, the section of a piece of wood said to be *grooved*. *Figure* 20, the sections of two pieces of stuff, *grooved* and *tongued* together: No. 1 shows the *tongue*, and No. 2 the *groove*, so adapted to each other that they may be joined closely together. This method is used where it is required to join many boards together, so as to make one board, in order to prevent wind or air from coming through the joints between every two boards.

Figure 21 represents the section of a piece of stuff said to be *rebated* and *beaded*.

ON THE VARIOUS FORMS OF FRAMING BOARDS WITH THEIR EDGES JOINED, SO AS TO FORM A RIGHT ANGLE, ONE BOARD WITH ANOTHER. *Pl.* XXXI.

Figure 1 shows the method of *mitreing* the ends of boards for *dado,** or the like, at an external angle.

Figures 2 and 3, the method of joining troughs together. *Figure* 3 may also be applied to joining dado together, at an internal angle.

Figure 4, the method of joining any kind of linings together, at an external angle; a bead being stuck on the edge, in order to conceal the joint.

* By *dado* is meant the plane surface between the base and surbase of a room, or between the base and cornice of the pedestal of a column.

PLATE XXXI.

FRAMING OF ANGLES.

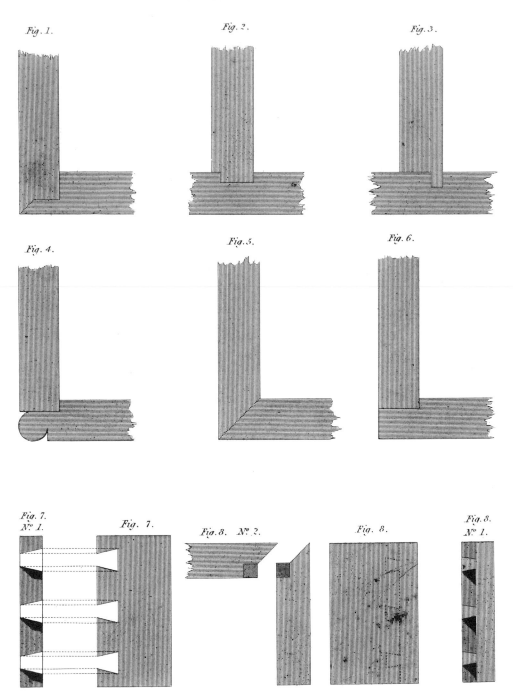

Fig. 1.   Fig. 2.   Fig. 3.

Fig. 4.   Fig. 5.   Fig. 6.

Fig. 7.
Nº 1.   Fig. 7.   Fig. 8. Nº 2.   Fig. 8.   Fig. 8.
Nº 1.

204

Figure 5, a plane *mitre,* used for various purposes; but, on account of its weakness, the method in *fig.* 1 is to be preferred.

Figure 6 is another method of joining angles by a plain *rebate.*

Figure 7 exhibits the method of *dove-tailing* : No. 1 represents the pins or male part, and the other the female dovetails.

Figure 8 shows the method of making secret dovetails. At No. 1 the ends of the male dovetails are shown; *fig.* 8 itself is the outside. No. 2 shows the section of both parts.

OF DOORS. (*Pl.* XXXII.)

Figure 1 represents a SIX-PANEL Door, having *ovolo* and *fillet* on the stiles, with plane panels.

Figure 2 represents FOLDING Doors, which meet together upon a lap-joint, exhibiting a bead on both sides of the door.

Figure 3 exhibits BEAD and BUTT.

Figure 4, BEAD and FLUSH. The difference between bead and butt and bead and flush is this: In bead and butt, the bead is run on the edges of the panel; but in bead and flush, the bead is run round all the four edges of the frame.

Figure 5, section of part of the stile and panel of a square frame.

Figure 6, section of part of a stile and panel moulded with quirk-ovolo and fillet; the panel being flat on both sides.

Figure 7, section of part of a stile and panel, having quirked ovolo and bead on the framing, with square panel.

Figure 8, section of a part of the stile and panel of a door, with quirked semi-reversa on the framing.

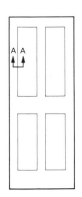

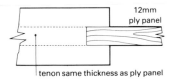

12mm
ply panel

tenon same thickness as ply panel

Figure 4.4

functions were established when man first built a home. In the past, doors were framed together from solid timbers in both hard and softwoods, the construction being held together by leather thongs, wood pegs, wrought iron nails and a series of joints of which the mortice and tenon is by far the most important.

Doors made of solid timber can range from the simple four-panelled domestic door to the most detailed and elaborate design, giving a very pleasing elevation and a source of pride to the craftsmen who construct them. Figure 4.4 shows a four-panel door, made either 32 mm or 44 mm finish thickness, using nominal 38 mm or 50 mm sawn material before bringing to thickness by machine. In section A-A note that the tenon is made to the same thickness as the panel; the panel groove is then run through the stile and so avoids extra work with the tenon haunching.

Figure 4.5 shows the same door but at section B-B a bed mould has been added and at section C-C a rebated bolection mould is fitted on the face side and a bed mould to the internal. These are mitred around the panel openings and nailed by panel pins or oval brads into the door framing.

A domestic entrance door with a shaped top rail is shown in Figure 4.6. The door, constructed entirely in solid timber, has 15 mm thick panels set in ovolo moulded framing. The top rail is most effective if the underside is slightly curved throughout the straighter elements. Note that a wider rail under the glass provides for a letter plate opening at a convenient height. A weather board is housed into the bottom rail and stiles, the housing being stopped on both sides and the tongue notched back at the ends. For the most effective weather protection, the weather board is constructed to the full door width and the frame housed out to the profile of the weather board. A rebate is formed in the base of the bottom rail to accommodate the water bar in the door frame sill.

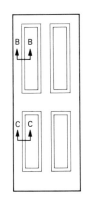

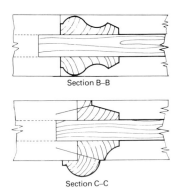

Section B–B

Section C–C

Figure 4.5

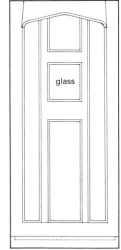

glass

Figure 4.6

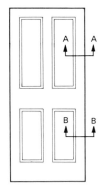

Section A–A

Section B–B

Figure 4.7

PLATE XXXII.

DOORS.

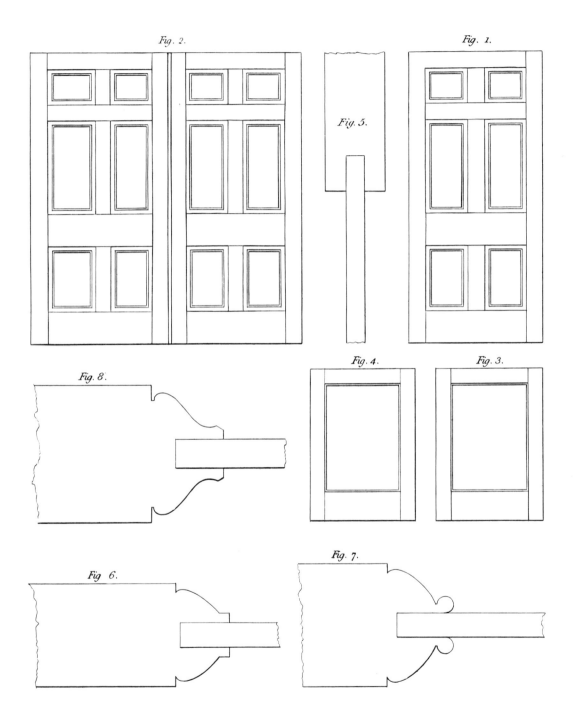

Fig. 2.   Fig. 5.   Fig. 1.

Fig. 8.   Fig. 4.   Fig. 3.

Fig 6.   Fig. 7.

The difference between a framed four-panel door with the top panels bead butt and the lower bead flush is detailed in Figure 4.7. In the case of bead butt, the beading runs vertically only along the length of panel; the panel can either be recessed on the reverse as shown or made to the full thickness with the bead on both faces. With a bead flush panel, the bead is run around the four edges of the panel. Modern machine practice requires the panel to be tongued all round and then a separate bead machined and mitred and pinned in place. It is not practical to work the bead and return the end across grain in the solid.

Figure 4.8 details a door constructed with diminished or 'gunstock' stiles. The advantage of this construction is to give extra glass area to a door without losing strength in the lower rail area. It is particularly useful with a pair of doors in a narrow opening, when the glass rectangles can be kept in proportion.

A double margin door is used in an opening of wide proportions (*Plate XXXII* page 207). Designed as a single door it would look too wide, and as a pair each half would be too narrow to admit a person. The doors are made as two equal doors, joined by a tongued centre fillet, the groove and tongue made the same thickness and in line with the tenons. The groove is made deeper than the tongue to avoid any movement from the tenon ends. Metal ties are housed in the top and bottom rails for additional strength.

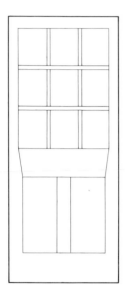

Figure 4.8

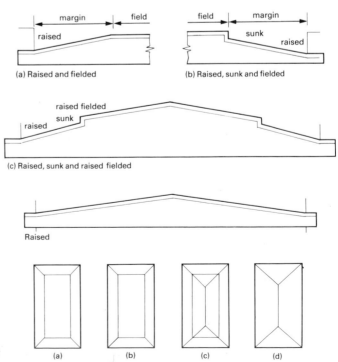

Figure 4.9   *Typical panels and their elevations*

Figure 4.9 details various panels that are fitted to doors, framed linings, wall panels, etc. As shown they are moulded on one face only; if thick timbers are a problem and the requirement is for the panels to be moulded both sides, they can be fitted back to back, but not glued together. This can have the added advantage of allowing different designs to be used on each face. Special doors are made with a different panel design on either side, with the rails at varying heights. This is usual in alteration work when an opening is required through a wall with different designs of panelling on either side and the lines of the existing work have to be picked up. It is possible to make a door with two different solid timbers used for each face, but the timbers have to be selected to be compatible.

WINDOWS

The size and position of window openings are influenced by room size to give light, ventilation, security and a pleasing external elevation to the building. Windows have sashes fitted within the surrounding frame, some fixed, some to open. The opening sashes can operate as side, top and bottom hung, to open in or out, vertical and horizontal, sliding, or in other forms of opening that ironmongery allows. Within the sash, allowance can be made for double-glazing for extra insulation.

Single and three light box sashes (Burwash, East Sussex)

OF WINDOWS. (*Pl.* XXXIII.)

Figure 1, No. 1, the elevation of a window.

No. 2, section of the meeting bars, with a small portion of the stiles fixed to each.

No. 3 shows the method of joining the intersecting bars, with the method of doweling them together.

No. 4, the elevation of the intersection; showing part of each branch or bar.

No. 5, the section of one of the bars, being *astragal* and hollow.

No. 6, a plane diminished bar for shop-fronts.

No. 7, section of a bar with a Gothic point, instead of an astragal.

No. 8, section of a Gothic bar.

No. 9, section of a clustered bar, with two reeds on each side of the centre.

No. 10, section of the stile of the sash-frame, with the astragal and hollow mouldings.

BASES AND SURBASES FOR ROOMS. (*Pl.* XXXIV.)

Nos. 1, 2, 3, and 4, are all sections of SURBASE-MOULDINGS, differently designed.

Nos. 5, 6, 7, and 8, are four different designs for BASE-MOULDINGS.

ARCHITRAVES AND PILASTERS. (*Pl.* XXXV.)

Nos. 1, 2, 3, 4, 5, 6, 7, 8, are sections for different designs of ARCHITRAVES.

Nos. 9, 10, 11, 12, 13, 14, and 15, sections for different designs of PILASTERS.

PLATE XXXIII.

WINDOWS.

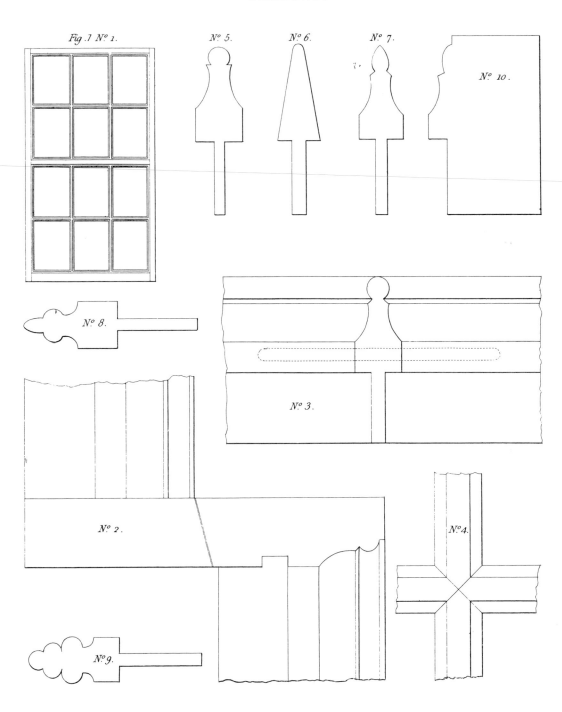

Fig. 1 Nº 1.

Nº 5.

Nº 6.

Nº 7.

Nº 10.

Nº 8.

Nº 3.

Nº 2.

Nº 4.

Nº 9.

PLATE XXXIV.

BASES AND SURBASES.

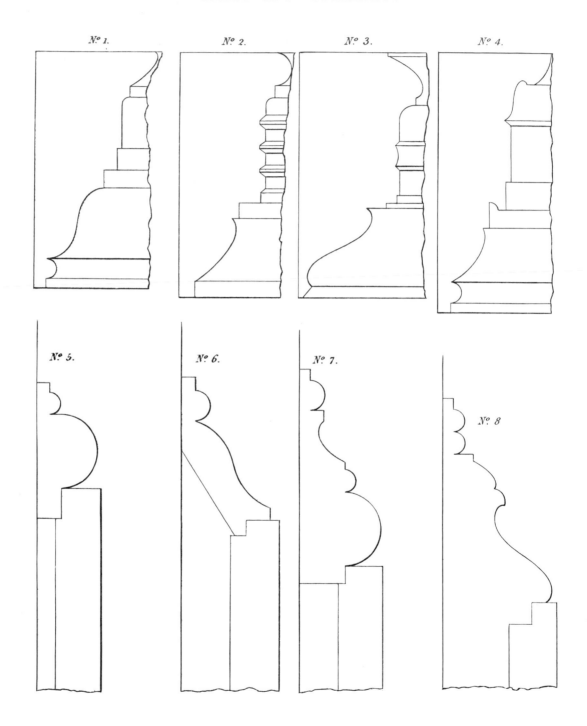

PLATE XXXV.

ARCHITRAVES AND PILASTERS.

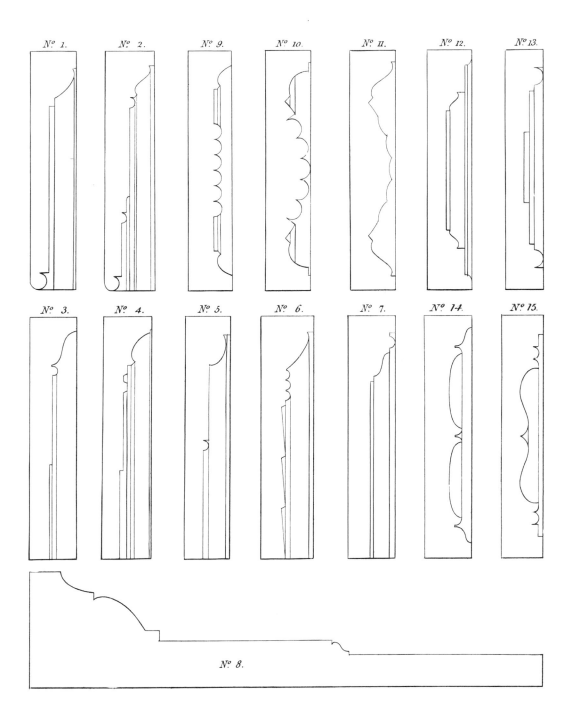

N.° 1. N.° 2. N.° 9. N.° 10. N.° 11. N.° 12. N.° 13.

N.° 3. N.° 4. N.° 5. N.° 6. N.° 7. N.° 14. N.° 15.

N.° 8.

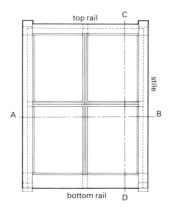

Figure 4.10 *Elevation of a fixed window frame*

A four-light sash is shown in Figure 4.10. The terms used are: stiles for the outer uprights, top rail, bottom rail, vertical bar, lay bar — mostly the same as those used for doors. With most sashes the vertical bar is run through the rails and wedged at both ends; this is particularly necessary with double hung sashes, since the meeting rails can be very thin and so the vertical through bars give extra strength. The lay or cut bar can be stub tenoned into the stiles. With most casement sashes and doors, the opposite applies, with the lay bar running through horizontally and the vertical bars becoming the cut bars. In other work the bar that is subject to the greater stress should be arranged as the through bar.

Figure 4.11 details the framing of the sash by mortice and tenon joints; the proportion of tenon thickness to the mortice sides is as near to equal thirds as practicable. In the case of extra thick sashes, double tenons would be used.

The joints between vertical and cut bars can be halved together (Figure 4.12). This is easy if the section consists of a rebated and splayed section, but as a rule the joint is stub tenoned as detailed, with the joint scribed around the face moulding.

Many sashes are described in a specification as 'in medium or small squares'. It is important to get each light in reasonable proportion by setting out the light width, A–B (Figure 4.13). Mark out the same length on line A–C at point D, scribe an arc to the vertical line B–E and connect point C–E. This will provide a good visual proportion.

The double hung box frame and pair of sliding sashes have been the traditional British window since the eighteenth century, in most cases the sashes being hung on cords that are balanced over the axle pulley by cast iron weights (*Plate XLVI*). In larger or better quality windows, the cords are replaced

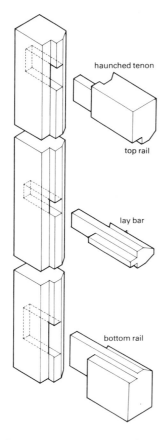

Figure 4.11 *Details of joints in sashes*

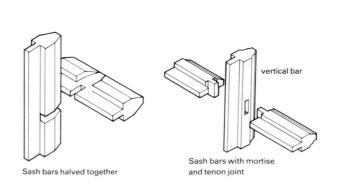

Sash bars halved together

Sash bars with mortise and tenon joint

Figure 4.12

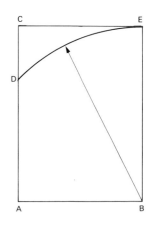

Figure 4.13

Eighteenth-century terrace houses in Bath, Avon, with both square and circular headed windows from which the astragals have been removed. There is a joggle or horn on the top sash of the right-hand windows but not on the left. The door is modern

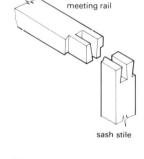

meeting rail

sash stile

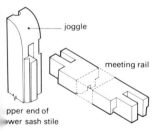

joggle

meeting rail

upper end of lower sash stile

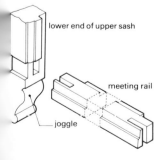

lower end of upper sash

meeting rail

joggle

Figure 4.14

by special steel or copper wire, or by steel or bronze chains in the extra large sizes. In these cases, the counterweights would have to be cast in lead. Before ordering the sash weights, the windows must be glazed and then removed and individually weighed. For the top sash 0.5 kg or so is added to each of the two weights to keep the window closed, and for the lower sash a similar weight is deducted for the same reason. In both cases they are almost counterbalanced, so that very little effort is required to open them.

As shown in Figure 4.14 the arrangements of the meeting rails have an extended depth that allows for the parting bead thickness. The meeting edges

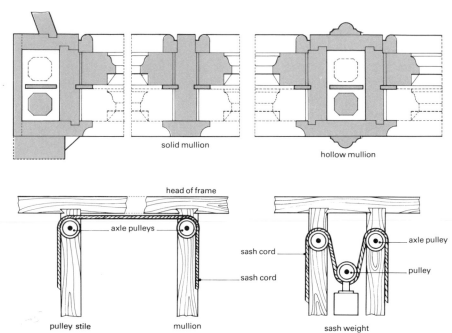

Figure 4.15

are either straight or rebated splayed; the joggle or horn is an extension of the stiles and gives greater strength and a decorative arrangement.

The Venetian box frame has three pairs of sashes to each frame (see Figure 4.15). They can be arranged for all to slide or for the middle pairs to open with the outer pairs fixed; the mullion section can be solid or boxed. The axle pulley must be fitted to the top of the head and not about 150 mm down the pulley stile, as in single windows. Where the sash cord passes over the outer sash top rail, it is usual to contain it in a grooved fillet that is cup and screw fitted for ease of access for cord replacement. Alternative arrangements of counterweight design are also shown.

When box frames need replacement, the two most important measurements to be taken are the width between pulley stiles (this is equal to the external width of brickwork) and the height taken from under head lining to under cill (this again conforms with the external opening). Should the head brickwork have a sprung soldier brick or other form of arch, then the measurement is taken from the springing line.

BASES, ARCHITRAVES AND PILASTERS

A base or plinth is that part of a column between the pedestal and shaft. It is usually named as the lowest member of anything in construction.

Architraves are plain or ornamental mouldings planted around door and window openings, pediments and other decorative features in building finishes, often terminating with a plinth.

Pilasters are rectangular piers, usually shallow in depth, projecting from the face of a wall or panelling. They can be tapered like columns and finished with a capital modelled after the classic order with which they were used.

Nicholson details a variety of bases to columns. The range of design is wide each related to the particular order, but the base should be in proportion to the shaft to be most effective (*Plate XXXIV*, page 212). The plinth has two particular advantages. First, an ornate moulding run to the ground can get damaged, particularly in cleaning, whereas the plinth has a smoother face to prevent damage. Secondly, the plain end of a plinth is suited to terminate the skirting, particularly if it is of heavy section with a considerable projection from the wall (Figure 4.16).

Very wide architraves should be built up with a number of pieces tongued and grooved together (Figure 4.17). This saves material, simplifies manufacture, and most important, the member is liable to less movement than would occur if the same section were moulded from one piece of timber. The architrave can be butt

Detail of door case and pediment in pine with six-panelled eighteenth-century door (Ludlow, Shropshire)

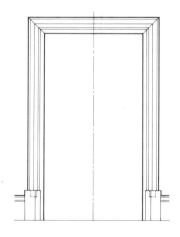

Figure 4.16

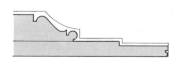

Figure 4.17 *Architraves and plinth blocks*

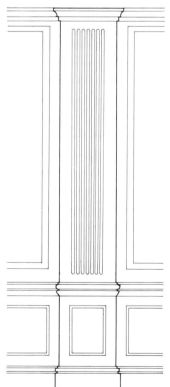

Figure 4.18

jointed to the plinth, but for superior work a barefaced tenon is made at one end and housed into the plinth back. This is a workshop operation and the legs must be made handed. The mitre cut at the head is normally regarded as a site operation but it can be made in the workshop and with very wide cuts a loose tongue helps to keep the mouldings in line.

Figure 4.18 details a plan and elevation of a pilaster. Pilasters are particularly useful for incorporating in large elevations. With internal panelled rooms they allow for the main panels, recessed back from the face of pilasters, to be made in manageable sections. In any design the first consideration is access into the building for the completed joinery assemblies. In some cases a wall will have to remain unbuilt until panels are installed, but in most work door openings are usually the only access. Pilasters also have the advantage of providing spaces for a duct system to accommodate service pipes. It is simple to make part of the face panel hinged to allow for maintenance or later alterations to the services without the complete removal of the wall panels.

COLUMNS

Strictly speaking a column is a long, solid body called a shaft, whereas a column that is built of segments and is hollow should be called a pillar or pile, but today they are both called columns.

Many buildings contain examples constructed from solid logs to give strength, where the columns formed part of the building construction. The problem here is in the ageing process. The surface will split or shake and, although in most cases this does not affect the compressive strength, it can be very unsightly.

A column can be laminated, but as a general rule it would be constructed in eight or more segments, depending on the diameter of the shaft. With this type of construction, a column can still be loadbearing as a steel stanchion can be run through the centre. Whether solid or sectional, the shaft will require to be turned on a lathe. The surface should not be straight but curved in length, so that all faces or surfaces on the vertical section of the shaft are convex. The curvature in length is called entasis; this gradual swelling towards the middle of the shaft increases the appearance of strength and corrects the illusion of concavity.

With the exception of the Doric order a column will stand on a turned base and a turned or square plinth to the lowest section, both shaft and head distinguished by the classic order of architecture to which it belongs: Doric, Ionic, Corinthian or Tuscan. A column can remain plain on the surface but in

DIMINUTION OF COLUMNS. (*Pl.* XXXVI.)

To *diminish a column* is to give such a form to the surface, that the sections through the axis will all form convex curves on their edges.

To DIMINISH THE SHAFT OF A COLUMN, as in *fig.* 1.—Draw the line representing the axis, on which set off the height of the column; then, from any point in the continuation of this line, at the bottom, describe a semi-circle, of a radius equal to that of the bottom of the column, and let the diameter of this semi-circle be perpendicular to the line of the axis. Through each extremity of the axis, draw the diameter of the shaft, at the top and bottom of the column. Through one extremity of the diameter of the top of the column draw a line parallel to the axis, to meet the circumference of the semi-circle. Divide the portion of the arc, between the point of section and the diameter, into any convenient number of equal parts; the more, the truer the result will be. Divide the height, or axis, of the column into as many equal parts as those contained in the arc of the semi-circle; and through the points of division, both in the semi-circle and in the axis, draw lines perpendicular to that axis. Through each point, beginning at the bottom of the arc, draw a line, parallel to the axis of the column, to meet its respective diameter; then, through all the points of section, draw a curve, which will form the contour of the shaft, or a section of the column through its axis.

In *figure* 2, instead of dividing the arc into equal parts, divide the distance intercepted on the axis and on the radius of the semi-circle into equal parts, and proceed as in *fig.* 1.

To DRAW THE FLUTES OF A COLUMN, as in *fig.* 3.—Draw a semi-circle and the axis of a column, as before. Divide the arc of the semi-circle into as many equal parts as it is to contain flutes; and, because the number of flutes are twenty, and the middle of a flute in the middle of the elevation of

PLATE XXXVI.

DIMINISHING COLUMNS.

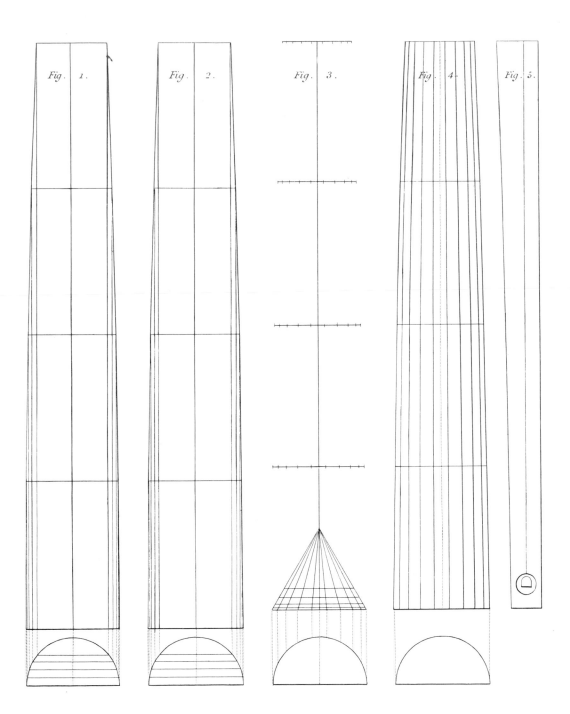

Fig. 1.   *Fig. 2.*   *Fig. 3.*   *Fig. 4.*   *Fig. 5.*

the shaft, the semi-circle is divided into ten equal parts, and half a part, at the extremity of the diameter. Then, having found the diameters at the different heights of the shaft, as in *fig.* 1, on the lower diameter describe an equilateral triangle. Draw lines through each point of division in the semi-circle, parallel to the axis, to cut the base of the equilateral triangle. From the points of section in the base, draw lines to the vertex. Apply each diameter from the vertex, on the side of the equilateral triangle, and mark the extremity of that side. Through each point of section, on the side, draw lines parallel to the base; and these lines will give the divisions of the flutes, which, being placed on the lines passing through the axis of the shaft, will give the points through which the flutes are to be drawn.

In the corresponding points stick in pins, or nails, and bend a pliable slip of wood round the nails, which will form the curve-line of one side of a flute : do the same for all the remaining sets of points, and we shall obtain the representation of the flutes required. The representation of the shaft thus fluted is shown in *fig.* 4.

Figure 5 exhibits the *diminishing rule,* which is to be applied to the side of the shaft, in order to form the curve of the surface of the shaft, as required.

ON THE METHOD OF SETTING-OUT THE FLUTES AND FILLETS OF PILASTERS AND COLUMNS. (*Pl.* XXXVII.)

To SET OUT the FLUTES and FILLETS of a PILASTER; *figure* 1.—Let us now suppose that the breadth of a flute is to that of a fillet as four to one; and, that the breadth of the fillet, at the corner, is double to one of the intermediate fillets, or half the breadth of one of the flutes.

In the line BC, set off any convenient distance; set another interval, double of that distance; then the next part equal to half: repeat the intervals, so that an interval of one may be between every two intervals of

PLATE XXXVII.

FLUTINGS OF COLUMNS AND PILASTERS.

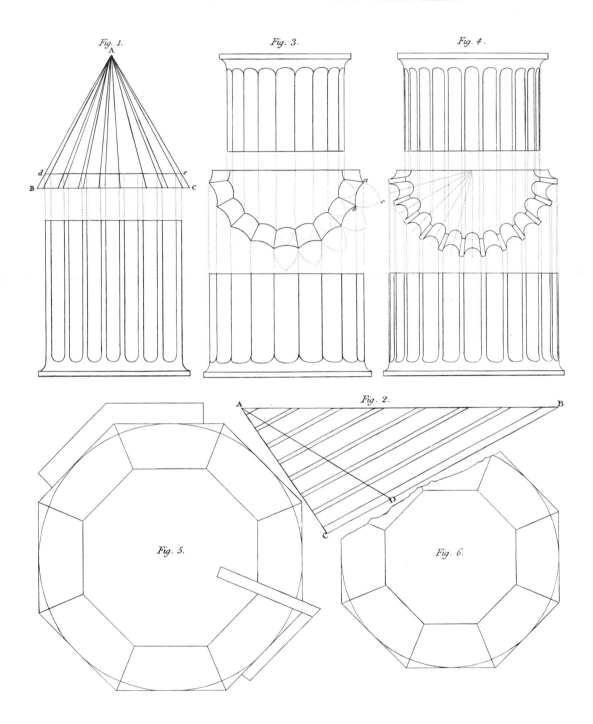

four; and that the intervals of four may be seven in number, and the intervals of one six in number; and that there may be an interval of two upon each extreme.

Then, with the distance BC, containing all the intervals, describe an equilateral triangle ABC. Draw lines to A from every point of division in BC. Now, it being understood that the distance BC is not less than the breadth of the pilaster to be divided; therefore, on each of the sides of the equilateral triangle, make A*d* and A*e* equal to the breadth of the pilaster, and draw the line *de*; then will *de* be equal to the breadth of the pilaster, and will be divided into the number of flutes and fillets required.

Nothing farther is necessary than to lay the parts of the line thus divided upon the edge of a rod; and thus the divisions may be transferred to each end of the pilaster.

Figure 2 exhibits ANOTHER METHOD of DIVIDING the FLUTES and FILLETS of a PILASTER. The parts being placed on the line AB, in the manner before described, draw BC at any angle, so that the distance between the point A and the line BC may be less than the breadth of the pilaster. Through all the points of section in AB, draw lines parallel to BC: then take the breadth of the pilaster, with a rod or compasses; and with that distance, as a radius, describe an arc from A, cutting the line BC in D, and draw AD: then apply AD as before.

If the sides of the pilaster are convex, the several breadths must be taken equi-distantly throughout its length, and the divisions applied to the lines in the breadth of the pilaster at each part.

The flutes and fillets may be transferred to different circles, taken equi-distantly on the surface of a column, in the same manner; but, instead of applying the parts upon a rod, they must be applied upon as many slips of parchment as the number of circumferences taken in the height of the column. But, in order to regulate the flutes, so that their edges may be all in planes passing through the axis of the column, draw a line on the surface of the column, so as to form the edge of a flute or fillet, or the middle of a flute or fillet; then one of the ends of the slip may be applied to the line where each circle intersects it, and the slip itself stretched round the circumference till the other end meets the line again; then mark the divisions of the flutes and fillets on the circumference of the column. Through every row of equi-distant points, on the circumference of the column, from the line previously drawn, draw a line, which will be the line of demarcation of a flute and fillet.

Figure 3 shows the METHOD of DRAWING the FLUTES and FILLETS of a DORIC COLUMN. One particular to be observed in this, is, that a plane, passing through the axis of the column, must pass through the middle of a flute, when that plane is perpendicular to the front, and when it is parallel to the front.

The whole circumference of the Doric column is generally divided into twenty equal parts, by the arrises of the flutes, which terminate upon each other, without the intervention of fillets.

Figure 4 shows the METHOD of DESCRIBING the FLUTES and FILLETS on the shaft of the IONIC, CORINTHIAN, and COMPOSITE COLUMNS: and here we must observe that, as in the Doric, a plane passing through the axis, perpendicular to the front, in which the column stands, generally passes through the middle of a flute; and, that a plane, passing through the axis, parallel to the front, passes also through the middle of a flute.

The number of flutes and fillets in the Ionic, Corinthian, and Composite orders, are generally twenty-four each; the fillet being about one-fifth part of the breadth of a flute.

Figures 5 and 6 show the METHOD of GLUING UP the SHAFT of a COLUMN in *staves*. The number may be more as the diameter of the column is greater. In the example before us, the number of staves is eight; therefore we must describe circles, one to the diameter of the top, and another to the diameter of the bottom, of the column, and circumscribe an octagon round each circle; then draw another octagon, of which the sides are parallel to those of the octagon already drawn; so that the distance of the parallel sides of the octagons may be equal to the proper thickness of stuff required to make the shaft of the column. From the angles of the octagon draw lines to the centre, which will give the directions of the joints; but, though the angle shown by the bevel in *fig.* 5, would not differ sensibly from the truth, the proper method to find it is the same as finding the backing of a hip-rafter; and, if the outside of the column is curved, it will be eligible to apply the bevel from the inside; because, if applied to the convex side of the column, every different place would require a different angle.

METHODS OF TAKING DIMENSIONS AND HINGEING.

THE TAKING of DIMENSIONS depends upon the method of describing a triangle, from the three sides being given: therefore, let ABC, *(fig.* 1, *pl.* XXXVIII,) be the three given sides of a triangle: draw the straight line A in any convenient place, as DE: from D, with the straight line B, as a radius, describe an arc at F; and, from E, with the straight line C, as a radius, describe another arc, cutting the former in F; join DF and FE: then will DEF be the triangle required.

In order to take the dimensions of a place which is to receive a piece of framing, make an eye-draught, as in *fig.* 2, No. 1; and upon each line mark the dimensions of the sides; then take the lengths of these sides from the scale, *fig.* 3, and find the angular points of the triangle, No. 2: having cut each piece of stuff to its proper length, scribe each edge down to its place; then lay together the ends which are to meet, one piece being on the top of the other, and draw the shoulders of the joints.

When the place which is to receive the framing consists of more than three sides, sketch the figure, as before; draw lines from one corner to every other corner, and mark the dimensions upon these lines, and the dimensions of each side of the figure upon its respective line. This is fully exemplified in *figures* 4 and 5, taken from the same scale.

most cases hollow flutes are worked into the surface. These flutes, stopped at both ends, are not parallel but made wider at the widest shaft point.

The shaft, when glued up in sections, should be grooved on the bevelled joints for tongues, to keep the pieces stable while cramping up. The tongue should be located nearer the inner face since, during the turning process, the surface will be worked nearer to the tongue at the smaller diameters near the top. In addition, allowance has to be made for the flute hollows.

Columns should not be constructed with octagonal shaped internal division pieces. This might aid gluing up but there is bound to be some movement in the structure and experience has shown that these gusset pieces tend to hold some parts too rigidly and cause other joints to move.

In most workshops, the construction of columns is an occasional job and it is not worth making elaborate jigs to house the flutes by fixed machinery. By far the quickest and most economical way is to use a portable router, with two thin strips of wood that are pinned to the surface as guides, and to finish off by hand if required.

HINGEING

Hinges are made of metal, steel, brass or bronze, the last being the most effective. They allow for doors, sashes and screens to be suspended within their frames and the operation of fixing them is known as 'hanging' the component part. Plain hinges are also called butts.

Hinges are purpose made for special functions, such as counter hinges and parliament hinges, with projecting knuckles to allow doors to open past 90° where heavy architraves obstruct. In most cases the hinge knuckle is visible but others are concealed when the door is shut and these require great skill in hanging, as well as the use of a stable timber, if a fine joint is required. It is usual to fit three hinges to the average height door as, apart from strength, it keeps a parallel joint between the stile and rebate. If a hinge is sunk too deeply, the door will bind as there is no clearance between stile and frame; the door is then said to be 'hinge- or butt-bound'. Care must be used in sinking the fixing screws square to the leaf and flush, or slightly under flush; any projection will prevent the hinge closing together and strain the knuckle and pin component parts.

MOULDINGS ON THE SPRING AND RAKING MOULDINGS

The term 'spring' refers to the change of direction in any form of construction, from a straight line to a circular or sprung line in elevation or plan. The junction between these two points, as with an arch, is referred to as the 'springing line'.

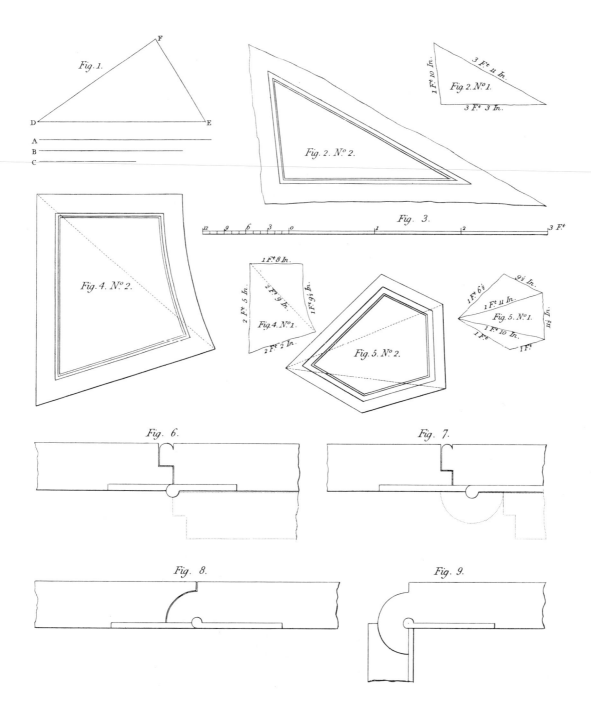

PLATE XXXVIII.

THE METHOD OF TAKING DIMENSIONS AND HINGEING.

Fig. 1.

Fig. 2. N.º 2.

Fig. 2. N.º 1.

3 F.ᵗ 11 In.

1 F.ᵗ 10 In.

3 F.ᵗ 3 In.

Fig. 3.

Fig. 4. N.º 2.

Fig. 4. N.º 1.

1 F.ᵗ 8 In.

2 F.ᵗ 5 In.

2 F.ᵗ 9 In.

1 F.ᵗ 9½ In.

2 F.ᵗ 2 In.

Fig. 5. N.º 2.

Fig. 5. N.º 1.

1 F.ᵗ 6½ In.

9½ In.

1 F.ᵗ 11 In.

1 F.ᵗ 10 In.

1 F.ᵗ

11 In.

Fig. 6.

Fig. 7.

Fig. 8.

Fig. 9.

227

Figure 6 exhibits the METHOD of HINGEING ONE FLAP TO ANOTHER, the joint being what may be termed a *lap-joint*. The centre of the hinge is placed opposite to the joint.

When one flap revolves upon another, it is sometimes required to throw the edge of the flap, when folded close upon the back of the other, at a given distance: to do this, the centre of the hinge must be placed at half that distance from the joint: this is exemplified in *fig.* 7.

Figure 8 shows the METHOD of HINGEING a RULE-JOINT, the axis of the hinge being in the axis of the cylindric surface that forms the rule-joint.

Figure 9 shows one of the flaps folded upon the other.

This method is sometimes used in window-shutters, though mostly in furniture.

HINGEING DOORS AND SHUTTERS. (*Pl.* XXXIX.)

Figure 1, Nos. 1 and 2, represents the form of the joint of two stiles, in order to fit each other. No. 3 shows the same when hinged together.

Figure 2, Nos. 1 and 2, exhibits a plane-joint, beaded alike on both sides: No. 3 shows the same when hinged together.

Figure 3, Nos. 1. and 2, exhibits the same thing with a double-lapped joint. No. 3 shows the two parts put together.

Figure 4, Nos. 1 and 2, shows the same thing, with a single-lapped joint.

Figure 5 exhibits the manner of hingeing the shutter to the sash-frame.

Figure 6 exhibits the manner of hanging the door upon centres.

Figure 7 shows the method of hingeing shutters, so as to conceal the hinges.

PLATE XXXIX.

HINGEING DOORS AND SHUTTERS.

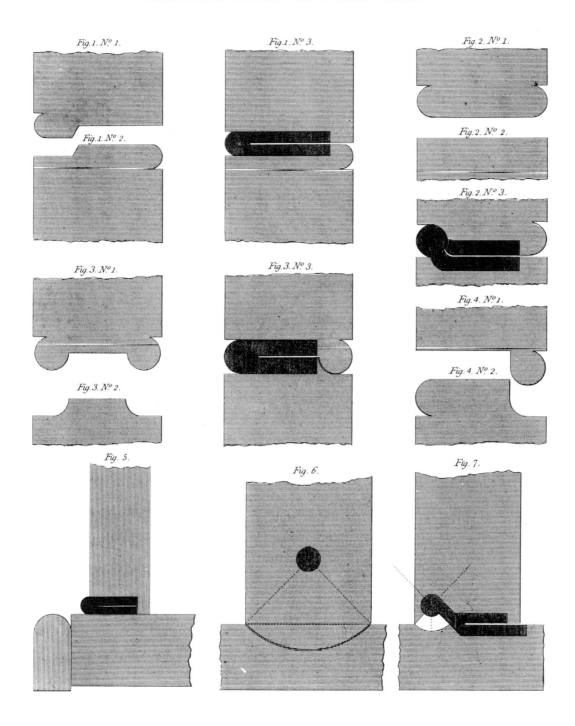

Fig. 1. Nº 1.

Fig. 1. Nº 2.

Fig. 1. Nº 3.

Fig. 2. Nº 1.

Fig. 2. Nº 2.

Fig. 2. Nº 3.

Fig. 3. Nº 1.

Fig. 3. Nº 2.

Fig. 3. Nº 3.

Fig. 4. Nº 1.

Fig. 4. Nº 2.

Fig. 5.

Fig. 6.

Fig. 7.

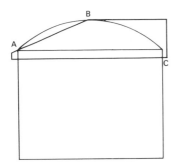

Figure 4.19

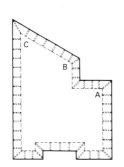

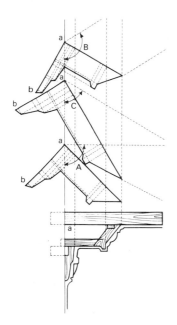

Figure 4.20

joinery is constructed circular on plan and also elevation, this is referred to as 'circle on circle work'. Unless the mouldings are very thin and can be bent, the work has to be set out full size, so that the shape required may be developed. The developed shape is then transferred to thin plywood and described as a face mould, with which it is easy to select the most economical cut from the timber required and also to avoid any defects in the material.

Raking mouldings are those which are inclined from a horizontal line. As a general rule, the projection of the mould in plan remains constant if it is in one plane, but its shape changes in width to give a true intersection.

An easy way to strike an arch without the use of trammels when its width and rise are known, is to use a thin piece of ply cut just a little longer and wider than the arch (Figure 4.19). Mark the points A and B and cut a straight bevel on the mould. Put a pin at points A and B and then slide the mould round, keeping the pencil at point B. take out pin A and put in to point C, reverse the mould and draw the other half of the shape. By this method one can draw direct onto the timber to be shaped without first setting out a detailed rod or making a face mould.

Plate XLI (page 234) shows part of a raking mould with the horizontal part of the moulding to the left of the figure. Also shown are a raking moulding on the spring, the method of describing a section of raking mould perpendicular to the raking line and further developed mouldings.

ENLARGING AND DIMINISHING

Many projects require mouldings produced in definite proportions to those in another part of the building; for example, smaller architraves around windows compared with those surrounding the doors. Nicholson details the various projections of brackets required to support a built-up cornice mould in an irregular shaped room. The alterations of sizes are all examples of geometrical projection and quite easy to follow. Plate XLIII shows how a moulding can be changed to any smaller or larger size by working between the radiating lines, and the method of determining the shape of supporting brackets for a built-up cornice to an irregular shaped room is detailed in Figure 4.20. A further example of a diminished mould from the original height, A–B, using an isosceles triangle can be seen in *Plate XLIII*, page 238.

CONSTRUCTION OF SEMI-CIRCULAR HEADED FRAMES AND SASHES

The shaped heads of frames and sashes may be constructed in a number of ways. A joiner will choose from experience the best method of assembly and

MOULDINGS ON THE SPRING. (*Pl.* XL.)

Figure 1 is the elevation of a cylindric body. At the upper end, G and I are the profiles of a cornice, or section of a cornice, to be put round the cylindric body. If the moulding is formed from a solid piece, it must be formed in short lengths; for, if the pieces are very long, the grain will run across them, and will render the pieces weak, and make the moulding very ugly.

In order to prevent the crossing, as much as possible, the best way is to reduce it, by cutting off the right angle by a plane, as nearly parallel to the face as possible; and the moulding may be bent in the same manner as in covering the frustum of a right cone. Thus may the moulding be got out of a thin board. Bisect the breadth DF, in the point E, and draw EH parallel to FG or DI. Produce the back of the cornice, *kl*, to meet the line of axis in *m*; then, from the point *m*, as a centre, with the distances from *m* to each edge of the fillets and moulding, describe arcs, and these will represent the lines for working the mouldings on the board.

Figure 2 shows the method of describing the mouldings when put round the segment of a cylinder. Here the whole semi-circle must be completed, and the moulding placed as before, and described after the same manner.

Figure 3 exhibits the method of describing the moulding for the interior surface of a cylinder.

Figure 4, the section of a base moulding, to be bent on the spring.

Figure 5, a cornice, where the mouldings are almost in a straight line. This is well adapted for the surface of a cylindric body.

Figure 6 is the profile of a cornice, where the cyma-recta only is intended to be sprung. Here this part must be bracketed behind, in order to keep it firmly in its place. The corona and the bed-moulding are made of a solid piece.

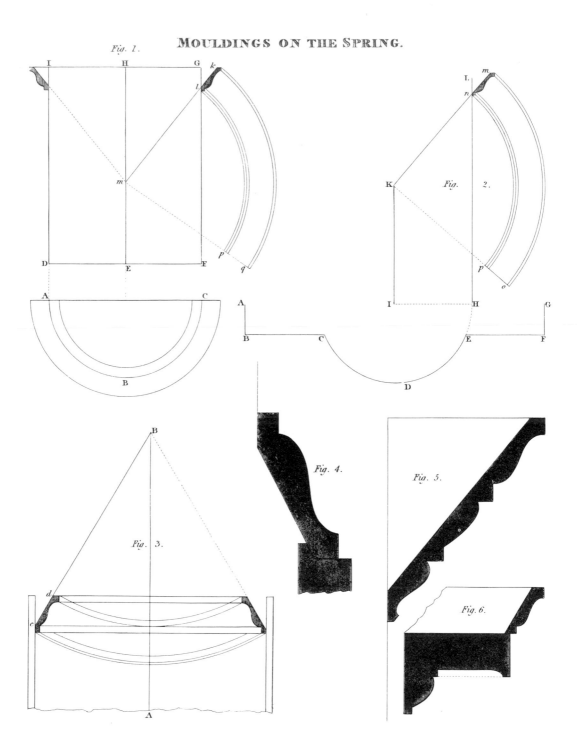

PLATE XL.

MOULDINGS ON THE SPRING.

Fig. 1.

Fig. 2.

Fig. 3.

Fig. 4.

Fig. 5.

Fig. 6.

RAKING MOULDINGS. (*Pl.* XLI.)

When a building has a pediment, with mouldings or a horizontal cornice, crowning the walls, and a pediment, with a similar cornice, upon the rake, the upper mouldings are mitred together, so that the mitre-plane may be perpendicular to the horizon: this renders the sections of the upper member of the horizontal cornice, and that of the pediment, dissimilar in their right section: the question then is, having the section of the one, how to find the section of the other. But, since the horizontal cornices are generally wrought first, the section of the horizontal moulding at the top is given, in order to find that of the pediment.

Therefore, in *fig.* 1, there is given the horizontal section, $abcdefg$, to find the section of the inclined moulding. Let the points a, b, c, d, e, f, g, be any number of points taken at pleasure; draw lines through these points, parallel to the rake; and, also, draw lines through the same points, perpendicular to the horizontal cornice, so that all shall cut any horizontal line in the points h, i, j, k, l, m, n. Transfer the distances between the points h, i, j, k, l, m, n, any where upon the raking line, to $h', i', j', k', l', m', n'$; and, from these points, draw lines perpendicular to the rake, cutting the inclined lines at the points $a', b', c', d', e', f', g'$; then, through the points $a', b', c', d', e', f', g'$, draw a curve, which will be the section of the inclined moulding.

Again, suppose it were required to return the moulding upon the rake to a level moulding at the top: Upon any horizontal line, transfer the distances between the points h, i, j, k, l, m, n, to $h'', i'', j'', k'', l'', m'', n''$; and, from these points, draw lines perpendicular to the level cornice, cutting the raking-lines before drawn at the points $a'', b'', c'', d'', e'', f'', g''$; then, through the points $a'', b'', c'', d'', e'', f'', g''$, draw a curve, which will form the return-moulding at the top.

PLATE XLI.

RAKING MOULDINGS.

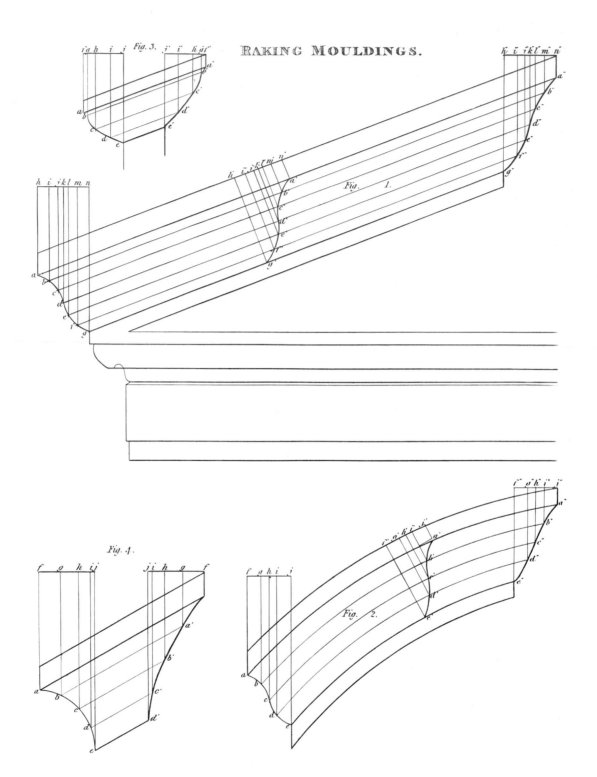

Fig. 3.

Fig. 1.

Fig. 4.

Fig. 2.

Figure 2.—The lower section is the horizontal part, and the upper section is that of the upper return-moulding, found in a similar manner to *fig.* 1, excepting that, as the mouldings themselves are circular, the lines drawn through the points b, c, d, must also be circular; and, instead of laying the parts between the points, b, c, d, &c., upon the raking-line, they must be laid upon a straight line, which is a tangent to the circle.

Figure 3 shows the method of finding the return mouldings for a *raking ovolo;* the lower section being the given moulding, and the upper one that of the return horizontal moulding.

Figure 4 exhibits the method of finding the return of a *raking cavetto.*

PLATE XLII, *fig.* 1, shows the steps of a stair, where the base-moulding continues along the rake, and returns both at the bottom and top of the stair. *Figure* 2 exhibits the moulding upon the nosing: *fig.* 3, the raking-mouldings, found as in *fig.* 1, *pl.* XLI. *Figure* 4 shows the same thing, when the mouldings are to be placed around an internal space.

Figure 5 represents raking-mouldings for angle-bars of shop-fronts: $a b c d$, &c., is the given moulding. Take any number of points, a, b, c, d, &c., in the curve, and draw lines, aa', bb', cc', dd', &c., parallel to the face of the window; draw a line perpendicular to the mitre line; then, through the points a, b, c, d, &c., draw lines perpendicular to the line of the face of the window, cutting it at the points e, f, g, h, i. Transfer the distances between the points e, f, g, h, i, upon the line which is drawn perpendicular to the mitre-line, at e', f', g', h', i'; then draw lines parallel to the mitre-line, cutting the lines drawn parallel to the front at the points a', b', c', d', &c., and, through the points, a', b', c', d', &c. draw a curve, and it will form one side of the angle-bar: then, making the other similar, the whole angle-bar will be formed.

Figure 6 shows another design of a bar, where the window returns at an obtuse angle. The method of forming the angle-bar is the same as in *fig.* 5.

235

PLATE XLII.

RAKING MOULDINGS.

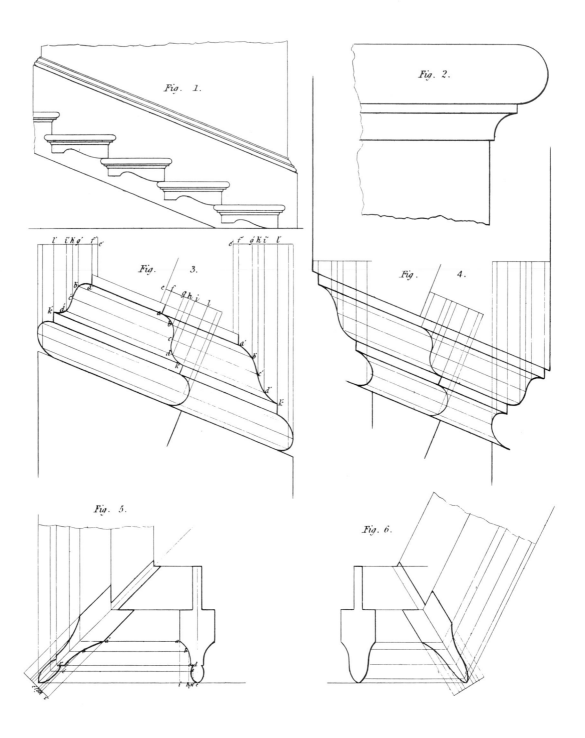

Fig. 1.

Fig. 2.

Fig. 3.

Fig. 4.

Fig. 5.

Fig. 6.

METHOD OF ENLARGING AND DIMINISHING MOULDINGS. (*Pl.* XLIII.)

THIS depends entirely on the proportion which any two lines, of different lengths, have to one another, when divided in the same ratio. Euclid proves, and indeed it is self-evident, that, if a line be drawn parallel to one side of a triangle, and if lines be drawn from the opposite angle, through any number of points taken in one of the parallels, to cut the other, these two parallels will be divided in the same ratio. This is one of the principles of proportioning cornices. Another method of proportion, emanating from a similar principle, proved by the same geometrician, and which is equally evident, is, when any number of straight lines are drawn parallel to one side of a triangle, so as to cut each of the other two sides in as many points, each of the two sides thus divided have their corresponding segments in the same proportion. Hence we have only to construct a triangle, which shall have two of its sides given; for, if the divisions in one of these lines be given, we may divide the other in the same ratio, by drawing lines parallel to the third side of the triangle : or, according to the first principle, if a straight line be drawn parallel to one side of a triangle, this straight line will divide the triangle into two similar triangles; therefore, if the triangle to be divided be equilateral, the smaller triangle, when divided, will also be equilateral. Therefore, if the divided line be greater than the undivided line, we have only to construct an equilateral triangle, and set the length of the undivided line from one of the angular points upon one of the sides, and draw a straight line through the point of extension, parallel to the side opposite to that angular point; then, placing the parts of the divided line on the greatest of the two parallel lines, we have only to draw lines, through the points of division, to the opposite angle, and the lesser parallel line will be divided in the same proportion.

PLATE XLIII.

METHOD of ENLARGING and DIMINISHING MOULDINGS.

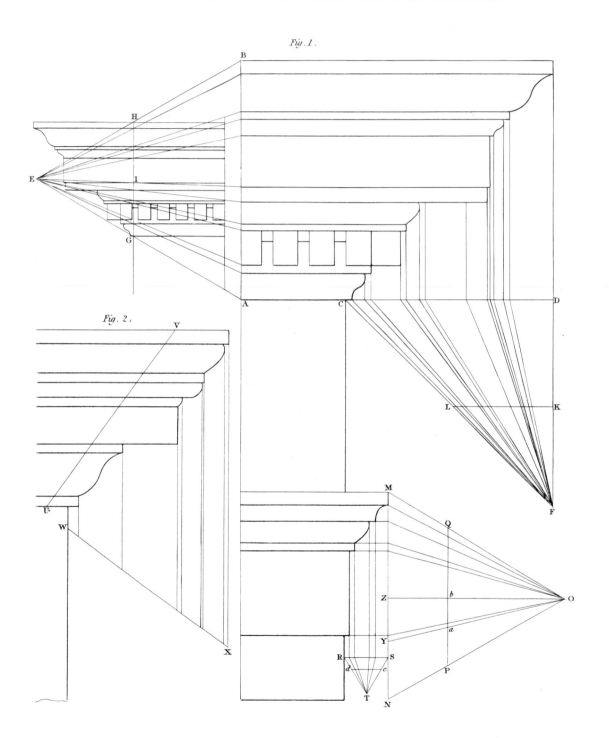

Fig. 1.

Fig. 2.

Let AB, (*fig.* 1, *pl.* XLIII,) be the height of a cornice, divided by the height of the members into as many segments. Upon AB describe the equilateral triangle ABE; from the points of division in AB draw lines to E. On the side EB or EA, of the triangle, make EH or EG equal to the height of the intended cornice, and draw GH parallel to AB; then GH will contain the heights of the members of the new cornice. The projections are found thus: AC, being the lower line of the cornice, produce AC to D; and, from all the points of projecture, draw lines perpendicular to CD, cutting CD in as many points as the lines thus drawn. The point D, being the extreme projecture, produce the line downwards from D to F, and make DF equal to the perpendicular of the equilateral triangle AEB. Draw lines from the divisions in CD to the point F. Make FK equal to the perpendicular EI, as terminated by the line HG, and draw KL parallel to CD, cutting all the lines drawn from the points of division in CD; then KL will contain the projectures of the new cornice, of which the height is GH: and thus, having the heights and projectures of the members of the new cornice, it may be drawn by the usual rules.

The mouldings of the architrave are proportioned in the same manner. Thus, describing an equilateral triangle MNO; on the height, MN, of the architrave, produce the lines of division in the height to meet the line MN; from the points of division in MN draw lines to O, the apex. Make OQ equal to the height of the new or intended architrave, and draw PQ parallel to MN, and PQ will be divided in the same proportion as MN. To find the projectures, draw RS perpendicular to MN, and describe the equilateral triangle RST. From the points of projecture, in the lines dividing the height, draw lines parallel to MN, cutting RS, the side of the equilateral triangle. Draw lines from the divisions in RS to the opposite angle T. Any where in the line MN make YZ equal to the side RS of the equilateral triangle, and draw YO and ZO, cutting PQ in *a* and *b*. On the side TS, of the small equilateral triangle, make T*c* equal to *ab*, and draw *cd* parallel to RS; then *cd* will be divided in the same proportion as RS.

To Enlarge a Cornice, according to any given height: *Figure* 2. From any point, V, with a radius equal to the intended height of the cornice,

jointing taking into consideration economy, strength and application to machine work.

1   The head can be made by gluing together a number of thin boards that can be bent around a jig with ease and held by cramps until the glue is set. This method, called laminating, is very satisfactory for strength and is free of later movement. Its drawback is expense, since extra material is required and there is the additional cost of the jig, usually only required for the one item.

2   By constructing the head in two parts in its thickness, a series of segments is made with the joint at half depth for a plane surface or at rebate depth if a door or sash is being fitted. The butt joints are then made to pass each other. By gluing (and the addition of screws in painted work) a strong and efficient head is made without the expense of extra thick timber.

3   By tradition shaped frame heads have been made from timber in one thickness. Very high quality material not readily available today is required for this work. Solid frames are made first in segments. The length of each segment depends on its radius or sweep in elevation. If it were made in excessive lengths the grain would be very short at the ends, which would reduce strength. The joints would be plain butt joints, which may be held together in one of a number of ways. The most effective is by the use of a metal handrail bolt, a double threaded bolt with a nut at each end. A dowel or cross tongue can be added to prevent twisting while the material is bolted up. An alternative is a hammer head key joint constructed in hardwood and housed into the back of the frame or sash, the joint pulled tight by wedges. Another method, much favoured to allow the full use of machinery, is a slip or double slip fillet housed in the back of a frame and held by glue. With modern high-speed machinery, the shaped head of a frame or sash would be glued up to its rectangular or squared section and the various rebates, moulds, grooves, etc., machined in one operation, rather than machining each segment before assembly.

Figure 4.21 details jointing by segments, and Figure 4.22 shows a handrail bolt made of mild steel with a twice threaded bolt. There is a square nut at one end and at the other a round slotted nut and washer which is tightened up by a handrail bolt punch. The mortice access to the nuts can be pelleted up, but those fitted to the back of a frame are usually left open.

A hammer head key joint constructed in hardwood is shown in Figure 4.23. The wedges are glued and driven home to give a strong joint. This joint is also used to hold a head section to the jamb with the half of the key joint worked in the jamb at the springing if required.

Figure 4.24 shows a double slip joint. The slip, made of hardwood or ply, has the advantage of being grooved through on the machine. By securing a block by G-cramp on each segment, it is easy to pull up the joint with sash cramps.

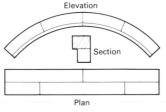

Figure 4.21

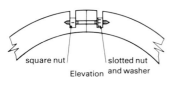

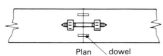

Figure 4.22

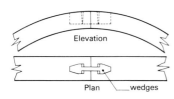

Figure 4.23

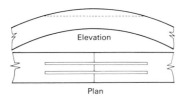

Figure 4.24

describe an arc cutting the opposite edge in U; and the line VU, being drawn, will contain the heights of the members of the new cornice.

To find the Projections.—Draw any line, WX, perpendicular to UV, between the extreme vertical lines of projecture; and, from all the extreme points of projecture, draw verticals to cut the line WX, which will be divided into the proper projectures.

CONSTRUCTION OF CIRCULAR SASHES IN CIRCULAR WALLS. (*Pl.* XLIV.)

To form the Cot-bar of the Sash-frame.—*Figure* 1 is an elevation of the window. Divide the half arc of the cot-bar, PR, into any number of equal parts, as six; and, from the points of division, draw perpendiculars to the horizontal line ag; transfer the parts of the horizontal line *ab, bc, cd*, &c. to *fig.* 2, from 0 to 1; 1, 2; 2, 3; 3, 4; &c., to 6; and reverse the order from the central point 6, and draw perpendiculars upwards from these points: make the heights of the perpendiculars, *fig.* 2, to correspond to those taken from the plan, *fig.* 1. Through all the points draw curves, which will be the form of the mould for the veneers to be glued in thickness.

To form the Head of the Sash-frame.—Divide the elevation round the outer edge into any number of equal parts, and draw perpendiculars to the chord of the half plan. From the points where these perpendiculars intersect the chord of the half plan, draw ordinates, perpendicular to the chord of the half plan. Make the ordinates FI, GK, HL, &c. equal to B1, C2, D3, &c.; and the ordinates of the inner curve equal to CM, DN, &c.; then, through the points E, I, K, L, &c., draw a curve; and within, through the other points, draw another curve; and this will form the face-mould for the sash-head.

Figure 3 is the development of the soffit of the under side of the sash-head. *Figure* 4, that which is applied to the convex side of the same: so that, by

PLATE XLIV.

CONSTRUCTION OF CIRCULAR SASHES.

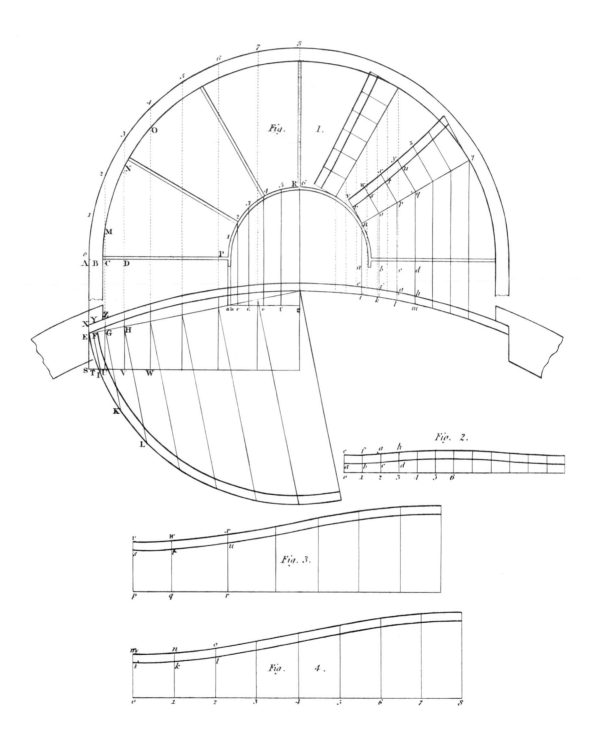

Fig. 1.

Fig. 2.

Fig. 3.

Fig. 4.

cutting away the superfluous wood on the outside of the space contained by the two lines, the sash-head will fit the surface of a cylinder made to the radius of the plan of the window.

To find the Radial Bars.—Let $n\gamma$, *fig.* 1, be the place of a radial bar. In $n\gamma$ take any number of points, n, o, p, q, &c., and draw the perpendiculars nv, ow, px, qy, &c., to $n\gamma$. Draw, also, ni, ok, pl, qm, &c., perpendicular to the base-line of the elevation, cutting the base-line at the points a, b, c, d, &c.; and cutting the convex side of the sash at the points e, f, g, h, and the concave side at i, k, l, m, &c. Make the distances nv, ow, px, qy, &c., respectively equal to ai, bk, cl, dm, &c.; and, through the points v, w, x, y, &c., draw a curve, which will form the convex edge of the radial bar. In the lines nv, ow, px, qy, &c., make the distances nr, os, pt, qu, &c., each respectively equal to ae, bf, cg, dh, &c.; and, through the points r, s, t, u, &c., draw another curve, which will give the inner edge of the radial bar.

Circular headed box frame sashes with frames concealed behind stone facing (Bath, Avon)

Figure 4.25

A circle-on-circle head for a door or window frame is detailed in Figure 4.25. The curved part is built up of a number of segments according to the width and springing of the head (each of necessity cut from a rectangular piece), and with the end joints cut before the curved surfaces are worked. The minimum thickness of material is the distance between MN and PQ in the Figure. The face joints are shown at XY, point X being obtained by drawing through 0 perpendicular to PQ. The edge joint at the lower end is perpendicular to the face side and the bevel for the edge joint at the upper end is shown at Z. The face moulds for marking out the curvature of the upper and lower faces are obtained by developing the vertical plane PQ for the outer (convex) side and the vertical plane MN for the inner (concave) side. The development in each case is an even curve drawn through points obtained by measuring, from PQ and MN respectively, ordinates equal in length to corresponding ordinates projected in elevation. After working these curved surfaces, the lines which cut the vertical curved surfaces are obtained by transferring the horizontal radiating lines — 1.1, 2.2, 3.3, etc. — to the upper and lower surfaces and measuring along these lines the points cc, dd, ee, etc., from the faces PQ and MN respectively. Even curves drawn through these points give the lines required.

SHUTTING OR SHUTTERING OF WINDOWS

The shutting, or shuttering, of windows refers not to the closing of the sashes but to the provision of shutters to close across the window opening. Shutters can be fitted to most windows, either internally or on the building face, when they are called a Jalousie, or Venetian blind if framed with louvred slats. In Britain shutters are usually fitted internally. They give added security to window and door openings and are very effective if constructed to match the wall panels of the main rooms when they are closed.

A deep window reveal, usually constructed on the splay, helps in the folding of shutters. Principal window shutters, where deep reveals are available, usually fold in two halves on each side, but they can be subdivided into more sections (*Plate XLVI*, page 247). With each additional leaf, the box to contain the folder shutters has to be made deeper. It is also possible to construct a shutter which is counter balanced as a double hung sash to slide vertically; or a shutter that slides horizontally and is hidden behind wall panelling when open (*Plate XLVII*, page 248). With the construction of vertical sliding shutters the floor is trimmed to allow space for the shutters to slide sufficiently low. To hide the grooves in which the shutters slide, a thin vertical flap is hung to the window frame and the window board is also hung on the front edge to allow the shutters to slide below the cill line.

SHUTTING JOINTS OF DOORS AND JIBB DOORS

Doors are hung within their surrounding frames at the hinged or butt joint by an extensive range of ironmongery, the designs of which are purpose made to overcome any problems. Many standard designs of butt are now made in a wide range of metals as described earlier. In most cases, the door edges and rebates to the frame are square, but splayed, rebated or rounded edges are sometimes required. When such designs are detailed, the joiner must consider very carefully the later problem of the locking on the closing stile, since it would be impossible to purchase from stock a splayed faced lock to suit the bevel of the splayed edge of the door. A purpose made lock would be very expensive and involve a long delivery period. Despite all the variants obtainable, by far the most extensively used hinge is the 'flat butt'. Flat butts are ordered by length × width opened flat, which also applies to the 'piano' or 'continuous' hinge. Butts can be purchased undrilled, so that the screw holes may be drilled in positions to avoid end grain if they clash with a tenon, or to allow extra projection of the knuckle. Three butts would normally be used in a quality door of normal height. The middle butt keeps the joint margin correct, particularly when temperature and moisture

DESIGNS FOR SHUTTING-WINDOWS. (*Pl.* XLVI.)

The parts A, B, C, D, E, F, G, H, *fig.* 1, form a Section of the Sash-frame.

A, Pulley-stile of the sash-frame.

B, Inside Lining.

C, Outside Lining.

D, Back Lining.

E and F, Weights to balance the sash-frame.

Here the pulley-stile, A, is tongued into the inside lining, B, and into the outside lining, C. The back lining, D, laps over the edge of the outside lining, C, and is tongued into the inside lining, B.

The parts K, I, B, form a recess for receiving the shutters, which recess is called the boxing.

I is called the back lining of the boxing, and is tongued into the inside lining of the sash-frame.

K is a ground, of which the outside is flush with the plaster. The inside lining of the boxing is also tongued into the ground K.

H, Section of the inside bead of the sash-frame.

G, Parting-bead, and serves to separate the upper from the lower sash, in order that they may work freely and independently of each other. R, architrave, or pilaster.

Figure 2, A Vertical Section of the Wood-work of the Sash-frame, and the parts attached to it.

PLATE XLVI.

DESIGNS FOR SHUTTING WINDOWS.

Fig. 1. Fig. 2.

Fig. 3.

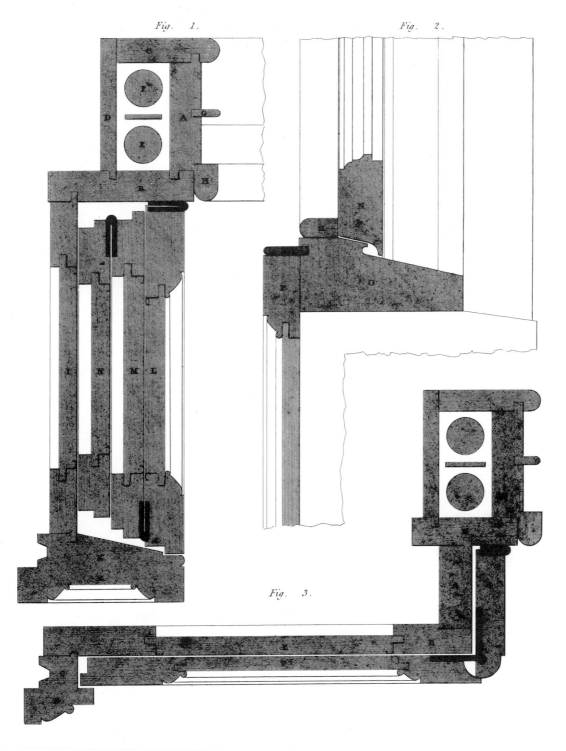

PLATE XLVII.

DESIGNS FOR SHUTTING WINDOWS.

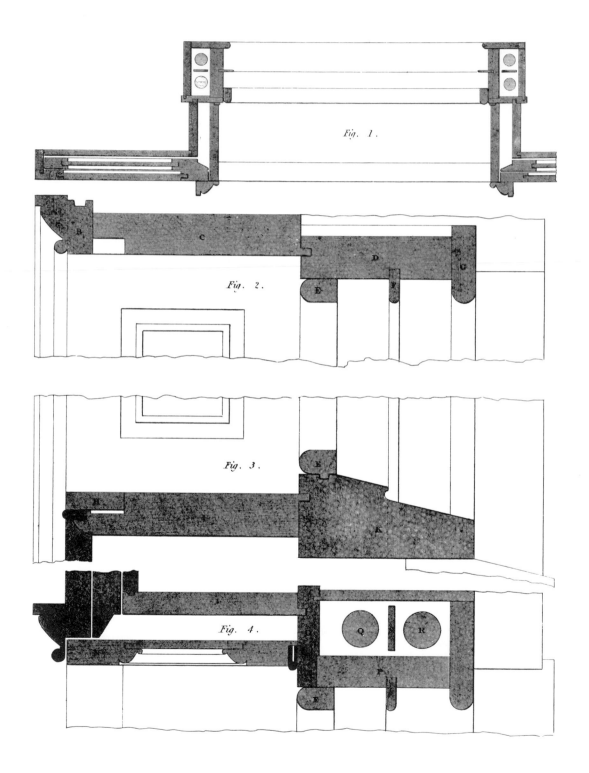

Fig. 1.

Fig. 2.

Fig. 3.

Fig. 4.

PLATE XLVIII.

DESIGNS FOR SHUTTING WINDOWS.

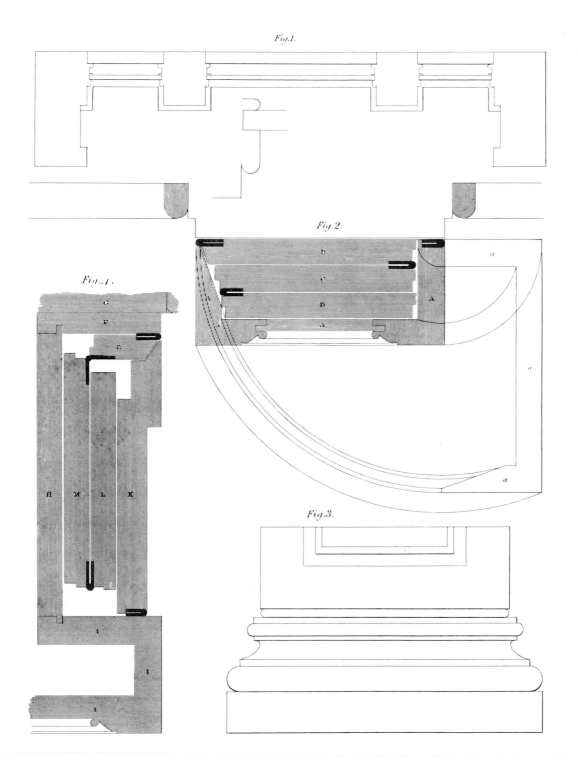

Fig. 1.

Fig. 2.

Fig. 4.

Fig. 3.

H, The Inside Bead, forming one side of a groove for the lower sash to run in.

N, The Bottom Rail of the lower sash.

O, Sill of the sash-frame, being of a different section to the uprights.

P, Section of the back lining of the window.

Figure 3, Section of the sash-frame and shutters, where the wall is not sufficiently thick to admit of boxing-room for the shutters. Here ABECD is a casing of wood, in order to receive the shutters, which is made in two folds, F and G, the one, F, being parallel to the wall, and connected to the other, G, by a rule-joint, and G is connected to the sash-frame by butt-hinges.

Figure 1, (*pl.* XLVII,) is a HORIZONTAL SECTION of a SASH-FRAME and SHUTTERS.

Here, instead of the rule-joint, shown in the preceding plate, the shutters are made to draw or slide out of the wall, as shown, and the end is covered by a flap, as if it were a front shutter; and this flap is hung to the sash-frame in the usual manner, and may be so framed together.

Figure 2 is a vertical section through the head of the sash-frame.

D, Head of the sash-frame.

E, Inside Bead.

F, Parting Bead of the sash-frame.

C, The Soffit, tongued into the head of the sash-frame.

B, Ground, flush on the front side with the plaster.

A, Architrave Moulding.

Figure 3, VERTICAL SECTION through the window.

K, Sill of the sash-frame.

E, Inside Bead or Stop of the sash-frame, forming one side of a groove.

I, Window Sill.

H, A small flap hinged to the back, M, of the recess under the window.

Figure 4, a HORIZONTAL SECTION through the sash-frame and shutters.

O, Inside Lining of the sash-frame.

P, Pulley-stile.

E, Inside Bead, forming a stop for the lower sash.

F, Parting Bead.

N, A Door hung to the sash-frame, in order to conceal the end.

T, Part of the section of the real shutter.

U, Architrave Moulding.

Q and R, Weights for balancing the sashes.

ON THE FORMATION OF THE SHUTTING-JOINTS OF DOORS.

Figure 1, *pl.* XLIX, represents a *common door,* supposed to be hinged at *a.* The face of the door is in the line *ac,* and the breadth is terminated at *a* and *c.* On *ac,* as a diameter, describe a semi-circle, *abc,* cutting the other face of the door at *b.*

Figure 2, on the same plate, represents the section of *folding-doors* with jambs, upon a straight plan. Here we must suppose that one of the doors is shut, while the other opens. Let the half which is shut be *edcbhgf,* and let *aedcb* be the other half, which opens. Draw the line *dc,* parallel to the face of the door, bisecting the thickness, so that the middle of *cd* may be in the middle of the breadth of the door. Draw the line *ad,* and draw *de* perpendicular to *ad;* also draw the line *ac;* and on *ac,* as a diameter, describe the semi-circle *abc,* cutting the other line of the door at *b,* and join *cb;* then will *edcb* be the form of the joint.

The principle of opening is evident; since no length can be applied in a place shorter than itself. The most remote point of the thickness in the moving part must pass, in the act of opening, every other part of the half that is stationary. The principal, therefore, amounts to this: that, since in the opening every point in the edge of the moving door describes the circumference of a circle, every line drawn from the point *a* to the line *bc,* ought not to be less than the line *ab;* and, because the angle *abc* is a right angle, every line drawn from *a,* to meet the line *bc,* will be the hypothenuse

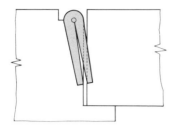

Figure 4.26

variations cause a door stile to cast or bend slightly, (see also 'Hingeing', page 226).

Figure 4.26 details a door frame with a double quirk bead moulded on the rebated edge. By moulding the bead the same diameter as the knuckle on the hanging butt and housing the butt in the frame and door the butt does not project, as does a butt housed in the door and frame in equal parts.

Jibb doors are constructed flush with the surrounding walls to make them inconspicuous. Since they are intended to be concealed, there are no architrave or finishings around them and skirtings and dadoes are carried across the face.

STAIRS AND HANDRAILING

To explore thoroughly the theory and practice of handrailing it is essential to deal first with the construction of the supporting staircase. As a primary vehicle for vertical circulation the staircase has been an important feature of interior design for at least six centuries and since the sixteenth century the development of the timber staircase, and its attendant and enclosing balustrade, has been an important feature of domestic joinery.

STAIRS

A staircase is a succession of steps arranged in such a way as to enable movement between two points at different heights in a building. A series of steps in a continuous line is called a flight of stairs and the termination of a flight is a landing. Stairs are identified by various names for example, closed string, dog-legged, open-newelled, circular, elliptical.

The principal component parts of stairs are the strings, treads, risers, newels, handrail, balusters, landings, winders, string capping, nosing, carriage and apron lining. In buildings of quality it is usual to make a special feature of the stairs. They give great interest and pride to those who construct them as well as providing aesthetic pleasure for the owner.

In smaller homes as with secondary stairs, space is at a premium and the staircase is relegated to a position which places limits upon the incorporation of special features. Today, new staircases have to meet certain British Standard requirements and satisfy the building regulations. Many existing stairs would not meet these requirements if they were to be replaced as the original construction. The regulations cover the pitch of the stairs, headroom, width between strings, winder construction, handrails and balustrades. In public buildings the fire regulations have also to be observed and for restoration and

PLATE XLIX.

FORMATION of the SHUTTING JOINTS of DOORS.

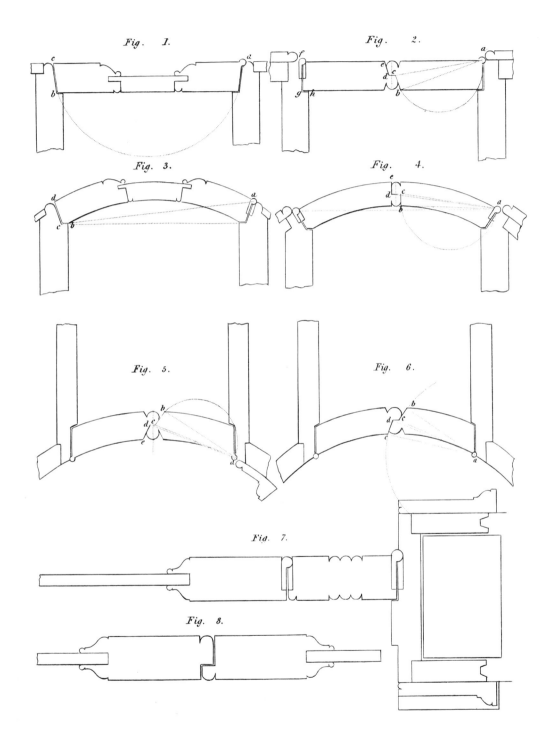

Fig. 1.

Fig. 2.

Fig. 3.

Fig. 4.

Fig. 5.

Fig. 6.

Fig. 7.

Fig. 8.

of a right-angled triangle, of which one of the legs is the line *ab*; therefore, *ab* is shorter than any line that can be drawn from the point *a* to the line *bc*; consequently, the point *b*, in the act of opening, would fall within the extremities of every line drawn from *a* to the line *bc*.

It may, also, be shown that, if any point be taken in *bc*, and a line be drawn from that point to the point *a*, the line thus drawn will be less than any other line drawn from *a* to any other point of the line *bc*, between the former point and the point *c*.

In the same manner, because *a de* is a right angle, the line *ad* is less than any other line that can be drawn from *a* to any point of the line *de*, between *d* and *e*; and every other line drawn from *a*, to any point between *d* and *e*, will be less than any other line drawn from *a* to any other point in *de*, between that point and the point *e*.

Having thus shown the reason of the method, the principle of *figures* 3, 4, 5, 6, will be evident on inspection; or, at least, by comparing it with the former part of this description.

Figure 7 is a section of the jambs of a pair of folding doors, with part of the section of the door : *fig*. 8, the section of the meeting-stiles of the doors.

OF JIBB-DOORS. (*See Plate* L.)

A JIBB-DOOR is one that has no corresponding door, and which is flush with the surface of the wall, being generally papered over, the same as the room; the design being to conceal the door as much as possible, in order to preserve the symmetry of the side of the room which it is in.

Let *fig*. 1 represent the side of a room, in which KLMN is a *jibb-door*, I the base of the room, and H the surbase, extending across the door.

Now, in order to make the jibb-door open freely, the mouldings must so be cut that no point of the moving part may come in contact with the jamb of the fixed part. This may be done by forming the end of the moving part,

PLATE L.

JIBB DOORS.

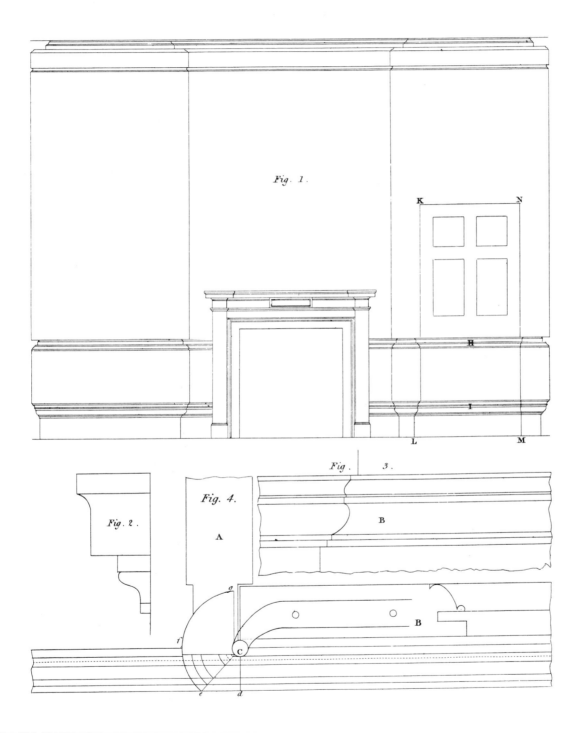

Fig. 1.

Fig. 2.

Fig. 4.

Fig. 3.

and the end of the jamb or stationary part, in such a manner that all the horizontal sections may be circles described from the centre of the hinge. In short, by making the end of the base and surbase, and the edge of the jamb, the surface of a cylinder, of which the axis line of the hinges is the axis of the cylinder. This is shown by *fig.* 4, where A is part of the jamb; B represents a section of the door, upon which the iron containing the centre is fixed. C is the centre. The parallel lines in front represent the projections of the mouldings. Draw C*d* perpendicular to the front line, and make *de* equal to C*d*: from C, with the radius C*e*, describe the circular line *ef*, and where the points of *ec* cut the parallel lines will be the extremities of the radii of the other circles.

Figure 2 exhibits the section of the surbase, marked H, in *fig.* 1; and B, *fig.* 3, is the elevation of the base, shown at I, *fig.* 1.

OF STAIRS AND STAIR-CASING.

Set the heights of the steps upon the perpendicular line FG, and through the points of division draw lines parallel to AF; then the horizontal parts meeting their corresponding heights will form the steps.

Figure 1, No. 4, is a development of the steps and rail next to the well-hole, found exactly in the same manner as No. 3.

These developments are of the greatest utility to the workman, as they enable him to judge of the proper form of his rail, so as to make it in the most agreeable and easy manner. Wherever there is an angle, that angle must be reduced, by taking it off in the form of a curve, which is more pleasant to the eye than a sudden change in the direction of the line. The taking away of an angle, either of the rail or string-board, is called by workmen the *easings* of the rail, or of the string.

Figure 1, No. 5, is the Plan of the Scroll to about one-sixth part of the real size.

Figure 1, No. 6, the side Elevation of the Scroll.

Figure 1, No. 7, the wreath or twisted part, at the turn of the rail above, between the winders and the upper flight of steps.

THE METHOD OF DESCRIBING THE SECTION OF THE HAND-RAIL AND MITRE-CAP FOR DOG-LEGGED STAIRS; (*fig.* 1, *pl.* LVI.)

Draw the straight line *ab*, and make it equal in length to the breadth of the rail. Bisect *ab* by the perpendicular *i*G, cutting *ab* at *w*; make *mi* equal to two-sevenths of the depth of the rail, and *wd* equal to five-sevenths of the said depth. Draw *dn* perpendicular to *di*. Produce *di* to *c*, and make *wc* equal to *wd*. From *d*, with the radius *di*, describe the arc *ign*. Join *nb*, and produce *nb* to *g*. Draw *gd*, cutting *ab* in *r*. Make *ws* equal to *wr*. Join *ds*, and produce *ds* to *f*. Join *cr, cs*, and produce *cr* to *h* and *l*, and *cs* to *e* and *k*. From *d*, with the radius *di*, describe the arc *fg*. From *r*, with the radius *rg*, describe the arc *gbh*; and from *s*, with the radius *sf*, describe the arc *fae*. Make *hl* equal to *hr*, *ek* equal to *es*, and join *kl*. From *k*, with the radius *ke*, describe the arc *et*; and from *l*, with the radius

---

HAND-RAILING.

THE ART OF FORMING HAND-RAILS round circular and elliptic well-holes, without the use of the cylinder, is entirely new. Mr. Price, the author of 'The British Carpenter,' is the first who appears to have had any idea of forming a wreath-rail. Subsequent writers have contributed little or nothing towards the advancement of this most useful branch of the Joiner's profession, and have contented themselves with the methods laid down by Price, which were very uncertain in their application; and, consequently, led to very erroneous results in the practice.

conservation work the significance of these various regulations must be considered.

What may appear to the designer to be problems in setting out are often resolved by the joiner with his workshop knowledge into a straightforward job. The joiner will pay a visit to site to examine the well area which is to contain the new staircase and to check any existing door or window openings. He will then check the plumb and evenness of the brickwork, since allowance must be made in the stair width if any part is to be fitted between walls which may be irregular before plastering. In the case of a straight flight, the only dimensions required are: the width, the total height from finished floor to finished floor level (taking care to allow for the flooring or finishes still to be applied), and the distance between a plumb line taken from the face of the trimmer (making an allowance for the thickness of the top riser plus a little packing, say 50 mm) to the required position of the face of the first riser (namely the 'going').

With this information, the process can be completed in the workshop. A storey rod is provided, i.e. a length of timber equal to the longest site measurement taken, and on one face, starting from one end, the total storey height is marked and then divided by the number of risers required. On the reverse face, from the same end, the total going is marked and divided by the total number of risers — less one, since the top of the final riser has a nosing as part of the landing and therefore cannot be considered in the setting out of the going of each step. From the two divided lengths detailed on the storey rod, a pitch board template is prepared. This is a thin piece of triangular zinc or ply, with a right angle formed by the going as a base line and rise set at 90°. The line which completes the triangle shows the pitch of the stairs.

When setting out a housed string, three further templates are required to work with the pitch board. One is the margin template, which is equal in width to the required distance from the nosing line to the string edge. The other two templates are for the wedges for the back of the tread and riser respectively. In most cases, the wedges would be machine cut and so both housings would have the same taper. Winders must be set out full size on a rod, so that the boards may be cut to the various splays before jointing with a minimum waste material. A full size detail is required of one tread and riser complete with its relationship to the string, handrail, any detailed work to the newel, moulded apron lining, balusters or special treads. Otherwise the setting out is done direct on to the strings, giving all angles for end cuts, lengths of handrail, etc. As a rule, a scale drawing is quite sufficient to identify the stair, hand and landing requirements to complete the work.

With a spiral or elliptical geometrical open-well stair, it would be necessary draw a plan full size. From this a mould or drum would be prepared to bend the

PLATE LVI.

STAIRS.

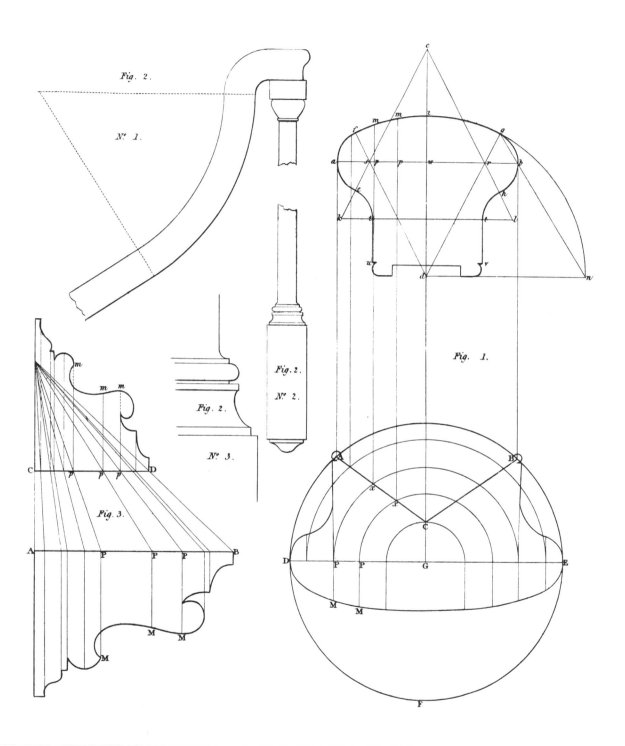

Fig. 2.

Nº 1.

Fig. 1.

Fig. 2.

Nº 2.

Nº 3.

Fig. 3.

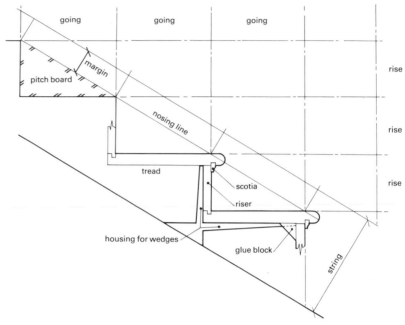

Figure 4.27

strings to build up the thickness of material required before the housing or cut string shape is undertaken. It is also necessary to build a small drum to bend an build up a string, rounded in plan, for an open-well staircase with straight wall strings and rounded ends to house the landing or perhaps a series of winders. Stairs over 900 mm in width may require the extra strength of a carriage for additional support. This is a central bearer that meets the underside of the tread with the addition of a cleat nailed on the side. In very wide stairs this may be two or more carriages. A carriage is liable to obstruct the soffit unless it is frame down. In the case of a geometrical stair, considerable skill is required to produc a strong and yet unobstructive carriage. Steel often has to be used in place of timber and the soffit may be covered with expanded steel mesh and plastered.

Figure 4.27 details a typical closed string with tread, riser and scotia housed into the underside of the tread. The initial marking out on the string is given wi the pitch board and margin. Once this is marked on the timber the back lines ca be added by allowing for the material thickness and wedges. From the pitch board the plumb cut to mark the newels and level cut for the floor line and skirtings are obtained. Where a stair is to be covered with full width carpeting, projecting nosing is not needed. In this case the riser is undercut to give the equivalent toe room. The principle of setting out with templates is the same as described before. Small easings are required to top and bottom of strings to pic up the skirting height or winders.

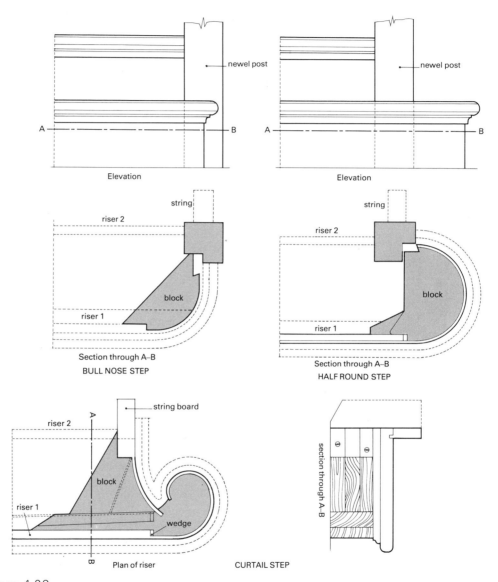

Figure 4.28

Figure 4.28 illustrates three possible methods of construction for a bottom tread when the newel and string terminate with the second riser. It will be noticed that the scotia mould under the tread is worked in the solid. If it is not possible to obtain suitable timber for bending the reduced thickness of riser around the shaped blocks, very thin plywood, about 1 mm thick, may be bent around blocks built up from blockboard.

Stairs with a closed wall string and a cut outer string have the latter cut to the face of the riser and then mitred, the tread or level cut being reduced by the thickness of tread.

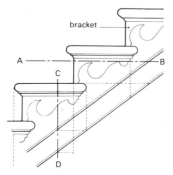

Figure 4.29

Shaped brackets (Figure 4.29) may be added as a decorative feature to a cut string, to form a cut and bracketed string. There is no limit to the amount of decoration, from the fret cut-out detailed here to elaborate carvings.

Figure 4.30 details a small drum with the string bent in one length. The string itself has to be reduced in thickness to about 4 mm thick in the portion to be bent. Depending on the radius of the drum, the timber has to be steamed or treated with hot water and carefully eased around the drum, using cleats across the string screwed to the drum and held in position. Tapered staves are then glued around the string to bring it to the original thickness. When the glue is dry and before removing from the drum the staves are flushed off and a good canva and two or three thicknesses of hessian are glued around them; this gives much added strength for handling, before the string is housed or cut according to the type of tread and riser to be fitted.

A stair string development which requires a series of winders radiating from the circular end is illustrated in Figure 4.31. In this case it would not be practica to construct the string from a solid piece of timber as detailed in Figure 30. The string would be built up by using either thin pieces of timber or plywood to form a laminated string; one or two thicknesses of material would be glued at a time, using a series of cleats screwed to the drum to hold them in position until dry, when the next pieces are added. If too many are bent at once, pockets can form inbetween the laminates which results in a loss of strength.

The straight and wreathed sections of string (Figure 4.32) are often made separately because of the lengths involved or for ease of access and handling whilst fixing on site. The sections are then jointed tightly with the use of counte

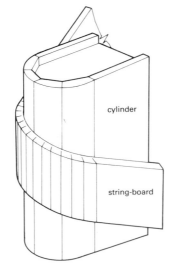

Figure 4.30

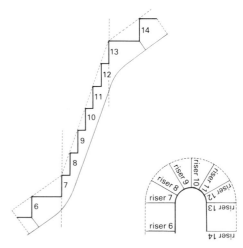

Figure 4.31

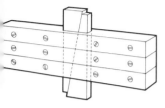

Figure 4.32

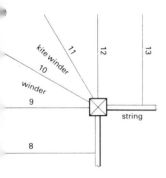

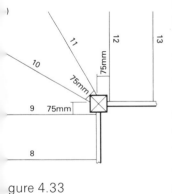

Figure 4.33

cramps. The string is never jointed at the springing line. The counter clamp consists of three pieces of hardwood. The two outer pieces are screwed at one end to the wreathed section, the middle piece is screwed to the straight section and a pair of folding wedges is driven through a central mortice. When the joint is pulled tight, additional screws are added to secure it. The string butt joint should be provided with a loose tongue or with dowels to hold the joint flush across its width.

The traditional method of setting out a quarter space of three winders to turn the stair 90° in plan is shown in Figure 4.33(b). The face of winders 9 and 12 are set in the middle of the newel with risers radiating from a common centre at 30° and 60° respectively. The current building regulations require alterations to the construction of tapered treads according to the 'Group' of building. Figure 4.33(b) illustrates one way of overcoming the requirement of the regulations relating to buildings in Groups 1 or 111: 'The going of any part of a tread within the width of a stairway to be not less than 75 mm'. In normal circumstances, the newel would remain its standard dimensional size and risers 9 and 12, normally housed into the newel, would now be housed into the string. This is not a very satisfactory construction. Alternatively; the risers may be moved round so that risers 9, 10 and 11 would be housed into the newel and riser 12 would be moved further along the string.

A two part newel where all the risers are contained within the angled, shaped newel can be formed from two sections of timber. The newel material need not be as thick as normal and it can be made into a feature without great expense.

In most cases winders are sent loose from the workshop. The straight flights of stairs are glued up in the workshop and fixed on site in the normal way, the winders being fed into the opening, working up from the lowest level. The treads (Figure 4.34) are rebated to take the risers and then screwed up from the underside. Special long wedges are made to be glued and driven home on the string side and blocks are screwed to the newel to hold the risers in position where it has been fully cut away to allow the parts to be angled into position.

HANDRAILING

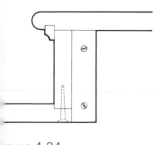

Figure 4.34

A handrail is the top member of a balustrade which surrounds a stairwell. It can also be fitted to a stair to assist and protect people going up and down the flight. Two basic designs are in use. The majority of rails are straight and terminate between newels with the addition of level and vertical bends, called easings, to bring the handrail to the required height off the rake of the stairs or the landing. These are described as handrails of single curvature. The second design has a continuous handrail, which forms part of a geometrical staircase.

The first successful method of squaring the wreath, upon geometrical principles, was invented and published by Mr. Peter Nicholson, in 1792, in a work called ' *The Carpenter's New Guide*,' a book well known to architects and workmen. No previous author seems to have had any idea of describing the section of a cylinder through any three points in space, making a mould to the form of the section, and applying it to both sides of the plank, by the principles of solid angles; so that, by cutting away the superfluous wood, the piece thus formed might have been made to range over its plan.

Since the first invention of the method, the author's experience and researches have produced many essential requisites, which were not thought of at first; so that this branch, as here presented, is now much improved.

The principle of projecting the rail furnishes the workman with a method by which he can ascertain, with great precision, the thickness of the plank out of which the rail must be cut. To do this in the most convenient way, the diagram must be made to some aliquot portion of the full size, which will supersede the necessity of laying it down on a floor. It must, however, be observed that the thickness of stuff found by this method is what will completely square the wreath or piece. But, as the rail is reduced from the square to an oval or elliptic section, much thinner stuff may be made to answer the purpose; so that, generally, for rails of the common size of $2\frac{1}{8}$ or $2\frac{1}{4}$ inches thick, instead of requiring a three-inch plank, one of two and a half may be made to answer the purpose.

1. The HAND-RAIL of a stair is that which is put up in order to prevent accidents, by falling into or through the well-hole.

2. The PRISMATIC MOULD, formerly used for forming the wreaths, and fitting the rail together, is now of no other use than merely to help the conception of the learner. In this case, we shall still be obliged to use the idea of such a prism, which was called by workmen a CYLINDER, whatever might be the form of the base or right section. But, as the word cylinder is used to define a geometrical solid, and has had the sanction of the learned for upwards of two thousand years, we must not use the word cylinder in two different senses without some word of qualification; as, otherwise, it will be

impossible to know which of the two bodies is meant. We shall therefore call the cylinder used by workmen *a cylindrome* or *working-cylinder*.

3. Supposing the working-cylinder to be covered with a thin pliable substance, as paper, and to be inserted in the well-hole, as if it were a newel, and the planes of the risers and treads to be continued, so as to intersect the covering; the indented line, formed by the intersections of the risers and treads, in the development of the covering, supposing it extended on a plane, is called the *envelope* of the well-hole.

4. The straight line formed on the envelope with the base of the cylinder is called the *base of the envelope*.

5. The straight line passing through the points of the external angles, on the development of the steps, is called the *line of nosings*.

THE THEORY OF HAND-RAILING.

Suppose any line to be drawn on the surface of the working-cylinder, and the working-cylinder to be cut entirely through, from this line to the opposite surface, so that a straight line, passing through any point of the line, drawn perpendicular to the surface, will coincide with the section made by cutting the solid, through the line thus drawn; every such line will be parallel to the base of the working-cylinder.

Suppose that the upper portion of the working-cylinder, separated from the lower, to be removed, and the lower to be inserted in the well-hole; then, if the surface of separation coincide with the nosings of the steps, while the base rests on the floor; and, if we again suppose the whole to be elevated to a certain height without turning, so that the base may be parallel to the floor, the surface of separation will form the top of the hand-rail in the square; and the two vertical sides of the hand-rail will be a portion of the vertical surfaces of the working cylinder.

Again, suppose that, while the portion of the working-cylinder, thus formed, remains in the situation now described, another portion next to the top is again separated from the lower portion, but not removed, in such a manner that the uppermost part may be every where of a certain thickness between the surfaces of separation; the upper part, thus separated, would exactly form the hand-rail in the square; and this the solid which we would wish to form, first in parts, and then to put the parts together, so as to constitute the whole solid *Helix,* as if it had been cut out of the solid of the working-cylinder.

The form of the solid helix, now defined, is called by workmen a square rail; the method of preparing the rail, in parts, of this form, is called the *squaring of the rail.*

The square rail is therefore contained between two opposite surfaces, which are portions of the surfaces of the working-cylinder, and two other winding surfaces, contained between each pair of curves of the helix.

The Plan of a Hand-rail is the space or area which the base of the working-cylinder would occupy on the floor. This area is therefore bounded by two equi-distant lines, on which each of the working-cylindric surfaces stand erect, and the breadth of the space between these two equi-distant lines is called the *breadth of the rail.*

The Story-rod is a rod of wood, equal in length to the height of the stairs, or the distance between the surface of one floor and that of another. It is divided into as many equal parts as the number of steps in the height of the story: its use is to try the steps as they are carried up.

For the conveniency of forming a square rail out of the least quantity of stuff, and in the shortest time, the rail is made in various lengths; so that, when joined together, the whole may form the solid intended.

If the rail thus joined be set in its true position, and if the joints be in planes perpendicular to the horizon, and to the surface of the working-cylinder, the joints are called *splice-joints.* But if each joint be in a plane perpendicular to one of the arrises, the joint is called a *butt-joint.*

It is evident that any portion of a hand-rail may be made of plank-wood of sufficient thickness and length: because such a portion of the rail may be considered as a portion of the working-cylinder, contained between two parallel planes, which may represent the faces of the plank; and the two sections of the working-cylinder, made on these planes, will represent a mould to draw the same upon the surfaces of the plank: then, if the surrounding wood be cut away in the same manner, the vertical sides of the rail will be formed agreeably to the definitions which we have given.

A mould made to form a section of the working-cylinder is called a *face-mould.*

A mould made to cover one of the vertical surfaces of a square rail is called a *falling mould.* A falling mould made to cover the convex surface of the square rail is called the *convex falling mould;* and that which is made to fit the concave surface is called the *concave falling mould.* The form of the falling moulds can be ascertained by geometrical rules; and, consequently, if the proper portion of the falling mould be rightly applied to the rail-piece, when cut out of the plank, and if lines be drawn by the two edges of the falling mould, and the superfluous wood cut away, so as to be every where perpendicular to the surface of the working-cylinder, that portion of the rail will be formed.

The Mitre-cap of a rail is a block of wood, turned to some agreeable figure, of a greater diameter than the breadth of the hand-rail. It is used in dog-legged stair-cases, for the purpose of giving a neat appearance to the termination of the rail, at a very little expense.

The Scroll is the termination of the hand-rail of a geometrical stair, in the form of a spiral, and is placed above the curtail-step, which is made to correspond with the scroll.

Balusters are vertical pieces fixed on the steps for supporting the hand-rail. In flights, the balusters are placed equi-distant, so that every step may have two balusters; and that one side of each baluster may be in the plane of each riser, and the whole thickness of each baluster so placed that it may stand within the solid of the riser.

In order to keep the hand-rail steady, and to provide against accidental violence, iron balusters must be inserted into the range, at equal distances, and strongly fixed to the steps. In common stairs, where wooden balusters only are used, the balusters are placed against the nosings, and let into the step-board below; and, being fastened to the nosings with nails, will be very secure.

The RAMP, in a dog-legged and open-newel stair-case, is the upper end of a hand-rail adjoining to the newel, formed, on the upper side, into a concavity, but straight with regard to the plan.

A SWAN-NECK, in dog-legged and open-newelled stair-cases, is a portion of the rail, consisting of two parts, the lower being concave and the upper convex on the top, and terminating in a framed newel, so as to be parallel to the horizon.

A KNEE, in a dog-legged and open-newelled stair-case, is the lower end of a hand-rail, next to the newel, formed either into a concavity on the upper side, or made to terminate upon the newel with a short level, mitred into the raking or sloping part of the rail, which follows the curvature of the steps.

The same part of a rail may therefore be both *ramped* and *knee'd*; that is, ramped at the upper end, and knee'd at the lower; or it may be *swan-necked* at the upper end, and *knee'd* at the lower.

When there is any sudden rise in the balusters, the top of the rail ought to be kept to the same height throughout, as nearly as possible; but, should the height of the steps lead the top of the rail to irregularity, in the curvature of the rail, the line of fall must be rendered agreeable, by taking away the angles, and reducing the whole to a uniform curve. These curves are called the *easings of the rail*. By this mean, the impediments which the hand might meet, in passing along the back of the rail, will be removed, instead of being suddenly interrupted at every junction. When the risers of three or more steps terminate in the same vertical line, in order to connect the lower and upper ends of the rail in the most agreeable manner, the intermediate part will require to be *ramped*, as is done in dog-legged stair-cases. But where not more than two risers terminate in the vertical line, the rail is frequently continued, so as to form an elbow in the intermediate part, in such a manner, that the top of the three parts thus connected may be all in one plane; which will be as pleasant to the eye as it is convenient; since the parts, thus joined, may be cut out of the thinnest wood possible.

To fix the rail in such a position as to differ the least from being parallel to the line of nosings, or the string-board, the top over the upper part may be depressed half the height of a step, while that over the lower part may be as much elevated; so that, though the rail may not be entirely parallel with the line of the nosings, the lower part rising higher as it advances towards the intermediate part, or turn, and the upper part approaching nearer to the line of nosings, as it is more remote from that part, the whole appearance will be more agreeable to the eye.

Where winders are necessary, and the well-hole very small, the top of the rail must be kept higher over the winders than over the straight part; as, otherwise, the person who ascends or descends will be in danger of tumbling over into the well of the stairs.

The rise of the rail, over the circular plan, cannot be regulated by geometrical principles, but must be left to the discretion of the workman. The rail ought not to be raised to any considerable degree over the winders, unless in very extreme cases, as it occasions not only a deformity in the fall of the rail, but a great inconvenience to the workman, by obliging him to prepare the semi-circular part of the rail to different face-moulds; whereas the same moulds might be alike applied to both parts of the rail. Where this practice is necessary, the easing of the rail, at the upper end, will be over the circular part of the plan; while that at the lower end will be entirely on the straight part below the winders; and thus, as it occasions the upper part to have less slope than the lower, so it occasions also the face-mould of the upper part to be considerably shorter than that of the lower part.

To find the Section of a Cylinder, when it is cut by a plane perpendicular to a given plane, parallel to the axis of the cylinder. (See *Fig.* 1, *pl.* LVII.)

Let ABC, (*fig.* 1,) be the base, and ACRP the plane parallel to, or passing along, its axis, and PR the line of section.

In ABC take any number of points, e, f, g, and draw the lines $he, if, jg,$ &c., parallel to AP or CR, cutting AC in a, b, c, d, &c., and PR in h, i, j, k, &c.: perpendicular to PR draw hl, im, jn, ko, &c. Make hl, im, jn, &c., respectively equal to ae, bf, cg, &c. Through all the points l, m, n, o, &c., draw a curve, which will be the section required.

If the cylinder be hollow, the inner curve will be described in the same manner.

When the plane of section makes an acute angle, as in *fig.* 2.

Let STU, (*fig.* 2, No. 2,) be the angle which the cylinder is to be cut at. Draw DU parallel to ST, at that distance from ST which is equal to the radius of the semi-circular base. Draw Br parallel to AC. From the centre, Z, of the semi-circle, draw ZW, parallel to AP or CR, cutting PR in W. Draw WX parallel to AC, and draw Xr parallel to AP or CR. Join Zr. Draw XY perpendicular to PR. From W, with the radius Zr, describe an arc, cutting XY at Y, and join WY.

In the arc ABC take any number of points, e, f, g, &c., and draw the ordinates ea, fb, gc, &c., cutting AC in a, b, c, &c. From the points a, b, c, &c., draw ah, bi, cj, &c., parallel to AP or CR, cutting PR in h, i, j, &c. Draw hl, im, jn, &c., parallel to WY, and make hl, im, jn, &c., respectively equal to ae, fb, cg: then, through all the points l, m, n, &c., draw a curve, and it will be the section required.

If the cylinder be hollow, the inside curve will be traced in the same manner, and from the same parallels Zr and WY, and by the very same ordinates; only observing the points where the inner semi-circle cuts these ordinates.

Upon the principle here shown, the sections of *figures* 3 and 4 are to be found: both these figures are segments of cylinders; *fig.* 3 being cut at an obtuse angle, and *fig.* 4, at an acute angle.

To FIND THE SECTION OF A CYLINDER, so as to pass through three given points in its surface, (*figures* 1 and 2, *pl.* LXIV.)

Let the seats of the three given points be ABC, in the base ABC of the cylinder, and let ADEC be the plane standing upon AC perpendicularly.

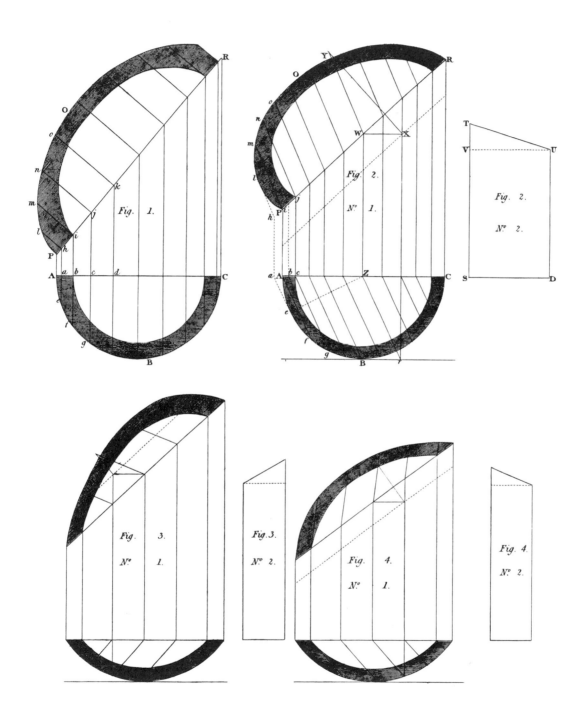

PLATE LVII.

HAND RAILING.

Join the points A and C, by the straight line AC, and produce AC to F, and draw BH parallel to AF. Draw AD, BG, and CE, perpendicular to AF or BH. Make AD equal to the height of the point, over its seat A, BG equal to the height of the point over its seat B, and CE equal to the height of the point over its seat C. Join DE and produce DE to F. Draw GH parallel to DF; and, through the points H and F, draw FI.

In AF take any point, J, and draw JI perpendicular to AF; and draw JK perpendicular to DF. From J, as a centre, with the radius Jl, describe an arc cutting JK at l. From J, with the radius Jl, describe the arc lm, cutting AF in m, and join mI.

In the base ABC take any number of points, a, b, c, d, &c., and draw the lines ae, bf, cg, dh, &c., parallel to FI, cutting AF in the points e, f, g, h, &c.

Draw ei, fj, gk, hl, &c., parallel to AD, BG, or CE, cutting DE in i, j, k, l, &c. Through the points i, j, k, l, draw ip, jq, kr, ls, &c., and make ip, jq, kr, ls, &c., each respectively equal to ea, fb, gc, kd, &c.; then, through the points E, p, q, r, s, &c., draw a curve, which will be the section of the cylinder as required.

The angle JmI is that which the plane of section now found, makes with the vertical plane ADEC.

The whole of the art of hand-railing depends on finding the section of a cylinder to pass through three given points on its surface; the reader is therefore requested to understand this thoroughly, before he actually commences his study upon hand-rails; for, if the principles are not comprehended, he will always be in difficulties, and liable to spoil his work.

The hand-rail of a stair is made in various lengths, and each portion is got out upon the principle of its being the section of a cylinder, and is cut out of a plank not exceeding two and a half inches in thickness. It would not be practicable to get a rail out in pieces for more than a quarter of a circle: a portion of the rail got out in one length, answering to the semi-circumference of the plan, would require a very great thickness of stuff; how much more then would a whole circumference require? for the thickness of stuff increases in a much more rapid ratio than the circumference.

PLATE LVIII.

HAND RAILING.

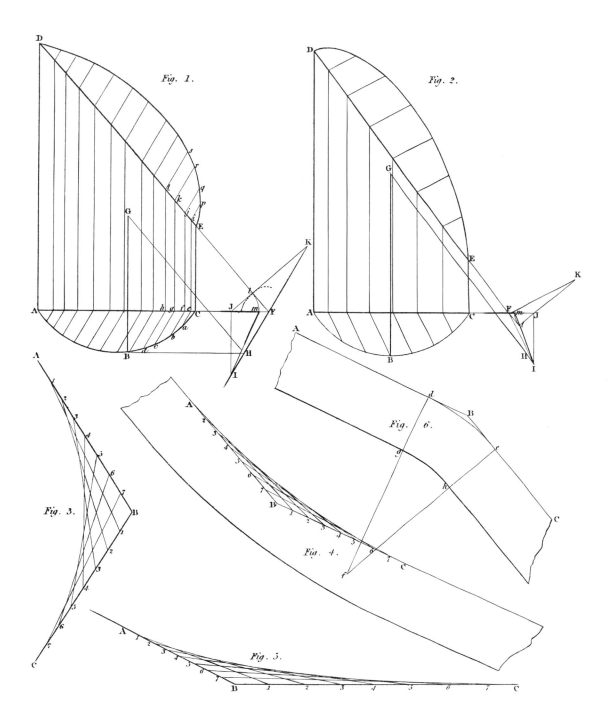

Fig. 1.

Fig. 2.

Fig. 3.

Fig. 4.

Fig. 5.

Fig. 6.

Figure 3 (*pl.* LVIII) is the method of drawing a curve, which shall touch two straight lines, AB, BC, in two given points A and C.

Divide AB, BC, each into any number of equal parts; beginning at A and B, draw the straight lines 11, 22, 33, 44, &c., through the corresponding points of division, and the lines thus drawn will be tangents to the curve.

The reducing of a piece of wood from an angle to a round is called by workmen the *easing of the angle.*

Figure 4 is an application of this to the hand-rail of a stair.

Figure 5 shows how the same may be done when AB and BC are unequal.

Figure 6 is another method of easing the rail at an angle. Let ABC be the angle, and let it be required to round it in a very small degree.

Make B*d* equal to B*e*. From *d* draw *df* perpendicular to AB, and *ef* perpendicular to BC. From *f*, with the radius *fd* or *fe*, describe the arcs *de* and *gh*, which will form what workmen call a *knee* in the rail.

THE METHOD OF DRAWING SCROLLS FOR HAND-RAILS, ANSWERING TO EVERY DESCRIPTION OF STAIRS. (*pl.* LIX.)

First, Let it be required to describe a spiral to any number of revolutions, between two given points, in a given radius.

Let E (*fig.* 1) be the centre, EB the given radius, and let the two given points be A and B, between which it is required to draw any number of revolutions.

Divide AB into two equal parts, in the point C, and divide AC or CB into equal parts, consisting of one part more than the number of revolutions; then, in the line EB, make EF and EI each equal to the half of one of these parts; then, upon FI, construct the square FGHI. Draw GE and HE. Divide GE and HE into as many equal parts as the spiral is to have revolutions; through these points construct as many squares, of which one side will be in the line FI, and the other sides terminate in the lines GE and HE; then the angular points of the outer square will be the centres for the first revolution, the angular points of the next less square the centres for the second

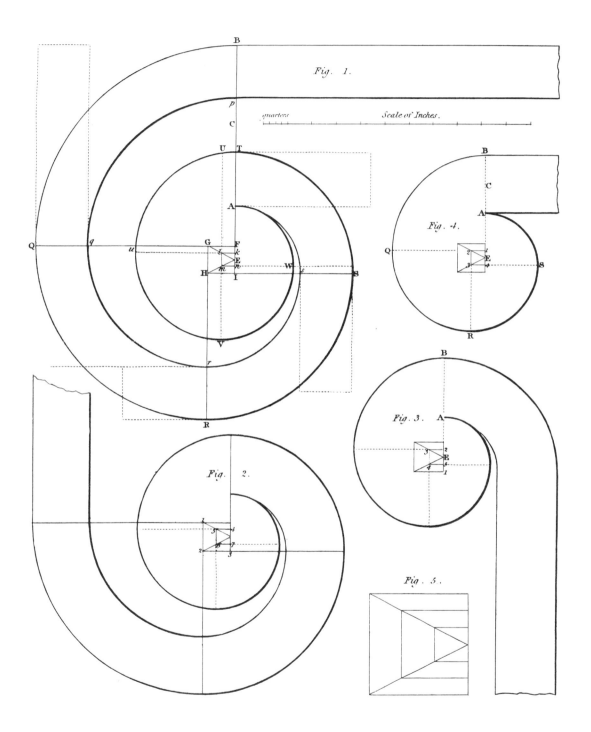

PLATE LIX.

HAND RAILING.

Fig. 1.

Fig. 2.

Fig. 3.

Fig. 4.

Fig. 5.

275

revolution; the angular points of the next less square will be the centres for the third revolution, and so on; one quadrant of a circle, which is one quarter of a revolution, being described at a time.

To apply this to the present example, which is to have two revolutions, divide, therefore, AB into two equal parts, as before, in the point C, and divide AC or CB into three equal parts; that is, into one part more than the number of revolutions. Make EF and EI each equal to half a part, and on FI describe the square FGHI. Join GE and HE, and divide GE or HE into two equal parts, being as many as the number of revolutions, and complete the inner square $klmn$. Produce FG to Q.

From the centre, F, with the distance FB, describe the quadrant BQ.

Produce GH to R; then, from the centre G, with the radius GQ, describe the arc QR.

Produce HI to S; then, from the centre H, and, with the radius HS, describe the arc RS.

From the centre I, with the radius IS, describe the quadrant ST; which finishes the first revolution of the spiral.

Again, produce kl to U, lm to V, mn to W; then, from k, with the radius kT describe the arc TU; from l, with the radius lU, describe the arc UV; from m, with the radius mV, describe the arc VW; from n, with the radius nW, describe the arc WA, which will complete the second revolution, and terminate in the point A, as required.

To draw the second spiral, and thereby to draw the scroll complete.—In the straight line EB set Bp towards E, equal to the breadth of the rail; then from F, with the radius Fp, describe the arc pq; from G, with the radius Gq, describe the arc qr; from H, with the radius Hr, describe the arc rs; from I, with the radius Is, describe the arc As, which will complete the scroll.

The whole breadth of this scroll, now drawn, is about twelve inches and five-eighths of an inch, and is intended for a very large step. The breadth of the scroll, *fig.* 2, is ten inches and a half; the breadth of the next scroll, not shown here, is eight inches and three-eighths of an inch; which will be a proper breadth for an ordinary sized step. The breadth of *fig.* 3 is six inches and seven-eighths of an inch; which is applicable to hand-rails where there is very little room.

All these scrolls are only portions of the great scroll, *fig.* 1, and show that one mould may be made so as to answer any number of revolutions: these scrolls are all drawn from the same centres as that of *fig.* 1. ***Fig.*** 1 consists of eight quadrants; *fig.* 2, of seven quadrants; the other, consisting of seven quadrants, is not shown, from want of room. ***Fig.*** 3 consists of five quadrants; and *fig.* 4, of four quadrants, and may be drawn, independent of *fig.* 1, by the very same rule, which must be adapted to one revolution: divide AB into two equal parts, in the point C, as before. Divide AC into two equal parts, that is, into one part more than the number of revolutions; because it is to consist of only one revolution. Then, making E the middle of the side of the square, describe the square 1234. From the centre 1, with the radius 1B, describe the arc BQ; from the centre 2, with the radius 2Q, describe the arc QR; from the centre 3, with the radius 3R, describe the arc RS; and, from the centre 4, with the radius 4S, describe the arc SA, which will complete the scroll, as required.

TO FIND THE MOULDS FOR EXECUTING A HAND-RAIL.

Let *fig.* 1, *pl.* LX, be the plan of the rail; AB and DE being the straight parts; BCD the circular part, which is divided into equal parts by the point C; and, consequently, BC and CD are each quadrants.

TO CONSTRUCT THE FALLING MOULD.

In *fig.* 2 draw the straight line AB; and through A draw CE, perpendicular to AB. Make AC and AE each equal to the stretch out of the quadrant BC or CD, (*fig.* 1,) together with the breadth B*g* or D*h* of a flyer. Draw CD (*fig.* 2,) parallel to AB. Make CD equal to the height of twelve steps; that is, equal to the ten winders, together with the breadth of the two flyers, one on each side of the winders. Make E*h* equal to the breadth of one of the flyers, and draw *hi* perpendicular to CE, and make *hi* equal to the

PLATE LX.

HAND RAILING.

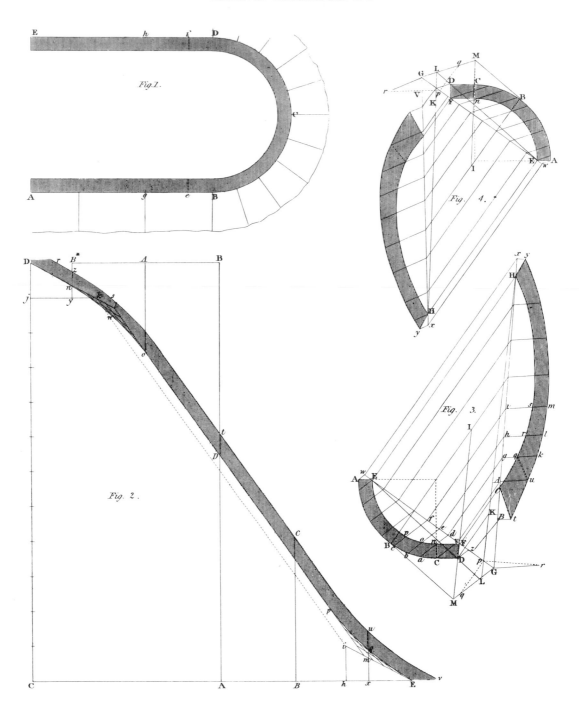

height of a step. Join iE. In like manner, in the straight line CD, make Dj equal to the height of a step. Draw jk parallel to CE, and make jk equal to the breadth of one of the flyers. Join Dk, and ki.

As it is customary with some workmen to raise the rail higher upon the winders than upon the straight part; and, as this is altogether arbitrary, draw lm parallel to ki, at such a height as the workman may think proper. Make ln, no, mp, each equal to mE; then ease or reduce each of the angles lno and pmE to curves nwo, pqE; then draw a line $rstuv$ parallel to D$nwopq$E, comprehending a distance equal to the depth of the rail, and this completes the falling mould of the rail.

TO FIND THE FACE-MOULD OF THE RAIL.

It is customary to execute a small portion of the straight rail along with the wreath, or twist, for each quadrant of the rail; and, as this distance is arbitrary, set off Be and Df, *fig*. 1, each equal to three inches. Transfer this distance to hx and ky, *fig*. 2.

In *fig*. 2, draw xu perpendicular to CE, cutting the upper edge of the falling mould at u; also draw yzB* perpendicular to CE, cutting the under edge of the falling mould at n, and the upper edge of the same at z.

Through any point B* draw B*B, parallel to CE, and divide Ax B*B each into two equal parts at the points B, A. Draw BC perpendicular to CE, cutting the top of the rail at C, and draw Ao perpendicular to B*B, cutting the under edge of the rail at o.

In *fig*. 3 lay down the plan for one quarter of the rail, *fig*. 1, taking in the straight part. ABC, *fig*. 3, being the quadrant, and CD the straight part of the rail.

It is found that, if the part of the rail over the plan ABCDFE, *fig*. 3, were actually executed, that a plane would touch the three points of the rail in the perpendiculars erected upon the plan EBD.

Join EF, (*fig*. 3,) and produce EF to G. Draw EH, BI, and DK, perpendicular to EG. Make EH equal in height to At, *fig*. 2; BI equal to BC, *fig.* 2; and DK equal to *xu, fig.* 2.   Join ED, and produce ED to L.   Draw BM parallel to EL.   Join HK, and produce HK to L; and draw IM parallel to HL.   Join ML, and produce ML to meet EG in G.   In GM, take any point, *q,* and draw *pq* perpendicular to EG, cutting EG in *p;* and draw *pr* perpendicular to HG.   From G, with the radius G*q,* describe an arc cutting *pr* in *r;* join G*r.*   In the curve CA take any number of points *a, b, c,* &c. and draw *ad, be, cf,* &c., parallel to GM, cutting EG in the points, *d, e, f,* &c.

Draw *dg, eh, fi,* &c., perpendicular to EG, cutting HG in the points *g, h, i,* &c.   Draw *gk, hl, im,* &c., parallel to G*r.*   Make *gk, hl, im,* &c. each respectively equal to *da, eb, fc,* &c; and, through all the points *k, l, m,* &c., draw a curve, which will give the outer edge of the falling mould.   The inner edge, *q, r, s,* &c., is found in the very same manner: viz. by transferring the ordinates *dn, eo, fp,* &c. to *gq, hr, is,* &c., and drawing the curve *qrs,* which is the inner edge of the falling mould.

Though the same principle serves to find the straight part of the rail, as well as the circular part, the straight part of the face-mould will be more accurately ascertained thus: Let FD (*fig.* 3) be the end of the straight part on the plan, and C*n* the line which divides the straight and circular parts of the rail.

Through the points *n*CD draw the ordinates *nd,* C*v,* and D*z,* parallel to GM, cutting EG in the points *d, v, z.*   Draw *dg, vA,* and *zB,* parallel to EH, cutting HG in the points *g, A, B.*   Draw *gq, Au,* and *Bt,* parallel to G*r.* Make *gq* equal to *dn, Au* equal to *v*C, and B*t* equal to *z*D.   Draw FC parallel to EH, cutting HG in *C.*   Join C*q* and C*t.*   Draw *qu* parallel to C*t,* and *tu* parallel to C*q;* then C*qut* will be that portion of the face-mould answering to the straight part *n*CDF on the plan.

The joint-line of the face-mould will be very accurately found thus:

Produce (*fig.* 3) GE to *w.*   Draw A*w* parallel to MG, and *wx* parallel to EH, cutting GH produced in *x.*   Draw *xy* parallel to G*r,* and make *xy* equal to *w*A; and by this method the whole of the face-mould is found in the most accurate manner.

To show the manner in which *fig.* 4 is determined, it is proper to observe here that the operation is inverted for the conveniency of finding the mould from the under side of the falling mould, instead of from the upper side.

In *fig.* 4, draw the plan ABDFE, and let the resting points be E, B, D. Join EF, and produce EF to G. Draw DK, BI, and EH, perpendicular to EF. Make DK equal to *B*n fig.* 2; BI equal to *Ao, fig.* 2, and EH equal to B*D*, *fig.* 2. Join ED, and produce ED to L; join HK, and produce HK to L. Draw BM parallel to EL, and IM parallel to HL. Join ML, and produce ML to G, and join GH. In GE take any point, *p*, and draw *pq* perpendicular to GE, cutting GM in *q*. Draw *pr* perpendicular to HG. From L, as a centre, with the radius L*q*, describe an arc, cutting *pr* at *v*, and join G*v*: then complete the falling mould as before.

TO FIND THE MOULDS FOR EXECUTING A HAND-RAIL, WITH FOUR WINDERS IN ONE QUARTER, THE OTHER BEING FLAT ROUND A SEMI-CYLINDRIC WELL-HOLE, HAVING FLYERS ABOVE AND BELOW.

To find the Falling Mould. (*fig.* 1, *pl.* LXI.)—Draw the straight line JI, in which take any point, *d*, and draw *d*C perpendicular to JI. In *d*C make *dt* equal to the greater radius of the rail, and, through *t*, draw *ab* parallel to JI. From the centre *t*, with the radius *td*, describe the semi-circle *adb*. In *t*C make *t*U equal to *tb*, together with three-fourths of *tb*. Join U*a* and U*b*. Produce U*a* to meet JI in T, and U*b* to meet JI in H. In JI make HI equal to the breadth of one of the flyers. Draw HG perpendicular to HI, and make HG equal to the height of a step, and join GI. Make TJ equal to the breadth of two of the flyers.

Draw JN perpendicular to JI. In JN make JK equal to the height of a step, K4 equal to the height of four steps, KL equal to the height of five steps, KM equal to the height of six steps, and KN equal to the height of seven steps. Draw 4*f* parallel to JI, meeting *d*C in *f*. Draw L*e* parallel to JI, and T*e* perpendicular to JI. Draw M*h* parallel to L*e*, and make M*h*

PLATE LXI.

HAND RAILING.

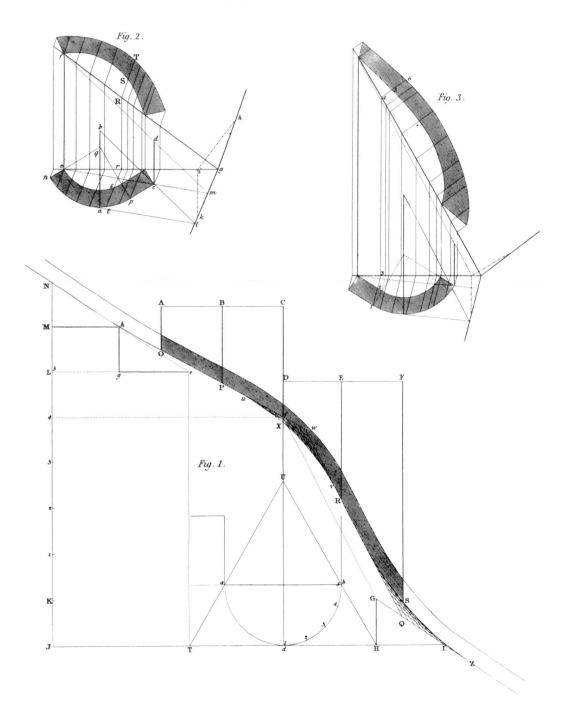

Fig. 2.

Fig. 3.

Fig. 1.

equal to the breadth of a step. In Le make Lg and ge each equal to the breadth of a step; and join Nh and he. Join also hf and fG. Produce $\hat{h}f$ to w, and draw wQ parallel to fG. In the lines wh and wQ make wu and wv each equal to the hypothenuse of a step. Draw the curve uv to touch the straight lines wh and wQ, in u and v. The same being done below, where the two straight lines join at Q, the crooked line NhuvSZ will be the under edge of the falling mould. From the under edge of the falling mould draw a line, at the distance of two inches above it, and the falling mould will be complete.

To find the Face-Mould. (*fig.* 2.)—Here $napc$ is the convex side of the rail, being one quadrant, and pc, a tangent at p, being a portion of the straight part.

Through C, *fig.* 1, draw AC perpendicular to dC, and make CA equal to the stretch out or development of the curve-line $cpan$, *fig.* 2. Let dC intersect the under edge of the falling mould in X. Bisect AC in B, and draw BP and AO parallel to CX, meeting the under edge of the falling mould in the points P, O.

Having completed the inner line of the plan, *fig.* 2, draw the chord-line eg. Draw the lines ef, ab, cd, perpendicular to eg; ab being drawn through the centre q. Make ef, *fig.* 2, equal to CX, *fig.* 1; ab, *fig.* 2, equal to BP, *fig.* 1; cd, *fig.* 2, equal to AO, *fig.* 1. In *fig.* 2, join ec, and draw al parallel to ec. Join fd: and produce fd to meet ec in m. Draw bl parallel to fm, and join lm, which produce to g. In lg take any point, k, and draw ki perpendicular to eg, meeting eg in i. Join fg; and draw ik perpendicular to fg. From g, with the radius gk, describe an arc intersecting ih in h; and join gh.

In eg take any point, r. Draw rt parallel to gl, intersecting the inner curve of the plan of the rail in s, and the outer curve in t. Draw rR parallel to ef, meeting fg in R, and RT parallel to gh. In RT make RS equal to rs, and RT equal to rt; then will S be a point in the concave curve of the face-mould, and T a point in the convex curve of the face-mould. In the same manner we may find as many points, and by this means complete the whole face-mould.

In the same manner, by means of the three lines DX, ER, FS, *fig.* 1, we may construct the face-mould, *fig.* 3, in every respect similar to that in *fig.* 2.

Then the face-mould, *fig.* 3, applies to the lower half of the winders, and *fig.* 2, to the upper half.

This system has the advantage of uninterrupted support, free of newel caps, ramps and bends. These are described as handrails of double curvature.

The curved rail in a geometrical handrail is described as wreathed. A turn of 90° in plan is called a wreath and a full half turn in plan, allowing the handrail to turn 180°, requires a pair of wreaths. In many joiner's shops the single curvature continuous rail is looked upon as a specialist job. The opportunities to undertake this kind of work are rare and consequently the specialist skills required are not always available, but the work can be approached on a step by step basis as the geometry is quite logical and a very interesting exercise.

With single curvature work, the entire shaping and moulding can be done by machine, leaving the jointing by handrail bolts to the bench joiner. Most of the work for a continuous rail can also be machined, including the wreaths. If only one wreath is required, the most economic method would have to be chosen between the setting up of a saddle jig to run a moulding on a spindle or router machine and employing the skill and knowledge of the specialist bench joiner.

For the single curvature type, the straight rails should be pitched parallel to the nosing line, but over a set of radiating winders or over a landing this rule is relaxed. In the joiner's shop, reference is made to the 'handrailer's eye'. The experienced operative will use his eye, when converting the timber wreath blank to form an easy falling line, often bending a very thin lath as a guide. Any wreath made with a nasty hump or an over sharp bend is described as having a 'cripple'. There are many examples of these, particularly on handrails which have been made by fitting to a metal core rail first. In quality work the timber rail should be made first and then the metal core rail forged to fit the timber. Here, the skill of the blacksmith is used, since the metal has to be bent without damaging the timber, particularly by burning which is very important when light coloured timbers are used.

For double curvature handrails, authors like James Newlands and George Ellis have added to the detailing and setting out since Nicholson wrote his text and further addition to the theory is impossible. The only part to change is the design of stair and handrail sections. The principle of placing the handrail over the stairs remains the same for the development of setting out the rods. References have been made in earlier texts to various systems of setting out, such as falling line, bevel cut, square cut and tangent. Today the square cut and tangent systems are used, or a combination of both.

A handrail of single curvature is brought from rake to level into a newel cap or into the newel post (Figure 4.35). The angle joint is referred to as a 'knee'. At the bottom end on a raking rail the angle of the level rail is referred to as a 'kneeling'.

The sharp angles formed by straight lengths bolted together are often

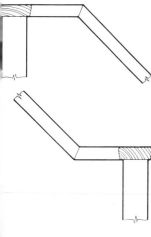

Figure 4.35 *Single curvature work*

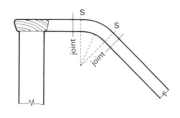

Figure 4.36

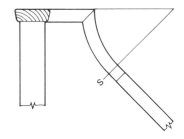

Figure 4.37

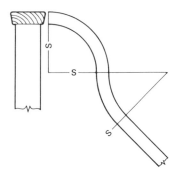

Figure 4.38

unacceptable; the angle may be formed between the rake and level by a curved section called an 'easing'. The illustration (Figure 4.36) is a curved knee, and the easing in reverse at the lower end of the rail would be a curved kneeling.

The height of a handrail at landing level has to be about half a riser higher than at the inclined part of the stairs. To overcome this problem, a ramp is introduced — Figure 4.37 shows a ramped easing.

Figure 4.38 details a 'swan's neck' which may also be used (invariably at the upper end of a handrail) and is in effect a combination of a ramp and a curved knee (*Plate LVI*, page 259).

The ultimate in the design for a 90° turn in a stair has a ramped easing, moulded newel cap, kneeling, turned and fluted newel with the Corinthian decorative style head, turned, spiral, fluted and part square turned balusters.

Figure 4.39 details balusters with spiral flutes turned handed and the turned members above and below the square shank ends.

The placement of a wreath which is to be bolted at the lower end to a straight rail and its relationship to an imaginary hollow cylinder is illustrated in Figure 4.40. In setting out, the centre line is found from the diagonal of the squared end which encloses the section of the finished handrail. Allowance for at least a 50 mm shank should be made, where the straight handrail is bolted to the wreath, by jointing a straight length of handrail to a wreath at the springing line. This will give the cripple effect mentioned earlier.

The setting out for a pair of wreaths over a half landing is shown in Figure 4.41. In workshop practice only a half would be set out covering the area A, B, C in plan and the development of the tangent lines. The face mould would be reversed to give the other hand to form the pair of wreaths, but for clarity the full plan and developed elevation are given. The full size part-landing and one riser line above and below are set out together with the width at AE in plan — this would be the centre line of any baluster. The centre line of the handrail is

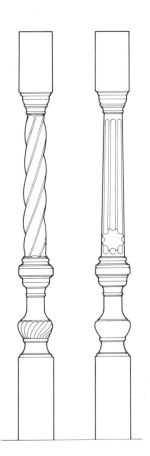

Figure 4.39

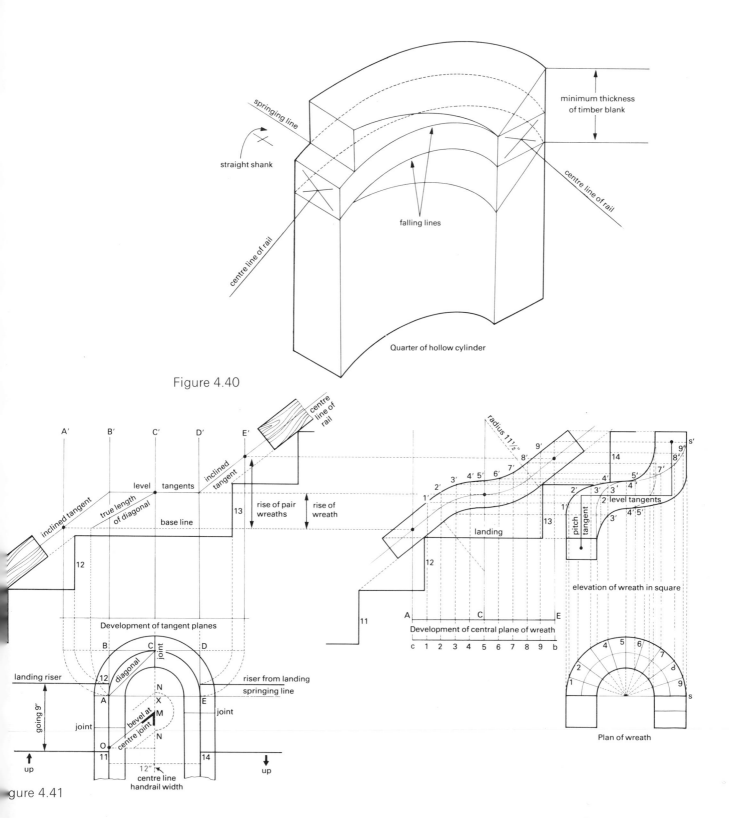

minimum thickness
of timber blank

springing line

straight shank

centre line of rail

centre line of rail

falling lines

Quarter of hollow cylinder

Figure 4.40

A' B' C' D' E'

centre line of rail

level tangents

inclined tangent

inclined tangent

true length
of diagonal

base line

rise of pair
wreaths

rise of wreath

13

12

11

Development of tangent planes

B C D
joint

12
diagonal

joint

landing riser

springing line

riser from landing

going 9"

A

N
X
M
N

E

bevel at
centre joint

joint

joint

O
11

14

up

12"
centre line
handrail width

up

radius 11½"

9'
8'
7'
6' 5' 4' 3' 2' 1'

14
9' s'
8' 7'
5' 4'
2' 3'
3' 3'
4' 5'

level tangents

pitch
tangent

landing

13

12

elevation of wreath in square

A   C   E
Development of central plane of wreath

c 1 2 3 4 5 6 7 8 9 b

4 5 6
2   7
d
1   9
s

Plan of wreath

Figure 4.41

287

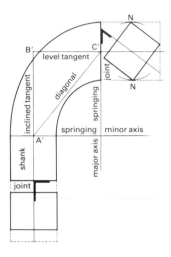

Figure 4.42 *The face mould*

enclosed by the tangent lines AB, BC, CD, DE, with the centre of the circle on the springing line at X. The developed tread, riser and landing lines are projected following the lines by adding the handrail on the rake, the centre line of which gives the inclined and level tangent. One other dimension, the true length of the diagonal, is required before the face mould can be started. This can be followed by examination of the elevation.

Figure 4.42 shows the face mould prepared on a thin piece of plywood or zinc. The length of inclined tangent A′ B′ and the length of level tangent B′ C′ are drawn the true length of diagonal connected. The angle at B′ will be 90°. The extra length for the shank end is allowed. Since there is no twist in the rail at the shank end, the full width of the handrail is marked on that end. One further width is required and obtained from the developed bevel (see Figure 4.41). The bevel of the centre joint is obtained by placing the length of the inclined tangent A′ B′ on the plan at OM. This gives the bevel at M. With a compass on the centre line a circle is described equal in diameter to the width of the rail in plan; this in turn will give the width on the face mould between

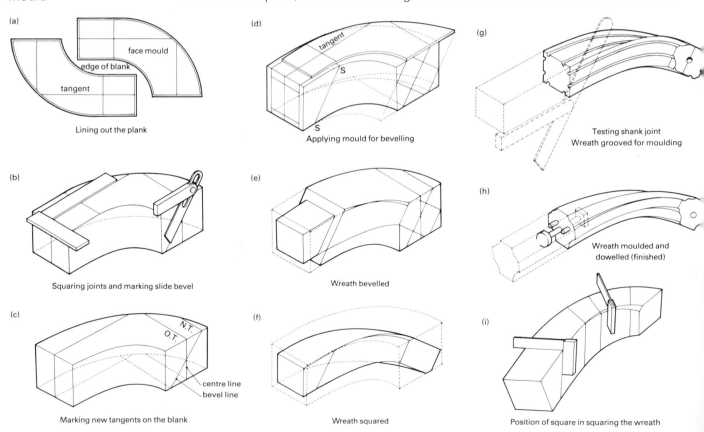

Figure 4.43

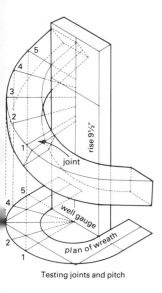

points NN. The width NN is now placed on the face mould middle joint (Figure 4.42). The lines are extended parallel to the tangents, giving a major and minor axis to the elliptical edges of the mould.

The evolution of a wreath from the timber plank to its moulded section is shown in detail in Figure 4.43(a)–(i). In most cases, the vertical side cuts would be carried out on a bandsaw. With Figure 4.43(d), after the face mould has been slid forward as detailed, the blank is pitched up to the height measured by the rise of the wreath detailed in Figure 4.41. An angled block of wood is pinned to the underside of the blank and then cut around by machine.

Figure 4.44 illustrates the testing of a pair of wreaths. As an aid to checking, especially when forming wreaths for the first time, a small drum is made to fit the inside of the handrail, the tread and riser line are marked and the joint and pitches tested on this.

This is a very simple form of wreathed work but once the principle of handrailing is understood, the more difficult forms follow automatically.

Testing joints and pitch

Figure 4.44

5. Plumber's Leadwork

Dennis Tyrrell

Since the publication of Nicholson's text, the role of the plumber has changed beyond all recognition. The advent of new materials and construction techniques has resulted in leadwork becoming a skill possessed and practiced by comparatively few craftsmen — the average plumber today would be more concerned with cold and hot water and heating installations than with any form of leadwork.

As with most trades, there have been improvements and changes in both methods and tools over the years. The basic art of working lead sheet to shape, known as bossing, has changed very little but because it is time-consuming much leadwork is now fabricated using lead welding techniques.

TOOLS

Most lead-working tools are made with specific tasks in mind, and always with the aim of working the lead with the minimum amount of damage to the surface. Most of these tools are therefore of peculiar shapes. They are usually made of boxwood although some hornbeam tools may be found; more recently toughened plastic has been used.

Dresser — this tool is used to 'dress' flat lead sheet and if properly used will leave very few marks on the lead.

Bossing stick — similar in appearance to a dresser, but with rounded edges and used when bossing lead into shape.

Bossing mallet — a round edged mallet, again used in the bossing process.

Chase wedge — a sharp edged tool used for setting in angles and folds.

Cutting or lead knife — a special type of knife used to cut sheet lead. Using this knife reduces the possibility of the ragged edges left when cutting with tin snips.

In addition to these special tools, hammers, chisels, hacksaws, tin snips, rule or tape and most general purpose tools are normally used in this work.

CAST LEAD SHEET

Very little cast lead is used today. The type of situation where it would be used is on the roofs of buildings undergoing conservation or restoration to match the existing work. The work is still carried out on a casting bench in much the same manner as it used to be, but under the Health and Safety at Work Act and the Clean Air Act great care has to be taken to ensure that lead fumes are not

CHAPTER XII.

PLUMBERY, or PLUMBING.

THE ART of PLUMBERY comprehends the practice of casting and laying sheet-lead, with the making and forming of pumps, cisterns, reservoirs, water-closets, &c.

The ductility of the metal in which he works enables the Plumber to effect his operations by means of tools, few in number and simple in construction. Of these the principal are as follow :

A HAMMER, which is made of iron, and which differs from the one in common use only in being somewhat heavier.

A JACK-PLANE, which is similar to that used by carpenters, and employed by the plumbers for smoothing the rough parts of the edges of sheet lead.

The TRYING-PLANE is similar to the carpenter's instrument of the same name; and is used for trying or finishing the edges of sheet lead, when they have been already smoothed by the jack-plane.

A CHALK-LINE is a line which, being rubbed on chalk, is used for marking out the lead into the different widths which may be required.

The DRESSING and FLATTING TOOL is made of beech, about eighteen inches long, and two and a half square; planed smooth on one side, and rounded into an arch on the other. It is used for stretching out and flattening the sheet lead, or dressing it into any required shape.

MALLETS are similar to those of the carpenter, and are of various sizes to suit different kinds of work.

GLASING or HEATING IRONS are of various sizes, generally about twelve inches long and tapering at both ends; the handle end being turned quite round, that it may be held firmly in the hand, and the opposite end spherical or of a spindle shape. They are used red-hot in soldering.

LADLES are of three or four different sizes, and are used for melting the solder.

CHISELS are of various sizes, according to the purposes to which they are applied.

GAUGES also vary in size according to their uses.

CUTTING KNIVES are of various sizes, and are used for dividing sheet lead at the mark left by the chalk-line.

FILES are likewise of various sizes. The name points out their use.

The MEASURING RULE is two feet in length, and is divided into three equal parts. Two of these legs are of box-wood, duodecimally divided, and the third of slow tempered steel. Its name points out its use.

CENTRE-BITS are of various sizes, according to the perforation they are intended to make.

COMPASSES are used for striking out circular portions of lead.

These are the principal tools; but the plumber must also be provided with weights and scales, as most of his work is charged by the weight.

LEAD, the metal in which the plumber chiefly works, is distinguished for its durability, maleability, and other properties, which render it of the highest importance. It is of a bluish-white colour, and, when newly melted, very bright, but it soon becomes tarnished by exposure to the air. Its specific gravity is 11,3523. It may be reduced, by the hammer, to very thin plates, and may also be drawn out into wire; but its tenacity is not great if compared with many of the other metals. A lead wire of one hundred and twentieth of an inch diameter is capable of supporting 18·4 pounds only without breaking.

Lead melts when heated to the temperature of 612° of Fahrenheit, and when a stronger heat is applied it boils and evaporates. If it be cooled slowly, it crystallizes. When exposed to the air it soon loses its lustre, and acquires at first a dirty grey colour; and, finally, by corrosion, its surface becomes almost white.

When taken from the mines, lead is almost always combined with sulphur, and hence it is called a *sulphuret*. The operation of *roasting* the ore, or *smelting*, consists :—1st. In picking up the mineral, to separate the unctuous, rich, or pure, ore, from the stony matrix, and other impurities. 2d. In pounding the picked ore under the stampers. 3d. In washing the pulverized ore to carry off the matrix by the water. 4th. In roasting the mineral in a reverberatory furnace, taking care to stir it, in order to facilitate the evaporation of the sulphur. When the surface begins to have the consistence of paste, it is covered with charcoal; the mixture is shaken, the fire increased, and the lead then flows down on all sides to the bottom of the basin of the furnace, from which it is drawn off into moulds or patterns, prepared to receive it.

The moulds are made so as to take a charge of metal equal to one hundred and fifty-four pounds; these are called, in commerce, *pigs*, or *pigs of lead*.

The plumbers use lead in sheets of two kinds; the one called *cast*, and the other *milled lead*. The cast lead is used for the purpose of covering the flat roofs and terraces of buildings, forming gutters, lining reservoirs, &c. In architecture it is technically divided into 5, $5\frac{1}{2}$, 6, $6\frac{1}{2}$, 7, $7\frac{1}{2}$, 8, $8\frac{1}{2}$, lbs. cast-lead; by which is understood, that every foot superficial of such cast-lead is to contain one or other of these weights; so that an architect, when directing a plumber to cover or line a place with cast sheet-lead, tells the workman that it is to be done with 6 or 7 lb. lead; meaning by it, that he expects each foot superficial of the metal to be equal in weight to six, seven, or other, number of pounds.

CASTING.—Every plumber, who conducts business to any extent, casts his sheet-lead at home; this he does from the pigs, or from old metal, or both. To perform this he provides a copper, well fixed in masonry, and placed at one end of his *casting-shop*, near to the *mould* or *casting-table*. The casting-table is, generally, in its form, a parallelogram, well jointed, and bound with iron at the ends, and varying in its size from six feet in width to eighteen or more feet in length. It is raised from the ground so high as to be about six or seven inches below the top of the copper, which contains

inhaled or permitted to get into the atmosphere above the prescribed level. There is no British Standard for cast lead sheet. The sizes of the sheet available are determined by the size of casting table used. These can vary from 2.5 × 1 m to 5 × 2 m, with thicknesses of 0.20 mm upwards. Cast lead can be obtained from most companies producing specialist leadwork (details may be obtained from the Lead Development Association).

MILLED LEAD SHEET AND STRIP

Milled sheet and strip lead is manufactured in accordance with BS 1178 (1969) Milled Lead Sheet and Strip for Building Purposes. In the past the thickness or gauge of milled sheet was determined by the weight in pounds per square foot, i.e. 4 lb, 5 lb etc.; but since the introduction of metric measurements BS 1178 was amended, giving a range of some six sizes of lead sheet with the thicknesses in millimetres. To avoid confusion and as the old sizes were similar, it was decided to retain the figures 3–8 as code numbers. For easy identification lead sheet and strip carry colour markings according to code. The standard range is as set out below.

BS code number	Thickness (mm)	Weight (kg/m²)	Colour Code
3	1.25	14.18	Green
4	1.80	20.41	Blue
5	2.24	25.40	Red
6	2.50	28.36	Black
7	3.15	35.72	White
8	3.55	40.26	Orange

Milled sheet is 2.40 m in width and up to 12 m in length. Milled strip is ready cut in widths from 75 mm to 600 mm by up to 12 m lengths in coils.

LAYING OF SHEET LEAD

The substrates on to which sheet lead is to be laid should have a smooth and even finish and be strong enough to support both the lead and the persons laying the lead. Timber substrates should be wrought finished, preferably of well seasoned, tongued and grooved softwood, and laid in either the direction of the fall of the roof or diaginally across it. Nail heads should be well punched in below the surface and all sharp arrises should be removed and angles rounded. It is advisable to use a good quality underlay, either waterproof building paper to BS 1521 Class A or Brown No 1 Inodorous Felt to BS 747 type 4a.

the metal, and stands on strongly framed legs, so as to be very steady and firm. The top of the table is lined with deal boarding, laid firmly and very even, and it has a rim projecting upwards, four or five inches all round. At the end of the table, nearest to the copper, a box, called the *Pan*, is adapted, which box is equal in length to the width of the table; at the bottom is a long horizontal slit, for the heated metal to issue from. This box moves upon rollers along the edges of the projecting rim of the table, and is set in motion by ropes and pulleys, fixed to beams over the table. So soon as the metal is found to be adequately heated, the bottom of the table is covered by a smooth stratum of dry and clean sand. These boxes are made to contain as much melted lead as will cast the whole of the sheet at the same time, and the slit in the bottom is adjusted so as to let through a sufficient quantity to cover it completely, of the thickness and weight per foot required. When the box has dispersed its contents upon the table, it is suffered to cool and congeal; after which it is rolled up and removed away. Other sheets are made in succession till all the melted metal in the copper be cast up.

The sheets thus formed, when rolled up, are weighed; as it is by the weight that the price is adjusted.

The other kind of sheet-lead made use of by plumbers, and called MILLED LEAD, is not manufactured at home, it being purchased of the lead merchant, as it is commonly cast and prepared at the ore and roasting furnaces. It is very thin, its weight being not more than four pounds in the foot superficial. Milled Lead is used by architects for covering the hips and ridges of roofs, or any part exposed either to great wear and tear, or to the effects of the sun. It is laminated in sheets of about the same size as that of cast sheet-lead; and, in the operation of making it, a laminating-roller is used, or a flatting-mill, which reduces it to the state in which it is used.

SOLDER is used for uniting the joints of leaden work, and it should more readily acquire a state of fusion than the metal intended to be soldered thereby, and be of the same colour. The solder generally made use of by the plumber is called *soft solder*, and is made of tin and lead, in equal parts, fused together, and run into moulds not unlike a common gridiron. In this state it is purchased of the manufacturer by the plumber, at so much per pound.

As thermal movement takes place in lead (coefficient of linear expansion is 0.0000297 per °C), allowance must be made to accommodate this property. It is therefore necessary to limit the size of lead that can be laid in one piece to 2.25 m², made up of 2.4 m maximum length and 1 m maximum width. These sizes include all turn ups, turndowns and allowances for joints. The British Standards Code of Practice 143 Part 2 (1970): Lead Roof and Wall coverings, gives recommendations on the spacing of joints on both flat and pitched roof coverings.

JOINTS

The functions of any metal roofwork joint are to allow for thermal movement, to retain the roof covering on the surface and to remain watertight under all weather conditions. Joints can be divided broadly into:

Transverse joints — those running across the slope of the roof.
Longitudinal joints — those running with the slope of the roof.

One of the problems that all joints must be able to overcome is that of capillary attraction and therefore the method of jointing will differ according to the pitch of the roof.

The transverse joints called a 'drip joint' is used on roofs below 15° pitch. The must be incorporated in the roof construction by the carpenter; Figure 5.1 shows the section of a drip. It can be seen that the undercloak is dressed into the groove while the overcloak has a straight finish. The undercloak should be close copper nailed in a rebate on the top edge.

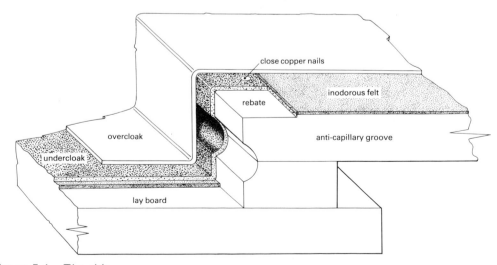

Figure 5.1 *The drip*

LAYING SHEET-LEAD.—The ground for sheet-lead, whether it be of plaster or of boards, should be perfectly even, otherwise the work will be bad, unsightly, and liable to crack. The sheets not being more than six feet in width, make it necessary that they should sometimes be joined. This is performed either by *seams* or *rolls*. The seams are formed by bending the two edges of the lead up and then over each other, and then dressing them down close. The rolls are formed by fastening a piece of wood, about two inches square, under the joints of the lead, and dressing one of the edges of the lead over the roll on the inside, and the other edge over both of them on the outside, and then fastening them down by hammering. Soldering is sometimes used for joining two sheets, but no good plumber would recommend it, as it always cracks after being exposed to one summer's sun. All sheet lead is laid with a *current* to keep it dry. This is done by the carpenter raising the boarding about one half or a quarter of an inch to every foot upon which the lead is laid.

Drips on Flats or Gutters are formed also as in the preceding manner, and by dressing the joints of the lead as described for rolls. This is used to avoid solder, and keep the work dry.

Flashings are pieces of milled lead, about eight or nine inches wide, and are fixed round the extreme edge of a flat or gutter, in which lead has been used. One edge is dressed over the lead of the flat or gutter, and the other fastened, either by passing it into the joints of brick-work, or by means of wall-hooks.

The Pipes used by the plumber are of various sizes and descriptions. The small sizes are called by their calibre, or bore, $\frac{1}{2}$, $\frac{3}{4}$, 1, $1\frac{1}{2}$, $1\frac{3}{4}$, and 2, inch pipes. Pipes below $1\frac{1}{2}$ inch calibre are charged by the foot run, and the larger size sometimes by the hundred weight.

Socket Pipes are those which are used for conveying superfluous water from roofs, &c., and are called 3, $3\frac{1}{2}$, 4, or 5-inch. They are generally made of milled lead, in lengths of eight or ten feet, dressed on a rounded core of wood, and fastened at the vertical joint with solder. The horizontal joints are formed by an astrigal moulding, in a separate piece of lead, about two or three inches wide, which laps completely over it, both above and below the joint, and hence it is called a *lap-joint*. Two broad pieces of lead, called

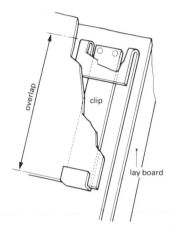

Figure 5.2 *Overlap*

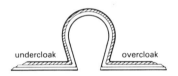

Figure 5.3 *The woodcore roll*

Figure 5.4 *Single welt*

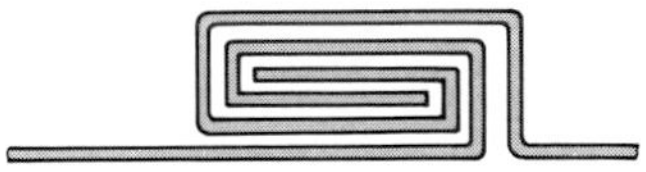

Figure 5.5 *Double welt*

Overlaps are used on steep slopes, and vertical and curved surfaces and vary from 100 mm to 150 mm according to the slope. Fixing is done on the top edge by close copper nailing; the bottom edge is left free and supported by straps (Figure 5.2).

Of the longitudinal joints the 'woodcore roll' is used mainly on flat roofs. The roll is screwed down to the decking. The undercloak is dressed two thirds of the way over the roll and fixed by close copper nailing. The other end is left free and dressed over the whole of the roll. The lower end of the roll should be splay cut to allow for easy covering (Figure 5.3).

Two types of 'welts' are in general use: Single welts are used mainly on vertical and curved surfaces (Figure 5.4); double welts are used on medium and steep pitches and also on curved surfaces (Figure 5.5). Fixing the welt is achieved by clips fixed to the decking and built into the welt.

ALLOWANCE FOR JOINTS

All allowances form part of the maximum sizes of lead that can be used in one piece. The average allowances that should be made, including lead required for bossing, are set out below.

Joint	Allowance (mm)	
	Overcloak	Undercloak
Drip 50 mm high	200	75
Drip 60 mm high	225	100
Roll	225	75
Single welt		
Finished size 20 mm	40	20
Double welt		
Finished size 25 mm	75	50

Where the roof abuts a wall or vertical 100–125 mm should be allowed. The outline of a bay with allowances is shown in Figure 5.6.

SOLDERS

As solder and lead expand at different rates the use of solder on sheet lead work is not recommended. It is, however, still used for the joining of lead rainwater and soil pipes. Modern solder is manufactured to BS 219 (1959): Soft solders. The type mainly used is Grade D, which is a composition of 68.3 per cent lead, 30 per cent tin, 1.7 per cent antimony.

tacks, are attached to the back lap-joints and spread out, right and left, for fastening the pipes to the wall by means of wall-hooks of iron. The *cistern-head,* which is fixed at the head of rain-water pipes, is either made of sheet-lead or cast in a mould, and is fastened by tacks, as above.

RESERVOIRS are generally formed of wood, or masonry, lined with sheet-lead united with solder.

PUMPS, made by the plumber, may be divided into *Sucking, Lifting,* and *Forcing, Pumps.* The last is now but little used.

The *Sucking-Pump* consists of two pipes, the barrel and suction-pipe, the latter being smaller in diameter. These are joined by flanches, filled with leather, and pierced with holes, to fasten them with screw-bolts. The lower end of the suction-pipe is spread out to facilitate the entry of the water, and it frequently has a grating to keep out filth or gravel. The working barrel is cylindrical, and as evenly bored as is practicable, to give the piston the least possible friction.

The *Piston* is generally made of wood, in the form of a truncated cone, the small end being cut off at the sides, so as to form a kind of an arch, by which it is fastened to the iron-rod or spindle. The two ends of the conical part may be hooped with brass, and the larger end of the cone uniformly surrounded with leather to some distance below its base. This leather band should be sufficiently large to render the piston air-tight, without causing much friction. This is the pump which is generally used for raising water for the common purposes of life.

The *Lifting-Pump* consists, as in the former, of a working-barrel, which is closed at both ends. The piston is solid, and its rod passes through a collar of leather in the plate, which closes the upper end of the working barrel. The barrel communicates laterally with the suction-pipe, and above with the rising main. This pump differs from the preceding only in having two valves, the lower one moveable and the upper one fixed.

The *Forcing Pump* consists of a working-barrel, a suction-pipe, and *serving-main,* or raising-pipe. The last is usually in three parts, the first consisting of one piece, and making part of the working-barrel; the second is joined to it by flanches forming an elbow with it; and the third is the beginning of the main, and is continued to where the water is delivered, where it is furnished with two moveable valves. The perfection of the barrel and piston of this pump is so great, as to require neither wadding nor leather. It is used for forcing water to any great height.

There are two or three other kinds of pumps which require a short description, and they are as follows:—

Mixed Pumps are formed by combining the principles of the forcing and sucking-pumps together: when the lower valve of a forcing-pump is above the surface of the water it can raise it only by suction, the manufacture remaining as before. The mechanism of a pump may be employed for converting the weight of water descending in its barrel so as to work another pump.

The *Spiral Pump* is formed by winding a pipe round a cylinder with an horizontal axis, and then connecting one end with a vertical tube, while the other is at liberty to turn round and receive water and air at each revolution. Such a pump is said to be able to raise a hogshead of water in one minute 74 feet high, through a pipe 760 feet long.

The *Water Screw Pump* consists either of a pipe wound spirally round a cylinder; or of one or more spiral excavations, formed by means of spiral projections, from an internal cylinder covered by an external coating, so as to be water-tight. These pumps are used for removing water out of the foundations of bridges, and for supplying pieces of artificial water, as, by means of the Archimedian screw, in the Royal Gardens, at Kew.

The materials of these pumps are manufactured to almost every required purpose, and thus sold to the plumber, who only put them together, so as to make them produce their desired effects.

The different parts of *water-closets* are made in a similar way, and sold to the plumber, who places the basin, apparatus, traps, socket-pipe, cistern, and forcing or lifting pump together, so as to put them into action.

Plumbers charge their sheet lead by the hundred weight, according to prices arranged at intervals by the Warden and Court of Assistants of the Plumbers' Company. Milled lead is two shillings per hundred weight more than the cast-lead.

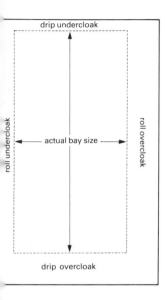

Figure 5.6 *Maximum area of one piece of lead that can be laid in one piece .25 m² including allowances*

FABRICATION OF LEADWORK

For speed, ease of assembly and laying, much work is cut, folded and assembled using lead welding techniques. These replace bossing methods but do not affect the maximum size of sheets laid or the method of joining them together. Skill must be gained by the operative using the equipment, which must be available as and when required. This method enables small items, such as chimney weathering, to be produced within the workshop and placed in site position in the minimum of time.

LEAD PIPE

As with sheet lead, new lead pipe work has almost disappeared except for conservation and restoration work, and the specification has altered with metrication. BS 602 and 1085 (1970) laid down code numbers and grades for various uses of the pipe. These range from Code 1: (0 mm nominal bore weighing 2.67 kg per metre to Code 29: 125 mm nominal bore weighing 14.62 kg per metre). The method of jointing the smaller bore pipes is usually a soldered wipe joint. Larger bore pipes can be socketted, soldered or lead welded.

Fixing of vertical pipes is by clips around the pipes or ears soldered or welded to the pipe through which screws provide fixing to the walls. Horizontal pipes require more support to prevent sagging with the weight of the pipe. Circular pipes from 10 mm to 125 mm nominal bore are formed by extrusion and are, therefore, seamless. Recommended coded sizes for differing uses are laid out in publications available from the Lead Development Assocation.

6. Slating

Alan Foster

Slates are used today for roofing prestige buildings, renovating and restoring old properties and domestic housing which is close to a source of supply. Owing to the ever-increasing labour costs in production and the ready availability of cheaper synthetic products, roofing slate is no longer used on a large scale for roof covering.

In Great Britain roofing slates are quarried mainly in North Wales and Cumbria. Although a few other small quarries are still working, the slate is normally used for roofing buildings close to the quarry. Slate is still mainly mined for roofing purposes but it has a variety of other uses. The market is increasing for slate granules and powders and also for flooring slabs, sills, copings and claddings. With modern sophisticated machinery, slate can be sawn to most sizes and shapes and polished if required; the only limitation being the size of the block extracted from the quarry.

Slates have been imported into Britain but, as Nicholson pointed out, many of them have disintegrated. Over the last ten years, increasing quantities of Spanish slates have been imported, but in such a short span of time, no comment can be made as to their lasting properties. Spanish slates are more fragile than those found in Britain and should not be fixed by the traditional method.

Since Nicholson's time, the roofing slate industry has seen considerable changes. The Welsh quarries enjoyed considerable expansion in their business as urban populations grew. Quarrying techniques were improved considerably to produce roofing slates in large quantities — many engineering innovations had to be made to extract the raw material from the mountain side and then transport the finished slates to ports and rail heads. However, during the 1880s there was a steady decline in demand for roofing slate and it was not until after the first world war that demand started to increase again. In the 1930s, however, clay roofing tiles were manufactured on a mass-production basis and they quickly started to take the place of slate for cheap roof coverings. After the second world war, concrete tiles quickly superseded clay as the main coverings for roofs. Most of the Welsh quarries closed, leaving only two major quarries producing roofing slate on a much reduced scale. The fortunes of the slate industry in Cumbria have not fluctuated as much as in North Wales because their slate was rarely used on a large scale for housing.

There are four main quarries left today, each producing a completely different type of slate: Bangor slate from North Wales, commonly known as Bangor Blue although the colour is in fact heather purple with occasional green markings; Portmadoc slates, also quarried in North Wales, are a grey colour with a smooth face. Both types of Cumbrian slates are of a more rugged texture and are thicker, Westmorland slates being green and Burlington slates blue/grey in colour.

CHAPTER XI.

SLATING,

WITH AN EXPLANATION OF TERMS, &c.

SLATING, till lately, was employed only for covering the roofs of buildings; but it is now used for forming balconies, chimney-pieces, castings to walls, skirtings, stair-cases, &c.

The slates most in use about London are the Welsh and Westmoreland, but the latter are now almost superseded by the former. About eighty years ago French slates were much used: they are smaller than Welsh slates, and, being very thin, are consequently extremely light; and their thinness renders them liable to be easily penetrated by wet, and are, of course, considered unfit for our climate. Slates of this kind, after they have been long exposed to the atmosphere in these countries, are often shivered in pieces; and they may sometimes be found completely decomposed, or reduced to a powdered state. This imperfection, since it has been known, has prevented their being used in this country; nor is it probable they will be again introduced.

The WELSH SLATES are generally classed in the following order.

	ft.	in.		ft.	in.
DOUBLES, average size	1	1	by	0	6
LADIES	1	3	—	0	8
COUNTESSES	1	8	—	0	10
DUCHESSES	2	0	—	1	0
WELSH RAGS	3	0	—	2	0
QUEENS	3	0	—	2	0
IMPERIALS	2	6	—	2	0
PATENT SLATE	2	6	—	2	0

The Doubles are so called from their small size. These are made from the fragments of the larger qualities, as they are sorted, respectively.

The Ladies are made up from fragments, as above, in pieces that will square up to the size of such a description of slate.

Countesses are in size the next gradation above *ladies;* and duchesses still larger.

Slate is extracted from the quarries in the same manner as other stony substances; that is, by making perforations between its beds, into which gunpowder is placed and fused. This opens and divides the beds of the slate, which the quarry-men remove in large blocks. These blocks are afterwards split by wedges of iron, driven between their layers, which separate the blocks into such scantlings as may be required. When slate is to be exported in this state, its edges are sawn to the sizes ordered; for it is not necessary to use the saw to the horizontal stratum of the slate, as that can be divided nearly as correct by the ready method above-mentioned.

The works in Wales, for sawing slate, are furnished with excellent machinery, which is set in motion either by steam or by water, and keeps in action a vast number of saws, each sawing the scantlings of slate into pieces adapted to their respective purposes.

The Imperial Slating, for roofs, is particularly neat, and is known by having its lower edge sawn; whereas all the other slates, used for covering, are only chipped square on their edges.

Patent Slating is so called, among the slaters, from the peculiar mode of laying it on roofs, but we are not aware of any patent for it being ever obtained. It was first brought into notice by the late James Wyatt, Esq. the architect of our late revered king, George the Third. Patent slating may be laid on rafters of much less elevation than any other kind of slating; it is considerably lighter; because the breadths of the laps are much less than the slates adopted for the common sort of slating. Patent slating was originally composed of slates called the *Welsh Rags*, but at the present time it is composed of the *Imperials,* which are lighter, and much neater in appearance.

On the Westmoreland Slate some experiments were made by Dr. Watson, the late Bishop of Llandaff, whence it appears that there is very little difference in the natural composition of this kind of slate and that of Wales. The Bishop's comparison of their absolute weight, as compared with the weight of other materials made use of as a covering to buildings, may be of great utility, inasmuch as it may tend towards forming a datum for adding to, or diminishing from, the quantity of timber employed in roofs of different spans and elevations. " That sort of slate," says his lordship, "other circumstances being the same, is esteemed the best, which imbibes the least water; for the imbibed water not only increases the weight of the covering, but, in frosty weather, being converted into ice, it swells and shivers the slate. This effect of the frost is very sensible in tiled houses, but it is scarcely felt in slated ones; for good slate imbibes but little water; and, when tiles are well glazed they are rendered, in some measure, with respect to this point, similar to slate." He adds, " I took a piece of Westmoreland slate and a piece of common tile, and weighed each of them carefully; the surface of each was about thirty square inches; both the pieces were immersed in water for ten minutes, and then taken out and weighed as soon as they had ceased to drip, and it was found that the tile had imbibed about one-seventh part of its weight of water, and the slate had not imbibed a two-hundredth part of its weight. Indeed the wetting of the slate was merely superficial, while the tile, in some measure, became saturated with the water. I then placed both the wet pieces before the fire; in a quarter of an hour's time the slate was become quite dry, and of the same weight it had before it was put into the water; but the tile had lost only about twelve grains of the water it had imbibed, which was, as near as could be expected, the same quantity that had been spread on its surface; for it was this quantity only which had been imbibed by the slate, the surface of which was equal to that of the tile. The tile was left to dry in a room heated to 60° of Fahrenheit, and it did not lose all the water imbibed in less than six days." He adds, further, " that the finest sort of Westmoreland slate is sold at Kendal at 3s. 6d. per load, which will amount to 1l. 15s. per ton, the load weighing two hundred weight. The coarser sort may be had at 2s. 4d. a load, or 1l. 3s. 4d. per ton. Thirteen loads of the finest sort will cover forty-two square yards of roofing, and eighteen loads of the coarsest will cover the same quantity;

Slate today is quarried in much the same manner as Nicholson describes although modern machinery has partially replaced the considerable labour force which used to be employed. Slate is formed in pillars which are sawn, levered or blasted out of the mountain-side and brought to the surface by motor vehicles. The size of the pillars determines the width of the finished roofing slates which are sawn from the boulders into blocks, and then riven (split) by hand with hammer and chisel down the grain until the required thickness of slate is reached. The four edges are then dressed (cut) by machine or hand to give a finished slate in the largest possible dimensions. The dressed edge gives a bevelled finish to the face of the slate which is most attractive as no two slates appear the same. From Nicholson's description and on evidence from eighteenth and early nineteenth century buildings, roofing slates were only roughly dressed to size and the top edge in particular could be any shape. All Welsh slate production today is in regular rectangular sizes, available from Duchess 610 × 355 mm (24 × 12 in.) — to Doubles — 255 × 150 mm (12 × 6 in.). The Cumbrian quarries produce random slates in both length and width.

'Imperial slating' as mentioned by Nicholson is normally not available today. However, a similar slate with all four edges sawn can be manufactured which gives the roofing slate a more uniform appearance when laid. 'Patent slating' that he describes is not used at all today and it is doubtful whether this type of work could be successfully matched. Large slates are still available but mainly from the Cumbrian quarries and these should be fixed using modern techniques to give a fair imitation of patent slating. 'Welsh Rags' and 'Imperials' are rarely quarried in Wales as there is a shortage of the large rock required for their manufacture.

The Bishop of Llandaff's 'Westmorland Test' is particularly interesting and can be taken as the forerunner of today's British Standard for roofing slates (BS 680). This was introduced to ensure that only high quality slates are used for roofing and includes a wetting and drying test, a water absorption test, and, for areas where there may be atmospheric pollution, an acid immersion test.

Welsh roofing slate is a relatively light product and the comparatively high cost can be partially offset by having a lighter roof sub-structure. The comparison below shows the approximate difference in weights:

Best Welsh slate — 32 kg/m²
Cumbrian slates — 50 kg/m²
Clay plain tiles — 75 kg/m²
Concrete interlocking tiles — 48 kg/m²

The manner of laying slates has altered over the years since Nicholson's description, but the basic principles remain identical. In the eighteenth century

so that there is half a ton less weight put upon forty-two square yards of roofs, when the finest sort of slate is used, than if it was covered with the coarsest kind, and the difference of expense only three shillings and sixpence." It must be remarked, that this slate owes its lightness, not so much to any diversity in the component parts of the stone from which it is split, as to the thinness to which the workmen reduce it, and it is not so well calculated to resist violent winds as that which is heavier.

COMPARISON IN WEIGHT OF THE SUNDRY COVERINGS EMPLOYED ON ROOFS.

A *Common Plain Tile* weighs thirty-seven ounces, and they are used, at a medium, seven hundred to cover a single square of roof of one hundred superficial feet.

A *Pan-tile* weighs seventy-six ounces, or four pounds and three-quarters, and one hundred and eighty are required to lay on a single square of roof.

Both the plain and pan tiles are commonly bedded in mortar; indeed the former cannot be well laid on a roof without it. The mortar used may be about one-fourth of the weight of the tiles.

COMMON LEAD or COPPER, for covering roofs, generally requires seven pounds of the former, and seven ounces of the latter, for each superficial foot. A square of one hundred feet covered with the above materials stand relatively thus:

	cwt.	qrs.	lbs.
For Copper, per square.	0	3	16
Lead	6	1	0
Fine Slate	6	0	21
Coarser ditto	8	1	8
Plain Tiles	18	0	0
Pan-Tiles	9	2	0

Hence a careful builder may select such a covering as his building may be best adapted to support.

A multifaceted slate roof to a Devon cottage using hips to sweep round a curved end

the slater had to ensure that the slates, which were of differing sizes and shapes, had sufficient lap to protect the nail hole of the slate in the course below. To be safe, the slater always ensured that a considerable overlap was used, normally about a third of the length of the slate. Timber was comparatively inexpensive at this time and consequently boarding beneath the slates was often used which, of course, increased the insulation value of the roof. The slater often carried out timber work which a carpenter would do today.

Slating today is easier than in Nicholson's day because of the rectangular roofing slates, and with a square top edge the lap can be reduced. Selection of the correct size of the slate for the roof pitch is most important. The overall weight of an individual slate has also to be considered in conjunction with the width and lap. Rainwater on slates tends to run downhill, by the most direct path, and when it enters the narrow vertical joints between slates, it creeps in a fanshape. This creeping or spreading is caused by capillary attraction between the smooth surfaces of the slates. The roofing slates are fixed by nails, and the hole for them should always be made as close to the side of the slate as practicable, as this hole must be covered by the centre of the lower edge of the slate above it. The bond (or width) together with the lap of the slate has to be related to the roof pitch and 'angle of creep'.

308

The versatility of slate as a roofing material is well shown in this work to the Butter Market at Dunster, Somerset

When laying roofing slates, each slate should be inspected and the thicker end used for the tails. The slates are then holed by hand or machine from the back towards the face, leaving a small countersunk hole which allows the nail head to be fixed flush with the surface of the slate. Each slate is twice holed close to the side edges slightly above centre, to ensure sufficient lap. The slates are then graded according to thickness so that the thicker slates can be used on the bottom portion of the roof, with the thinner slates at the top. Any broken slates are saved and dressed for under-eaves, top and half-slates.

Slating is laid with a broken bond and secured with nails to softwood timber, battens or boards. Before fixing, perpendicular lines should be marked giving the correct bond, allowing approximately 4 mm between the vertical joints of each slate, thus ensuring a free thoroughfare for water running down the slope. Slating is started at the eave and fixed diagonally up and across the roof slope, enabling each slate to be fixed with two nails. The slating can be cut square or on the rake, to form various finishes at the eaves, verges, hips or valleys.

Roofing slates today are fixed mainly with copper or aluminium alloy nails, the length being approximately 20 to 25 mm greater than two thicknesses of slate. The gauge of the nails is dependent on the weight of the individual slates. Battens are usually of sawn softwood with a minimum 19 × 38 mm section

OF THE MANNER OF LAYING SLATES.

ALL kinds of slate have a *lap* of each joint, generally equal to one-third of the length of the slate. The largest slates are reserved for the eaves. The slater, first picking and examining the slates to discover the strongest and squarest end, holds the slate over the edge of a small block of wood, cuts one of its edges straight, and having gauged the other thereby, cuts off that also; and, making two small holes on its opposite side, finishes the slate for the roof. All quarry slates require this preparation from the slater. The above holes are for the reception of the nails intended to fasten the slates to the roof. The copper and zinc nails are esteemed the best. When iron nails are used, they should be previously put into a tub of fluid white lead, till they are completely covered, and then left to dry. Iron nails, plated with tin, have lately been introduced, and are much cheaper than copper ones.

A base or floor is laid for receiving the slates. Boarding is essential for Doubles and Ladies, and this should be laid with even joints and well nailed down to the rafters. Then the slater, having provided himself with slips of wood, two inches and a half wide and one inch thick on one side, and chamfered away to an arris on the other, nails down these *tilting fillets*, as they are called, beginning with the hips, then the sides, eaves, and ridge. He next lays the eaves, setting their lower edge to a line, and nails them down to the boarding. A bond is then formed to the under sides of the eave, by placing another row under, so as to cross all the joints; this row is not nailed, but tightly pushed up and left dependent for support on the pressure of those above them and their own weight on the boarding. The slater then draws a straight line on the upper part of the row laid for a bond, and lays another course of slate crossing the joints of the other, and nails them down even with the line marked. This process is repeated till the whole roof is finished. All the larger kinds of slate may be made to lay upon battens, which saves an expense of about twenty shillings per square. A *batten* is a narrow piece of deal, about two inches and a half or three inches wide. For *Countesses* the bottoms may be about three-quarters of an inch thick, but for the larger kind of slate they should be an inch. The slater is the fittest person to lay them, as he may thus suit the length of his slates, and other particulars, which he best understands. This is the general method of laying all kinds of slate, except the *patent slating*.

The PATENT SLATING, so called, consists of the largest slates of an uniform thickness; *Imperials* are now generally taken. Neither battens nor boarding is required for these slates; but the common rafters should be left loose on the purlins, so that a rafter may be fixed under each of the meeting joints of the rows of slates. The work of covering is then performed, as above described, except that no bond is required, the slates being laid uniformly, and screwed down by two or three strong one and a half inch screws at each end into the rafters beneath.

Filleting is now commenced, which consists in covering the meeting-joints with fillets of slates, bedded in putty, and screwing them down through the whole into the rafters. These fillets are then neatly pointed up with more putty, and then painted, to resemble the slates. The hips and ridges of roofs are sometimes filleted, but lead is preferable. The Patent Slating may thus be laid, perfectly water-tight, with a rise of two inches in one foot of a rafter.

These are the general modes of laying slates; and for peculiar neatness they are sometimes laid in a lozenge form, but as, in this form, only one nail can be used to each slate, thus laid they soon become dilapidated.

The SLATERS' TOOLS are the *Saixe, Ripper, Hammer, Shaving-Tool*, and various kinds of *Chisels, Guages*, and *Files*.

The SAIXE is of steel, and not unlike a large knife, except having on its back a piece of iron, projecting about three inches, and drawn sharp to a point. It has a handle of beech, and is used for chipping and cutting slates.

The RIPPER is formed of iron, about the same length as the Saixe, with a very thin blade, tapering towards the top, where a round head projects about half an inch, with two little notches at the intersection of one with the other.

Nineteenth-century slated roof and tile hanging, with slate facing to the bargeboards in a typical West Country style (Totnes, Devon)

where rafters do not exceed 450 mm centre. For heavier slate and where maximum rafter spacings are 600 mm centres, the batten size is increased. Battens should be impregnated under pressure with preservative to help withstand rot and decay and attacks from insects and vermin. Underlays beneath slating are mainly felt to BS 747 standard and should be reinforced where used unsupported over open rafters. Insulating materials can be incorporated with felt underlay or positioned as boards beneath battens on top of rafters. Softwood boarding is used in some regions although the cost is generally prohibitive. Nailing slates to boards is not recommended; battens should be used with counter battens running down the roof slope to allow air to circulate.

The slater's tools as described by Nicholson have not altered over the years and they are all in current use. The only addition to the slater's tool-bag is a mechanical device for making holes in heavy slates.

Slating is now measured in metric values. The main area is measured in square metres, with an allowance for eaves, verges, hips, valleys etc. The slating terms given by Nicholson are all used today with the exception of patent slating. Welsh slates are still manufactured in various imperial and metric dimensions and each size is named. The larger slates are always known by a female name, from Princesses down to Narrow ladies and including amongst others, Duchesses, Countesses, Wide ladies and Broad ladies.

This tool is used for lifting up and removing the nails out of old slating, when it is to be repaired.

The HAMMER differs but little from the common tool of the same name, except that the upper portion of the driving part is higher and bent towards the handle, so as to form a claw, by having a notch in its centre. It is used for extracting nails that do not drive satisfactorily.

The SHAVING TOOL consists of a blade of iron, about eleven inches long and two wide, sharpened at one of its ends, like a chisel, and mortised into two round wooden handles. It is used for smoothing the surface or face of a slate, for skirtings, floors of balconies, &c.

The CHISELS, GAUGES, and FILES, need no description. They are used for finishing the better parts of the slater's work, as mouldings, chimney-pieces, skirtings, casings, &c.

The STRENGTH of SLATE to Portland Stone has been calculated to be as five to one, and consequently slate should be used where lightness is required combined with strength.

VALUATION OF SLATERS' WORK.

SLATERS' work is measured by Surveyors by the square of 100 feet superficial. Besides the nett dimensions of their work, slaters are allowed six inches for eaves, and four for hips, for common slating; and nine inches in addition for rags or imperials. Slating for roofing may be averaged thus per square.

	£.	s.	d.
Doubles	2	2	0
Countesses	2	12	6
Welsh Rags and Imperials	3	13	6
Westmoreland	4	14	6

Slaters' work, for galleries, varies, according to the mouldings, from 4s. 6d. to 5s. 6d. per foot superficial; skirtings and facings from 1s. 6d. to 2s. per foot. Chimney-pieces, &c. are sold at so much per piece.

EXPLANATION OF THE TERMS USED IN SLATING.

BACK OF A SLATE.—The upper side of it.

BACKER.—A narrow slate put on the back of a broad square-headed slate when the slates begin to get narrow.

BED OF A SLATE.—The lower side of it.

BOND OR LAP OF A SLATE.—The distance between the nail of the under slate, and the lower end of the upper slate.

EAVE.—The skirt or lower part of the slating hanging over the naked of the wall.

HOLING.—The piercing of slates for the admission of nails.

MARGIN OF A COURSE.—Those parts of the backs of the slates exposed to the weather.

NAILS.—Pointed iron, or copper, or zinc, of a pyramidal form, for fastening the slates to the laths or boarding. They are commonly of the description or shape of Clout-nails.

PATENT SLATES.—Those which are used without boarding, and screwed to the rafters, with slips of slates, bedded in putty, to cover the joints.

SCANTLE.—A gauge by which slates are regulated to their proper length.

SORTING.—Regulating slates to their proper length by means of the scantle.

SQUARING.—Cutting or paring the sides and bottom of the slates.

TAIL.—The bottom or lower end of the slate.

TRIMMING.—Cutting or paring the side and bottom edges of a slate, the head of the slate never being cut.

Eighteenth-century slate hanging incorporating box sashes and later shop front (Lewes, East Sussex)

Slating is much in demand for conservation work and skilled craftsmen can match most old slated buildings. Slates from reputable quarries are of such a high quality that they will last in excess of a hundred years. Many roofs have failed over the years, because the fixing nails have rusted away, although the slates may be in perfect condition. This means that second-hand slates are usually available for restoration work. Some, however, are foreign or were damaged when they were removed from the old roof. Great care should be taken when specifying this material, as a considerable proportion of the slate is hidden from view when laid and a poor slater could form the new nail-holes too close to the centre of the slate, allowing water to penetrate the roof. Slates quarried nowadays are of an excellent quality, with a variety of textures and colours. Matching old slates is usually no problem, so that any risks involved in using second-hand slates can be avoided without difficulty.

7. Glazing
Charles Brown

The 1823 edition of the *Practical Builder* was published at a turning point in the development of the craft of glazing. The choice of glass was limited and the size was even more restricted. Most windows were produced by blowing and spinning a large flat disc of glass. The disc was then cut into small sheets and the quality assessed by the distance the glass was cut from the heart of the disc. The nearer the centre, the more irregular was the surface of the glass until at the very centre was found the 'bullion'. The bullion or 'bull's eye', not even mentioned by Nicholson, was used, if at all, for windows of little importance such as stables or outbuildings. Bullions are currently fashionable and our manufacturers are unfortunately pressing out false bullions for use in houses with the aim of producing an antique effect. Genuine bullions should be preserved. The installation of false ones is an affectation to be avoided.

The disc spun glass was the 'crown glass' described by Nicholson, but he clearly thought it inferior to 'plate glass' which he calls 'the most beautiful glass made' and, although expensive, 'much to be preferred'. The new plate glass was available in larger sizes and this swiftly led to the omission of the astragals or glazing bars so necessary to support the smaller panes of crown glass. In 1845 the tax by weight on glass was abolished and this was a further incentive to use the new plate glass. It was used increasingly with the gradual elimination of astragals, not only in new building design, but in alterations to existing windows.

Nineteenth-century villa with astragals removed from ground floor windows showing loss of scale compared with windows on upper floors (Cheltenham, Gloucestershire)

CHAPTER XIV.

GLAZING.

ON glass very little has been communicated in the works of the antients. It, indeed, appears, from the ruins of several Grecian buildings, that they had apertures or windows; and it would seem, from the nature of their construction, they were adapted to receive a frame filled with some transparent substance. In some of the apertures discovered at Pompeii and Herculaneum, squares of amber were found; yet, though many of the Roman authors mention glass, it was so rare as to be employed only in the mansions of the opulent.

BEDE is the first who mentions glass as applied to glazing windows. He likewise informs us that Abbot Benedict was the first who introduced the art of making glass into this kingdom, about the year 669; and, from the specimens that now remain, it is evident that not only the making of glass, but the art of staining it, made rapid strides towards perfection in a very short time after.

Glazing, as now practised, embraces the cutting of glass, and fixing it into sashes of wood or casements of lead; and likewise the ornamenting of windows with stained glass.

Plain coloured glass may frequently be used with a very pleasing effect, and is very little more expensive than good common glass: Coloured glass is charged by the pound; Claude Lorraine, green, red, &c., at about six or seven shillings, and blues somewhat more.

Today, the very irregularity of crown glass is prized. The reflections in small panes in the typical sash window produce a lively animated effect; a sparkle is given to a façade, sadly lacking when the same small panes are filled with modern glass. Even more bleak is the appearance of large single pane windows of plate glass. Furthermore, the divsions produced by the astragals were invariably more in scale with the materials of the neighbouring wall surface, whether brick or stone.

Glass by its very nature is a material easily broken and lost and, therefore, crown glass when discovered should be treasured and conserved. As the process of removal from frames is hazardous, the sashes themselves should be repaired if at all possible. Otherwise, the crown glass can be cut out and stored for use in smaller sashes.

Green glass is mentioned by Nicholson and this is still obtainable but only from specialist suppliers. It is now found mostly in leaded light panes and a good substitute is essential in repair work.

Crown glass is not made today, but a close substitute can be obtained if a special order is made. Alternatively, the poorest quality of sheet glass now available, often called greenhouse glass is an acceptable substitute as it has irregularities of surface. The restoration of astragals to sashes is outside the scope of this chapter, but the above comments can be seen to contain reasons for considering such a possibility.

The late nineteenth century saw the end of the manufacture of crown glass o any scale and the production of modern glass sheet or plate in enormous quantities. Some nineteenth century glass is itself of quality and should not be destroyed. Particularly of merit are the polished plate sheets with bevelled edge which produce a rich effect. Also to be treasured are the etched glasses, not produced in Nicholson's day.

Apart from waved plate glass, there is no reference to the obscured glasses available today. Such glass should normally be avoided in conservation work. I any waved plate glass (later term fluted sheet glass) survives finding a match will not be easy. However, such lightly obscured glasses can be sought in Germany where a greater variety of glass types is available than in this country. As an alternative, 'antique' glass can be used.

A conservation problem is the repair of false or dummy windows. These, where they incorporate real window frames and glass, often have back painted glass. If the original glass remains, it must be preserved. If not, new black glass can be inserted or new greenhouse glass back painted black or British Standard colour OOE.53. Although not mentioned by Nicholson curved glass was used but is now only available from three suppliers and it must be ordered specially.

The restoration of the more ancient practice of leaded lights, although a

Glazing in lead-work is of the most antient description; sashes being of modern date. These sashes are formed with a groove or rebate, on the back of their cross and vertical bars, for the reception of the glass, which the glazier cuts to its proper size, and beds in the composition called *putty*.

PUTTY is made of pounded whiting, beat up, with linseed oil, into a tough tenacious cement. When used for mahogany frames, a little red-ochre is mixed with it to suit the colour of the wood.

The beauty of glazing depends principally on the colour of the glass. Glaziers now use chiefly what is called *crown glass*, which is divided into three kinds, called *firsts, seconds,* and *thirds,* according to their qualities, on which its value depends. The glass is bought by the crate, which consists of twelve tables of the best, fifteen of the seconds, and eighteen of the thirds. These tables are each about three feet in diameter. A crate of the best glass is valued at about four guineas; of the seconds, about three; and the thirds, two guineas. The crown glass manufactured at Newcastle and its neighbourhood is esteemed the best: the prices of glass are various.

GREEN-GLASS is another sort, much used for common purposes, being not more than half the price of the crown-glass. From many old windows, it appears that this kind of glass was the most antient made use of.

WAVED PLATE-GLASS is very thick and strong, presenting an uneven surface, as if indented all over with wires, so as to leave the intermediate spaces in the form of lozenges; it was formerly much used in counting-houses, &c. to prevent the inconvenience of being overlooked; but though it has lately been superseded by ground-glass, it is still to be obtained in London.

Ground or *Rough Glass* is used for the same purpose as the above, and is no other than the common crown glass, rendered opaque by having its polish taken off, and rubbing it with sand and water or emery.

PLATE-GLASS is the most beautiful glass made use of, being nearly colourless, and sufficiently thick to admit being polished in the highest degree. The tables of this glass will admit of pieces being taken out of them much larger than can be obtained from any other kind of glass. The British Plate-Glass Company, in Albion-Place, London, is the most celebrated depot

specialist trade, is easier to achieve today than the restoration of crown glass. The types of glass painted or coloured are available at a price and the technique of employing lead cames is a craft which has continued unbroken from the medieval period. One important point must, however, be made. Nicholson recommends the use of vertical and cross bars of iron (often called 'ferramenta'). Such usage has now been discontinued because of the resultant damage to surrounding masonry (where there is no timber frame) by the rusting of the iron. The iron, in rusting, expands causing the masonry to split. Restoration should include the substitution of bronze or non-ferrous bars for the original iron. Alternatively, an alloy bronze, such as delta metal or stainless steel can be used.

The conservation of windows with panes set in lead cames is a frequent occurrence in secular buildings as well as churches. Re-leading may be involved and it is in fact the need to re-lead such windows, usually on a hundred-year cycle, which has helped to keep the craft alive. The removal of atmospheric corrosion on the surface of the glass may also be necessary and specialist

Eighteenth-century iron casements with glass quarry glazing, showing original quadrant stay (Burwash, East Sussex)

320

for this species. There it is sold by the inch, in porportion to its size, the value increasing accordingly. Though the expense of this glass, by far, exceeds that of any other, yet is now so much preferred, as to be used in many shop-windows in the leading streets.

GERMAN SHEET is another species of glass much esteemed, and would be superior to the preceding, had it not a disagreeable appearance, from being very wavy or uneven.

BOHEMIAN PLATE-GLASS is similar to the above, only possessing a red teint; and though much used about thirty years ago, it is now quite rejected.

GLAZIERS value their work by feet, inches, and parts, according to the size of the panes, or squares, employed. The charges are regulated by the Masters, Wardens, and Court-Assistants of the Company of Glaziers, and at present run thus:

				s.	d.
Best crown, not exceeding 3 feet, per square........				3	10
Ditto,	ditto	2 ft. 6 in.,	ditto..........	3	4
Ditto,	ditto	2 ft.	ditto..........	3	2
Ditto,	under	2 ft.	ditto..........	3	0

Seconds of the same dimensions are about ten per cent. cheaper; and Thirds, of similar dimensions, are 10 per cent. cheaper than the seconds. Green glass is the cheapest, never exceeding eighteen pence per foot.

The price of all kinds of bent glass, for circular and other windows, varies according to the size, the trouble of obtaining it, and fitting it in.

Cottage and some kinds of church windows are glazed in squares, or other figures, in leaden rebates, which are cast and drawn for the purpose, and soldered together at the interstices. This leaden work is of various sizes, according to the strength required, and is used instead of the cross bars of sashes. The grooves left in it for the glass have their cheeks sufficiently soft to be pressed down all round to admit the glass, and again raised up, when the glass has been put in. to keep it firm. Such windows are strengthened by vertical and cross bars of iron, with bands, which, having been soldered to the lead, are twisted round the iron. In cottage windows the bars, instead of being of iron, are often of wood.

Glaziers formerly cut their glass out with an instrument called a *grozing-iron;* but this process was not only tedious but difficult, and has therefore been entirely superseded by the introduction of the diamond, which is as complete a tool for the purpose as can possibly be required. This instrument consists of a diamond spark, in its natural *unpolished* state, fixed in lead, and fastened to a handle of some hard wood by means of a brass ferrule. The handle is about the size of a moderate drawing pencil. The diamond is the principal working tool of the glazier. His other tools are a rule and several small *straight edges.* The former is divided into thirty-six parts, or inches, and is used for dividing the tables of glass into any required size. The straight edges are merely thin pieces of some hard wood, about two inches wide, and one quarter of an inch thick, and are used for the diamond to work against. Glaziers are likewise furnished with *stopping knives,* which resemble dinner knives, with the blade reduced to about three inches in length, and ground away on each side of its edges to an apex. They are used for bedding the glass in the rebates, and for spreading and smoothing the putty.

A Hacking-out Tool is an old broken knife, ground sharp on its edge, and used for removing old putty out of the rebates, which are to be filled with new squares of glass.

The glazier's hammer is similar to the smaller kinds used by other artificers.

Glaziers are also furnished with a pair of compasses, which has one of its legs formed with a socket to receive the handle of the diamond, for drawing and cutting out any peculiar shapes of glass for fan-lights, &c.

Good GLAZING requires that the glass be cut full into the rebates; for, when too small or too large, it is liable to be broken by the least pressure within, or even the wind from without: moreover, the putty should never project beyond the line of wood in the inside, and large squares should be further secured by small sprigs being driven into the rebates of the sash, and covered over with another coat of putty.

The business of a glazier includes the cleaning of windows, and this forms no inconsiderable portion of the trade in London; some masters keeping one or two men constantly employed therein. The charge is regulated by the number of windows cleaned, and the number of squares in each frame. Windows, exceeding twelve squares, are charged at from 6d. to 8d. per dozen, the large squares of French sashes being raised about one-third more. The master-glazier takes upon himself the risk of windows being broken by his men, when employed in cleaning them.

In many parts of the United Kingdom it is the custom to measure all the wood-work appertaining to the sashes, for the quantities of glass contained in the respective squares; also, the lead-work. And such is the prejudice in favour of the practice in some places, that if any intelligent person was to attempt to reason them out of it, he would be considered a most inequitable valuator, and unworthy of being countenanced. Time and concurring circumstances, it is presumed, may, at some period or other, equalize our customs, weights, and measures; but until that period arrives, the system of valuation must be dependent upon local customs. The net quantities of glass should, in all cases, be measured, except in circular fan-lights and similar works, where the glass should be measured in the widest part; and because the pieces cut off to make the glass fit the apertures can be considered only as waste glass, the price or allowance for which is not embraced in the value charged by the glazier for his glass so consumed.

techniques are now available. Repair of broken panes by modern glass is possible and sometimes very precious glass is repaired by forming a sandwich of the ancient glass between outer layers of new.

If replacement glass is needed in leaded work, antique glass can often be used successfully. It is available in various tints and with its irregular surfaces, is a passable imitation of old glass.

Virtually no changes have occurred in cutting techniques in the glazing contractor's workshop, or on site, since Nicholson's day. Neither has there been any change in the use of the putty specified by Nicholson. This type of putty should still be used and there is now a British Standard specification (BSS 544 (1969)) covering its manufacture. In leaded lights a Butyl mastic is sometimes used to provide a more effective and resiliant seal. Care should be taken to prime any new woodwork in window rebates with a good quality lead primer before applying putty. Where iron astragals are discovered any rust must be removed, the iron treated with an inhibitor and primed with a red lead primer.

It is doubtful if the 'Standard Method for Measurement of Building Works' is sufficiently precise to exclude the thickness of glazing bars and leads. However when bills of quantity are prepared from measurement after completion, Nicholson's desired practice of honesty should hold! It is interesting that in 1823 the charges for glass were regulated by the Master and Wardens of the Company of Glaziers — today, the charges are based on the manufacturer's tariffs and there are too few of them to create sufficient competition.

As far as is known, the practice of glaziers subsequently cleaning the glass they had fitted has fallen into total disuse — such cleaning now falls to the occupiers.

Suppliers of special glass including the equivalent of crown glass: Hartley, Wood & Co., Portobello Road, Monkwearmouth, Sunderland, Tyne & Wear SR6 ODN; James Hetley & Co. Ltd, 10/12 Beresford Avenue, Wembley, Middlesex HAO 1RP.

Suppliers of curved glass: Bradford Glass Co. Ltd, Spring Mill Street, Manchester Road, Bradford, West Yorkshire BD5 7D7; Hills Glass & Windows Ltd, Glass Works, Chester Street, Aston, Birmingham B6 4AG; T. & W. Ide, Glasshouse Fields, London E1 9JA.

8. Plastering

Brian Pegg and Donald Stagg

In all building internal plastering fulfils two main functions. First, to cover joints and other irregularities in various backgrounds and to provide a smooth or textured surface for the decorator and secondly, to provide three-dimensional decoration within itself, again providing an excellent base for the decorator. In addition many modern gypsum plasters will assist in the thermal insulation of a building, accoustic plasters assist in the control of sound, and types of backing coat can be designed to provide a water resistant surface.

Decorative plasterwork may be applied *in situ* especially in reconstruction and repair work. Today decorative plasterwork is produced in fibrous plastering.

External plastering will in general fulfil the same two functions. It will also improve the durability of buildings and in certain cases it may be used to provide a waterproof covering. The finishes will vary from plain to heavily textured and may be self-coloured. External ornamental work can also be carried out by plasterers; cornices, arches, pediments and similar features are all within the scope of a good craftsman.

External rendering on to brick illustrating skills of plasterer in moulded and run work (Cheltenham, Gloucestershire)

CHAPTER IX.

PLASTERING.

IN modern practice, PLASTERING, by its recent improvements, occurs in every department of architecture, both internally and externally. It is more particularly applied to the sides of the walls, and the ceilings of the interior parts of buildings, and, also, for stuccoing the external parts of many edifices.

In treating on this subject, we shall divide Plastering under its several heads: as *plastering on laths*, in its several ways; *rendering* on brick and stone; and, finally, the finishing to all the several kinds of work of this description; as well as modelling, and casting the several mouldings, both ornamental and plain; stuccoing, and other outside compositions, which are applied upon the exterior of buildings; and, the making and polishing the *scagliola*, now so much used for columns, and their antæ, or pilasters, &c.

LIME forms an essential ingredient in all the operations of this trade. This useful article is vended at the wharfs about London in bags, and varies in its price from thirteen shillings to fifteen shillings per hundred pecks. Most of the lime made use of in London is prepared from chalk, and the greater portion comes from Purfleet, in Kent; but, for stuccoing, and other work, in which strength and durability is required, the lime made at Dorking, in Surrey, is preferred.

The composition, known as PLASTER OF PARIS, is one on which the Plasterer very much depends for giving the precise form and finish to all the better parts of his work; with it he makes all his ornaments and cornices, besides mixing it in his lime to fill up the finishing coat to the walls and ceilings of rooms.

The stone, from which the plaster is obtained, is known to professional men by several names, as *sulphate of lime, selenite, gypsum,* &c.; but its common name seems to have been derived from the immense quantities which have been taken from the hill named *Mont-Martre,* in the environs of Paris. The stone from this place is, in its appearance, similar to common free-stone, excepting its being replete with small specular crystals. The French break it into fragments of about the size of an egg, and then burn it in kilns, with billets of wood, till the crystals lose their brilliancy; it is then ground with stones, to different degrees of fineness, according to its intended uses. This kind of specular gypsum is said to be employed in Russia, where it abounds, as a substitute for glass in windows.

According to the chymists, the specific gravity of gypsum, or Plaster of Paris, is from 1.872 to 2.311, requiring 500 parts of cold and 450 of heat, to dissolve it; when calcined, it decrepitates, becomes very friable and white, and heats a little with water. In the process of burning, or calcination, it loses its water of crystallization, which, according to Fourcroy, is 22 per cent.

The plaster commonly made use of in London is prepared from a sulphate of lime, produced in Derbyshire, and called alabaster. Eight hundred tons are said to be annually raised there. It is brought to London in a crude state, and afterwards calcined, and ground in a mill for use, and vended in brown-paper bags, each containing about half a peck; the coarser sort is about fourteen-pence per bag, and the finest from eighteen to twenty-pence. The figure-makers use it for their casts of anatomical and other figures; and it is of the greatest importance not only to the plasterer, but to the sculptor, mason, &c.

The working-tools of the plasterer consist of a *spade,* of the common sort, with a *two or three-pronged rake,* which he uses for the purpose of mixing his mortar and hair together. His *trowels* are of two sorts, one kind being of three or four sizes. The first sort is called the *laying* and *smoothing-tool;* its figure consists in a flat piece of hardened iron, very thin, of about ten inches in length, and two inches and a half in width, ground to a semi-circular shape at one end, while the other is left square; on the back of the plate, and

327

Traditional 'fine stuff' is today pure lime putty with no hair added, and stucco has become 'lime setting stuff', a mix of three parts lime putty to two parts of fine washed sand. This particular material is rarely used today except in the reconstruction of old buildings and repair work and even then the addition of a small quantity of Class A gypsum plaster is usually considered necessary. Mortar or gauged stuff is still in use today although usually referred to as 'coarse stuff'. It normally consists of one part lime to three parts sand and then either ordinary Portland cement or a Class C plaster may be added. It is used as a backing plaster and may have hair or some similar firbrous material added to assist with binding when it is worked on wood or metal lathing.

Wood laths are only used as a solid plastering background when specified for restoration work. Otherwise, in new work, either plasterboard or metal lathing would be used for ceilings and non-load-bearing partitions. Metal lathing would be treated by the plasterer in a similar way to wood lathing. It would be given three coats of either traditional gauged lime/sand plasters or three coats of the correct grade of premixed lightweight plasters.

Internally a traditional mix of Portland cement, hydrated lime and sand to a ratio of 1:1:6 may be used as an undercoat. In this case the finish will be either neat gypsum plaster or plaster plus 10–20 per cent lime putty. The choice of plaster to be used internally as a backing coat may well be determined by the type of background. To assist in this, backgrounds are normally placed under two headings, 'high suction' and 'low suction', depending on their ability to absorb water. When undertaking restoration work, where repairs have to match the material as well as the surface levels, it is always advisable to use traditional mixes. The expansion that takes place as a conventional gypsum plaster sets, may cause problems to old work.

TOOLS

The tools a plasterer uses to apply material to walls and ceilings have changed little over the years: a hand hawk for carrying, a laying on trowel for spreading and another for finishing; a lath hammer for tacking lathings and when fixing wooden rules, and a gauging trowel when running mouldings and applying material to awkward positions and small areas. Wooden floats are used for flattening and scouring and water brushes for dampening down and lubricating the trowel when finishing. Small tools for modelling and carving, joint rules, angle trowels and a host of other specialist and general tools will all be required by a competent craftsman.

nearest to the square end, is riveted a piece of small rod-iron, with two legs, one of which is fixed to the plate, and the other, adapted for being fastened in a round wooden handle. With this tool all the first coats of plastering are put on; and it is also used in setting the finishing coat.

The trowels of the plasterer are made more neatly than the tools of the same name used by other artificers. The largest size is about seven inches long on the plate, and is of polished steel, two inches and three-quarters at the heel, diverging to an apex or point. To the wide end is adapted a handle, commonly of mahogany, with a deep brass ferrule. With this trowel the plasterer works all his fine-stuff, and forms cornices, mouldings, &c. The other trowels are made and fitted-up in a similar manner, varying gradually in their sizes from two to three inches in length.

The plasterer likewise employs several small tools, called *stopping* and *picking-out tools;* these are made of steel, well polished, and are of different sizes, commonly about seven or eight inches long, and half an inch wide, flattened at both ends, and ground away till they are somewhat rounding. With these he models and finishes all the mitres and returns to the cornices, and fills up and perfects the ornaments at their joinings.

The workman in this art should keep all his tools very clean; they should be daily polished, and never put away without being wiped and freed from plaster.

In the practice of plastering many rules and models of wood are required. The rules, or *straight-edges* as they are called, enable the plasterer to get his work to an upright line; and the models guide him in running plain mouldings, cornices, &c.

The CEMENTS made use of, for the interior work, are of two or three sorts. The first is called *lime* and *hair*, or coarse stuff; this is prepared in a similar way to common mortar, with the addition of hair, from the tan-yards, mixed in it. The mortar used for lime and hair is previously mixed with the sand, and the hair added afterward. The latter is incorporated by the labourers with a three-pronged rake.

FINE-STUFF, is pure lime, slaked with a small portion of water, and afterwards well saturated, and put into tubs in a semi-fluid state, where it is allowed to settle, and the water to evaporate. A small proportion of hair is sometimes added to the fine-stuff.

STUCCO, for inside walls, called *trowelled* or *bastard stucco,* is composed of the fine-stuff above described, and very fine washed sand, in the proportion of one of the latter to three of the former. All walls, intended to be painted, are finished with this stucco.

MORTAR, called *gauge-stuff,* consists of about three-fifths of fine-stuff and one of Plaster of Paris, mixed together with water, in small quantities at a time: this renders it more susceptible of fixing or setting. This cement is used for forming all the cornices and mouldings, which are made with wooden moulds. When great expedition is required, the plasterers guage all their mortar with Plaster of Paris. This enables them to hasten the work, as the mortar will then set as soon as laid on.

PLASTERERS have technical words and phrases, by which they designate the quality of their work, and estimate its value.

By LATHING is meant the nailing up laths, or slips of wood, on the ceiling and partitions. The laths are made of fir or oak, and called *three-foots* and *four-foots,* being of these several lengths: they are purchased by the bundle or load.

There are three sorts of laths; viz. *single laths, lath and half,* and *double laths.* Single laths are the cheapest and thinnest; lath and half denotes one third thicker than the single lath; and double laths twice their thickness. The laths generally used in London are made of fir, imported from Norway, the Baltic, and America, in pieces called *staves.* Most of the London timber-merchants are dealers in laths; and there are many persons who confine themselves exclusively to this branch of trade.

The fir-laths are generally fastened by cast-iron nails, whereas the oaken ones require wrought-iron nails, as no nail of the former kind would be found equal to the perforation of the oak, which would shiver it in pieces by the act of driving.

In lathing ceilings, it is adviseable that the plasterer should make use of laths of both the usual lengths, and so manage the nailing of them, that the joints should be as much broken as possible. This will tend to strengthen the plastering laid thereon, by giving it a stronger key or tie. The strongest laths are adapted for ceilings, and the slightest or single laths for the partitions of buildings.

LAYING consists in spreading a single coat of lime and hair all over a ceiling or partition; taking care that it is very even in every part, and quite smooth throughout: this is the cheapest manner of plastering.

PRICKING-UP is similar to *laying*, but is used as a preliminary to a more perfect kind of work. After the plastering has been put up in this manner, it is *scratched* all over with the end of a lath, in order to give a key or tie to the *finishing coats*, which are to follow.

LATHING, LAYING, and SET, are applied to work that is to be lathed as already described, and covered with one coat of lime and hair; and, when sufficiently dry, finished by being covered over with a thin and smooth coat of lime only, called by the plasterer *putty*, or *set*. This coat is spread with the smoothing trowel, and the surface finished with a large flat hog's-hair brush. The trowel is held in the right hand, and the brush in the left. As the plasterer lays on the set, he draws the brush backwards and forwards over it, till the surface is smooth.

LATHING, FLOATING, and SET, consists of lathing and covering with a coat of plaster, which is pricked up for the floated work, and is thus performed: The plasterer provides himself with a strong rule, or straight-edge, often from ten to twelve feet in length; two workmen are necessarily employed therein. It is began by plumbing with a plumb-rule, and trying if the parts to be floated are upright and straight, to ascertain where filling up is wanting. This they perform by putting on a trowel or two of lime and hair only: when they have ascertained these preliminaries, the *screeds* are prepared.

A SCREED, in plastering, is a stile formed of lime and hair, about seven or eight inches wide, guaged exactly true. In floated-work these screeds are made, at every three or four feet distance, vertically round a room, and

APPLICATION OF PLASTER

The application by hand of all plasters to a wide variety of backgrounds has changed very little since Nicholson's day. Whether the backing coat is premixed lightweight gypsum plaster or gauged ordinary Portland cement/lime/sand, it will still be laid on in a succession of thin coats until the required thickness is obtained. It will then be ruled flat with a straight edge and keyed with a wooden devil float ready to receive the finishing coat of plaster. Screeds or grounds (varying from hand applied plaster screeds, nail fixed wooden rules or plaster fixed metal beads) are positioned at internal and external angles and in intermediate positions so that they can be used as guides when the plasterer is ruling his backing coat flat. They will also act as guides for the correct thickness of material.

Where the work has to be matched to the existing plaster, all old edges must be cut to clean regular lines and slightly undercut to assist with the bonding of the new to the old. The old background must be thoroughly cleaned free of all dust, dirt, grease and oil and all joints well raked out. The whole area is then dampened down (including the edges) and coated with a diluted PVA adhesive. This will perform two necessary functions. First, it will greatly assist bonding between old work and new and secondly it will help to prevent the spread of damp into the old work from the new wet plaster. This will also help to control the suction which can be considerable from old lime hair mixes.

The backing coat is applied by trowel in the usual thin coats and kept at least 2 mm behind the finish line of the old work. It must then be ruled flat and lightly keyed with a devil float. A suitable mix for this backing coat is three parts of ready mixed lime and sand (with hair or its equivalent) with either half or one Class A gypsum plaster added. This will enable the plasterer to apply the finish immediately the floating has set hard. Too strong a mix will cause problems both in the speed of set and expansion, which may cause cracking at the edges.

The finish or setting coat to all classes of work will be applied in either two or three coats, to a total thickness of 2 mm. With traditional mixes of Class C or D plaster and lime putty applied to a gauged OPC/lime/sand background, three coats are generally considered suitable. Between the two trowel coats mentioned earlier, a wooden float coat will be applied. This may add a little to the thickness, no more than 1 mm, but will have the effect of producing a perfectly flat and true surface. After the final application by trowel the whole finished area is then made smooth by trowelling in long sweeps, using a little brush applied water as a lubricant for the trowel. The water may be gently applied to a hardened surface but where the surface is still soft it is better applied to the bottom of the laying on trowel.

are prepared perfectly straight by applying the straight-edge to them to make them so; and, when all the screeds are formed, the parts between them are filled up flush with lime and hair, or *stuff*, and made even with the face of the screeds. The straight-edge is then worked horizontally upon the screeds, to take off all superfluous *stuff*. The floating is thus finished by adding *stuff* continually, and applying the rule upon the screeds till it becomes, in every part, quite even with them.

Ceilings are floated in the same manner, by having screeds formed across them, and filling up the intermediate spaces with *stuff*, and applying the rule as for the walls.

Plastering is good or bad, in proportion to the care taken in this part of the work; hence the most careful workmen are generally employed therein.

The SET to the floated work is performed in a similar way to that already described for the laid plastering; but floated plastering, for the best rooms, is performed with more care than is required in an inferior style of work. The setting, for the floated work, is frequently prepared by adding to it about one-sixth of Plaster of Paris, that it may fix more quickly, and have a closer and more compact appearance. This, also, renders it more firm, and better adapted for being whitened, or coloured, when dry. The drier the pricking-up coat of plastering is, the better for the floated stucco-work; but if the floating is too dry before the last coat is put on, there is a probability of its peeling off, or cracking, and thus giving the ceiling an unsightly appearance. These cracks, and other disagreeable appearances in ceilings, may likewise arise from the weakness of the laths, or from too much plastering, or from strong laths and too little plastering. Good floated work, executed by a judicious hand, is very unlikely to crack, and particularly if the lathing be properly attended to.

RENDERING and SET, or RENDERING, FLOATED, and SET, includes a portion of the process employed in both the previous modes, with the exception that no lathing is required in this branch of the work. By *rendering* is meant that one coat of lime and hair is to be plastered on a wall of brick or stone; and the *set* implies that it is again to be covered and finished with fine stuff, or

For a much harder and perfectly true surface it is better to use Class D gypsum plaster (Keene's cement) to produce this finish. When using this plaster it is best to scour well after the final coat of finish plaster has been applied. Scouring is carried out on a hardening plaster surface by applying water and then rubbing flat with a crossgrain float. This will bring a degree of surplus fat to the surface which must be trowelled off completely. The whole area is then polished by water lubricated trowel applied in long vertical sweeps.

Where plastering is required to curved backgrounds (such as domes, lunettes, niches, groined and vaulted ceilings), the system for carrying out this work will fall into one of two categories. In the first the plasterer will press screeds into shape using a purpose made rule or run screeds using a radius rod. The alternative, which can happen when working on rather small items, is to run the whole of the feature using a variety of moulds. No shape or curve should be beyond the scope of a craftsman.

CORNICES

Plaster cornices today will, in the majority of cases, be made in precast fibrous plaster. This is especially true when the cornice includes any form of enrichment or ornament. However, where they are necessary (either by architect's specification, or work classified to be restored as the original) the process of running plaster cornices has altered little. Where bracketing is required it will again be spaced some 300, 350 or 400 mm apart, depending upon size and weight. Wood laths or metal lathing is fixed to the bracketing and rendered with the appropriate grade of premixed lightweight plaster, or a mix of 1 : 3 Class A plaster/sand with hair, sisal or similar material added.

The running mould, which consists of a metal profile cut exactly to form the required cornice shape, a wooden backing piece called the stock, a slipper, handles, braces and shoes are then prepared. The shoes, three in all and placed at the three bearing points — one at the nib and one at each end of the slipper — consist of soft metal and are there to prevent wear in the timber (Figure 8.1).

The cornice may be run in a traditional mix of 1 : 1 Class A plaster, lime putty or in a premixed lightweight finish plaster. In the case of the latter the cornice must be cored out to within 2–3 mm of the finish using the backing grade of premixed lightweight plaster. This is done by fixing a metal or hardboard muffle or false profile to the running mould so that it projects 3 mm in front of the metal profile.

Rules are fixed to the correct height on the walls of the room so that, when the mould slipper sits squarely on the rule, the nib will run smoothly on the ceiling. In modern practice it is usual to run on the finished wall and ceiling putty. The method of performing this is similar to that already described for the setting of ceilings and partitions. The *floated* and *set* is performed on the rendering in the same manner as it is on the partitions and ceilings of the best kind of plastering, which has been described.

TROWELLED-STUCCO is a very neat kind of work, much used in dining-rooms, vestibules, stair-cases, &c., especially when the walls are to be finished by painting. This kind of stucco requires to be worked upon a floated ground, and the floating should be as dry as possible before the stuccoing is began. When the stucco is made, as before described, it is beaten and tempered with clean water, and is then fit for use. In order to use it, the plasterer is provided with a small *float*, which is merely a piece of half-inch deal, about nine inches long and three inches wide, planed smooth, and a little rounded away on its lower edge; a handle is fitted to the upper side, to enable the workman to move it with ease. The stucco is spread upon the ground, which has been prepared to receive it, with the largest trowel, and made as even as possible. When a piece, four or five feet square, has been so spread, the plasterer, with a brush, which he holds in his left hand, sprinkles a small part of the stucco with water, and then applies the float, alternately sprinkling and rubbing the face of the stucco, till he reduces the whole to a perfect smooth and even surface. The water has the effect of hardening the face of the stucco; so that, when well floated, it feels to the touch as smooth as glass.

CORNICES are plain or ornamented, and sometimes include a portion of both; in the ornamented, superior taste has latterly prevailed, on principles derived from the study of the *antique*. The preliminaries, in the formation of cornices in plastering, consist in the examination of the drawings or designs, and measuring the projections of the members: should the latter be found to exceed seven or eight inches, *bracketing* will be necessary.

BRACKETING consists of pieces of wood fixed up at about eleven or twelve inches from each other, all round the place intended to have a cornice; on these brackets laths are fastened, and the whole is covered with one coat of plastering, making allowance in the brackets for the stuff necessary to form the cornice;

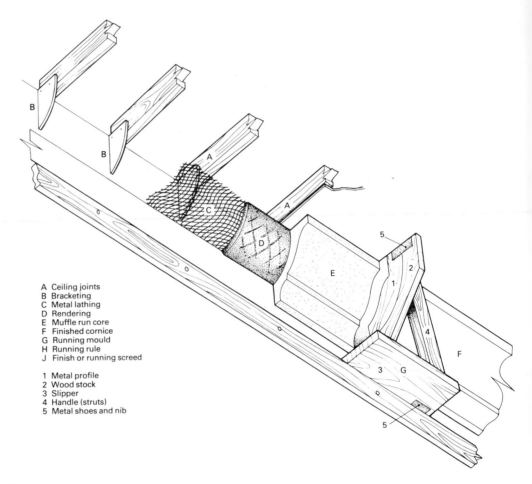

A Ceiling joints
B Bracketing
C Metal lathing
D Rendering
E Muffle run core
F Finished cornice
G Running mould
H Running rule
J Finish or running screed

1 Metal profile
2 Wood stock
3 Slipper
4 Handle (struts)
5 Metal shoes and nib

Figure 8.1

plaster or to use a rebate on the slipper so as to keep the front edge of the slipper just away from the wall. The finishing plaster is mixed to a wet creamy consistency and laid on over the core. After each application along the whole length of one wall, the running mould is passed over the entire length. More material is applied till a perfect shape is obtained. Mitres (internal and external) are formed by hand using small tools and joint rules.

Where it is necessary to run enriched cornices in solid, beds will be run in the moulding so that the enrichment may be hand planted after being cast from hot melt compound moulds. These are made from models as required.

Externally, cornices are frequently run in position using an OPC/sand mix of 1 : 3. The running mould will be constructed in a similar fashion to the internal

for this about one inch and a quarter is generally found sufficient. When the cornice has been so far forwarded, a mould must be made of the profile or section of the cornice, exactly representing all its members; this is generally prepared, by the carpenters, of beach-wood, about a quarter of an inch in thickness; all the quirks, or small sinkings, being formed in brass. When the mould is ready, the process of running the cornice begins: two workmen are required to perform this operation; and they are provided with a tub of set, or putty, and a quantity of Plaster of Paris; but before they begin with the mould, they guage a straight line, or screed, on the wall and ceiling, made of putty and plaster, extending so far on each as to answer to the bottom and top of the cornice, for it to fit into. This is the guide for moving the mould upon. The putty is then mixed with about one-third of Plaster of Paris, and incorporated in a semi fluid state, by being diluted with clean water. One of the workmen then takes two or three trowels full of the prepared putty upon his hawk, which he holds in his left hand, having in his right hand a trowel, with which he plasters the putty over the parts where the cornice is to be formed; the other workman applying the mould to ascertain where more or less of it is required; and, when a sufficient quantity has been put on to fill up all the parts of the mould, the other workman moves the mould backwards and forwards, holding it up firmly to the ceiling and wall; thus removing the superfluous stuff, and leaving in plaster the exact contour of the cornice required. This is not effected at once, but the other workman keeps supplying fresh putty to the parts which want it. If the stuff dries too fast, one of the workmen sprinkles it with water from a brush.

When the cornices are of very large proportions, three or four moulds are requisite, and they are applied in the same manner until the whole of their parts are formed. The mitres, internal and external, and also small returns or breaks, are afterwards modelled and filled up by hand.

ORNAMENTAL CORNICES are formed previously, and in a similar way to those described, excepting that the plasterer leaves indents or sinkings in the mould for the casts to be fixed in. The plasterers of the present day cast all their ornaments in Plaster of Paris; whereas they were formerly the work

cornice mould, though a nib rule will probably be needed. The technique of running is very different, as there is no quick set as with gypsum plaster. After coring out accurately to a muffle, a finish is obtained by applying thin coats of wet and dry OPC/sand alternatively and passing the running mould along the rule after each application.

EXTERNAL RENDERING

Ordinary Portland cement has completely superceded Roman cement for use as the cementatious material in the mix that plasterers use today for all external work. Portland cement is manufactured and the main constituents are limestone or chalk, and clay. It should be mixed with hydrated lime and a well graded sand to the following ratios, $1:\frac{1}{2}:4$, $1:\frac{1}{2}:5$, $1:1:6$, $1:2:8$, OPC/lime/sand as the specification requires. It may also be used with sand on its own ($1:3$), and with a proprietory brand of waterproofing material added to create a waterproof and

Detail of external rendering showing lining out to represent stonework. Excessive drying shrinkage shows as hair cracking on the surface (Cheltenham, Gloucestershire)

of manual labour, performed by ingenious men, then known in the trade as *ornamental-plasterers*. The casting of ornaments in moulds has almost superseded this branch of the art; and the few individuals now living, by whom it was formerly professed, are chiefly employed in modelling and framing of moulds.

All the ornaments which are cast in Plaster of Paris, are previously modelled in clay. The clay-model exhibits the power and taste of the designer, as well as that of the sculptor. When it is finished, and becomes rather firm, it is oiled all over, and put into a wooden frame. All its parts are then retouched and perfected, for receiving a covering of melted wax, which is poured warm into the frame and over the clay-mould. When cool, it is turned upside down, and the wax comes easily away from the clay, and is an exact reversed copy. In such moulds are cast all the enriched mouldings, now prepared by common plasterers. The waxen models are made so as to cast about one foot in length of the ornaments at a time; this quantity being easily removed out of the moulds, without the danger of breaking.

The casts are all made with the finest and purest Plaster of Paris, saturated with water. The casts, when first taken out of the moulds, are not very firm, and are suffered to dry a little, either in the air, or in an oven adapted for the purpose; and when hard enough to bear handling, they are scraped and cleaned up for the workmen to fix in the places intended.

The FRIEZES and BASSO-RELIEVOS are performed in a manner exactly similar, except that the waxen moulds are so made as to allow of grounds of plaster being left behind the ornaments, half an inch, or more, in thicknesses; and these are cast to the ornaments or figures, which strengthen and secure the proportions.

CAPITALS to columns are prepared in a similar way, but require several moulds to complete them. The Corinthian capital will require a shaft or bell to be first made, exactly shaped, so as to produce graceful effects in the foliage and contour of the volutes; all of which, as well as the other details, require separate and distinct reversed moulds when intended for capitals made to order.

339

suction free background. Waterproofing compounds are added to the manufacturer's specification. The only difficulty that could occur is when carrying out repairs to untreated or unpainted original Roman cement, as OPC is grey whereas the original Roman cement was brown. Colours may be added to Portland cement mixes or a ready coloured cement is also available. The Blue Circle Company produces a good range of coloured cements and these are also available from other sources.

When repairing old cement work the area to be repaired must be cut into a reasonable shape, all surrounding areas checked for soundness, and the background and joints thoroughly cleaned and dampened. Should any doubt exist concerning the adhesion of the backing coat to the background, a spatterdash coat may be applied. This consists of 1:2 OPC/sharp sand made up into a wet slurry. This is brushed into the wet background with a 2-knot washing off brush, stippled heavily and then left for twenty-four hours before the backing coat is applied. This must be laid on and cut back behind the original finish line to allow for the finish. Different textures and finishes will need different thicknesses. The backing should be keyed horizontally with a 'comb' scratcher for all textures.

DUBBING OUT

Dubbing out is carried out by the plasterer when for any one of a number of reasons the background is badly out of line or plumb. Most modern backing plasters are limited to a mean thickness of 12 mm, and when the plaster mixes are going to have to exceed this measurement, dubbing out should occur. Successive layers of OPC/lime/sand or OPC/sand should be applied until the irregularities in the background have been eliminated. Should several coats be required, they must be applied individually to a thickness of 10–12 mm, flattened, keyed by comb scratcher and left for a minimum of twenty-four hours.

The same practice should be followed for external finishes in OPC/lime/sand where necessary. Any plaster laid on to an excessive thickness during one application is liable to crack and break away from the background – dubbing ou will produce a good regular background ready for plastering in the normal way.

Large solid cornices may also require some form of dubbing out so that they conform to the reasonable thickness rule. In this case however the plasterer will refer to it as 'coring out'. The core will either consist of Class A gypsum plaster/sand, mixed in equal proportion and forced into the wall/ceiling angle and keyed, or a rendering coat applied to bracketing. In both cases the final application of the core will be shaped to a rough cornice by the use of a muffle attached to the running mould.

The plasterers, as before-mentioned, in forming cornices, in which ornaments are to be used, take care to have projections in the running moulds; which have the effect of grooves or indents in the cornices; and into these grooves are put the ornaments after they are cast, which are fixed in their places by having small quantities of liquid Plaster of Paris spread at their backs. Friezes are prepared for cornices, &c., in a similar way, by leaving projections in the running moulds, at those parts of the cornices where they are intended to be inserted, and they are also fixed in their places with liquid plaster. Detached ornaments, when designed for ceilings, or any other parts, to which running moulds have not been employed, are cast in pieces exactly corresponding with the designs, and are fixed upon the ceilings, or other places, with white-lead.

Plasterers require numerous models in wood, and very few or any of their best works can be completed without them. But, with moulds, good plasterers are capable of making the most exquisite mouldings, possessing sharpness and breadths unequalled by any other modes now in practice. This, however is, in some measure, dependent on the truth of the moulds. Good plastering is known by its exquisite appearance, as to its regularity, correctness, solid effect, and without any cracks or indications of them.

ROMAN CEMENT, or OUTSIDE STUCCO.—The qualities of this valuable cement is now generally known in every part of the *United Kingdom*. It was first introduced to public notice by the late JAMES WYATT, Esq. eminent for having planned and executed some of the most magnificent and useful structures in these countries. It was originally known as *Parker's Patent Cement*, and was sold by Messrs. Charles Wyatt and Co., Bankside, London, at *five shillings* and *sixpence* per bushel: it is now vended by different manufacturers in the Metropolis at *three shillings* per bushel, and even less, when the casks are returned. Equal quantities of this cement and sharp clean grit-sand, mixed together, will form very hard and durable coverings for the outsides of public and private edifices. If the sand is wet or damp, the composition should be used immediately. When the works are finished, they should be frescoed, or coloured, with washes, composed in proportions of five ounces of copperas to every gallon of water, and as much fresh lime and cement as will produce the colours required. Where these sorts of works are executed with judgment, and finished with taste, so as to produce picturesque effects, they are drawn and jointed to imitate well-bonded masonry, and the divisions promiscuously touched with rich tints of umber, and occasionally with vitriol; and, upon these colours mellowing, they will produce the most pleasing and harmonious effects; especially if dashed with judgment, and with the skill of a painter who has profited by watching the playful tints of nature, produced by the effects of time in the mouldering remains of our antient buildings.

The following are the average prices for Roman Cement, as charged in the Metropolis, at per yard superficial.

	s.	d.
Roman Cement, on the outsides of buildings, including all materials, and colouring in the manner described........	4	9
Ditto, without colouring............	4	0
Ditto, on strong laths.....	5	3
Plain fascias, pilasters, and belting-courses, or strings, per foot super.................................	0	6
Plain cornices, ditto.	2	2
Sinkings, per foot run............................	0	5
Arris', ditto...................................	0	2
Nine-inch reveals to windows, ditto.................	0	8
Four inches and a half reveals, ditto.................	0	5

Where the works are circular, *one-fourth*, *one-fifth*, or *one-sixth*, should be added to the above prices, in proportions to the quickness of the curvatures.

The expenses of dubbing-out, to make the works fair, must be added to the before-mentioned prices; also the value of the cement consumed in performing the same; together with all the time in erecting and taking down the scaffolding; as, also, the expenses of iron spikes, for twine, and other requisite materials, for creating extra projections to cornices, pilasters, &c.

One bushel of cement, used with discretion, care, and judgment, will perform from three to four yards superficial; that is, mixed with an equal portion of clean sharp grit-sand; and, in procuring the latter article, great pains should be taken to select such qualities as are of a lively and binding description, and free from all slime or mud. As soon as the sand and cement is mixed with clean water, the composition should be used as quick as possible, and not a moment lost in floating the walls, which will require incessant labour, until the cement is set, which is almost instantaneous.

ROUGH-CASTING is an outside finishing cheaper than stucco. It consists in giving the wall to be rough-casted a pricking-up coat of lime and hair; and when this is tolerably dry, a second coat of the same material, which is laid on the first, as smooth and even as can be. As fast as this coat is finished, a second workman follows the other with a pail of rough-cast, which he throws on the new plastering. The materials for rough-casting are composed of fine gravel, with the earth washed cleanly out of it, and afterwards mixed with pure lime and water, till the entire together is of the consistence of a semi-fluid; it is then spread, or rather splashed, upon the wall by a float made of wood. This float is five or six inches long, and as many wide, made of half-inch deal, to which is fitted a rounded deal handle. The plasterer holds this in his right hand, and in his left a common white-wash brush; with the former he lays on the rough-cast, and with the latter, which he dips in the rough-cast, he brushes and colours the mortar and rough-cast that he has spread, to make them, when finished and dry, appear of the same colour throughout.

SCAGLIOLA.—The practice of forming columns with SCAGLIOLA is a distinct branch of plastering. It originated in Italy, and was thence introduced into France, then into England. For its first introduction here our country is indebted to the late Henry Holland, Esq. who was for many years the favourite architect of his present Majesty, who caused artists to be invited from Paris to perform such works in Carlton-Palace; some of whom, from finding a considerable demand for their works, remained with us, and taught the art to our British workmen.

ROUGH CASTING

Rough casting is a two or three coat textured external finish, requiring moderate suction. A backing coat of 1:1:6 (OPC/lime/sand) is applied to a clean damp background. It is ruled flat and horizontally keyed by comb scratching. After a minimum of twenty-four hours the rough cast mix of 1:1:6 is made up as follows, one part OPC, one part lime, three to four parts coarse shingle, three parts coarse gritting sand. This is thrown on to the keyed background with a harling or dashing trowel, the design of which should ensure that a good even spread is obtained and not individual piles of material. Alternatively, a butter coat of 1:1:6 is applied to the hardened key backing coat and the rough cast mix, this time of 1::1:(5+1) is thrown into the butter coat. This should be limited to a thickness of 6 mm, and by using more stones or shingle in the rough cast coat a matching texture should be obtained.

FIBROUS PLASTERING

From the time of the earliest internal ornamental plasterwork in this country it was seen that relatively small repetitive features could be reproduced from moulds. Reproduced ceiling panels existed alongside the free modelling and carving of ceiling and wall ornament in lime putty and plaster of Paris mixes. The method was to press a dough-like mix into a plaster mould and strut the mould in position against the ceiling. On setting, the mix would stick to the ceiling. The mould was then removed. No undercut could be produced with this rigid type of mould but it could be carved in after the mould's removal.

Through Georgian and early Victorian times relatively small, unreinforced plaster casts were first removed from their moulds and then bedded in position with a plaster mix. This enabled plain run *in situ* mouldings to be dressed with enrichment such as blocks, egg-and-dart, bead-and-reel and leaves. Piece moulding was developed in order that undercut casts might be made from plaster moulds in the round. Gelatine came into use as a pliable moulding material that would bend away from, and pull out of, undercut sections. Fibrous plasterwork as we know it today, reproducing the whole of a surface (flat areas, plain moulded sections and enrichments), was introduced around the middle of the nineteenth century.

There are two reasons for using fibrous plasterwork as an internal finish for buildings:

1   Columns, niches and lengths of mouldings can be reproduced quickly and economically, each from just one unit that acts as a model from which a mould is taken.

In order to execute columns and their antæ, or pilasters, in Scagliola, the following remarks and directions are to be observed: when the architect has furnished the drawing, exhibiting the diameter of the shafts, a wooden cradle is made, about two and a half inches less in diameter than that of the projected column. This cradle is lathed all round, as for common plastering, and afterwards covered by a pricking-up coat of lime and hair: when this is quite dry, the workers in Scagliola commence their peculiar labour.

The Scagliola is capable of imitating the most scarce and precious marbles; the imitation taking as high a polish, and feeling to the touch as cold and solid as the most compact and dense marble. For the composition of it the purest gypsum must be broken in small pieces, and then calcined till the largest fragments have lost their brilliancy. The calcined powder is then passed through a very fine sieve, and mixed up with a solution of Flanders glue, isinglass, &c., with the colours required in the marble they are about to imitate.

When the work is to be of various colours, each colour is prepared separately, and they are afterwards mingled and combined nearly in the same manner as a painter mixes, on his pallet, the primitive colours which are to compose his different shades. When the powdered gypsum, or plaster, is prepared, and mingled for the work, it is laid on the shaft of the column, &c., covering over the pricked-up coat, which has been previously laid on it, and is floated, with moulds of wood, to the sizes required. During the floating, the artist uses the colours necessary for the marble intended to be imitated, which thus become mingled and incorporated in it. In order to give his work the polish or glossy lustre, he rubs it with a pumice-stone, and cleanses it with a wet sponge. He next proceeds to polish it with tripoli and charcoal, and fine soft linen; and, after going over it with a piece of felt, dipped in a mixture of oil and tripoli, finishes the operation by the application of pure oil.

This is considered as one of the finest imitations in the world; the Scagliola being as strong and durable as real marble for all works not exposed to the

2   Casts can be made self-supporting with extra large reinforcing sections of timber or metal. These are attached to the backs of the casts with plaster soaked canvas during the casting operation, and greatly reduce the number of on-site fixing members needed since each cast has only to be fixed at two points. This compares very favourably with the completely armatured background of shaped grid and lathwork required by a solid plastering system, for example for domes and pendentives, vaulting, pendants, etc.

A number of factors may determine the size of a fibrous plaster cast:

(a) the most suitable places for joints — masking by a decorative feature is taken into consideration;

(b) the desirability of producing single units (niches, ceiling centres, etc.) in one piece and symmetrical units (columns, lunettes) in two halves;

(c) where handling is the only consideration a convenient size for flat units is 2.5 × 1.25 m and for a length of moulding 3—4 m.

The term 'fibrous plaster' refers to units of plasterwork that have been cast from moulds and reinforced with fibres. Plaster of Paris is the most commonly used casting plaster but where extra hardness or resistance to damage is required, Keene's cement or special hard casting plasters may be used. The fibres are usually comprised of two layers of 6 mm square mesh jute hessian. In addition, 25 mm wide by 3 mm or 6 mm thick wood laths are positioned both ways to form squares no larger than 300 mm in size. The laths are placed between two layers of hessian or positioned over the back and covered by plaster-soaked strips of hessian. The hessian imparts tensile strength to the plaster. The wood lath forms reinforcing ribs and the means by which the casts are fixed. Metal angle or bar sections of 25 mm may be used for extra fire resistance or to give more strength where insufficient on-site fixing points are provided. The laths are placed flat when the cast is to be fixed to timber by nailing or screwing through them, and on edge when a galvanized tie wire is to be passed under them for subsequent wiring to metal fixings.

The casts are between 6 and 9 mm thick with the ribs 18 to 23 mm thick using flat laths, and 35 mm thick with the laths on edge. Timber fixings (battens, joist or studs) should be not more than 300 mm apart and metal fixing members not more than 450 mm apart. The casts are fixed at every point where the ribs in a cast cross a fixing member.

There are two methods for producing a fibrous plaster cast. One uses two 'gauges' or batches of plaster, and the other one gauge.

In the two-gauge method the first mix is used to form the face of the cast. The mix should contain just enough size retarder to control its set and is called 'the firstings'. It is applied to the face of the mould with a sisal splash brush, first by

346

effects of the atmosphere, retaining its lustre as long and equal to real marble, without being one-eighth of the expense of the cheapest marble imported.

COMPOSITION.—Besides the composition, before adverted to, for covering the outsides of buildings, plasterers use a finer species of composition for inside ornamental works. The material alluded to is of a brownish colour, exceedingly compact, and, when completely dry, very strong. It is composed of powdered whitening, glue in solution, and linseed-oil; the proportions of which are, to two pounds of whitening one pound of glue, and half a pound of oil. These are placed in a copper and heated, being stirred with a spatula till the whole becomes incorporated. It is then suffered to cool and settle; after which it is taken and laid upon a stone, covered with powdered whitening, and beaten till it becomes of a tough and firm consistence. It is then put by for use, and covered with wetted cloths to keep it fresh.

The ornaments to be cast in this composition are modelled in clay, for common plastering, and afterwards carved in a block of box-wood. The carving must be done with great neatness and truth, as on it depends the exquisiteness of the ornament. The composition is cut with a knife into pieces, and then closely pressed by hand into every part of the mould; it is then placed in a press, worked by an iron screw, by which the composition is forced into every part of the sculpture. After being taken out of the press, by giving it a tap upside down, it comes easily out of the mould. One foot in length is as much as is usually cast at a time; and when this is first taken out of the mould, all the superfluous composition is removed by cutting it off with a knife; the waste pieces being thrown into the copper to assist in making a fresh supply of composition.

This composition, when formed into ornaments, is fixed upon wooden or other ground, by a solution of heated glue, white-lead, &c. It is afterwards painted or gilded, to suit the taste and style of the work for which it is intended.

brushing or stippling (depending on the intricacy of the detail) and then by splashing to form an even coat. The outer edges of the mould are then cleaned off, and as the plaster stiffens, the first layer of hessian is laid over the mould, overlapping all joints slightly. As the plaster sets and so stiffens, the hessian is pressed into its surface with the hands or with a gauging trowel, depending on the contours of the mould. The partial setting of the plaster prevents the hessian being pushed through to the face of the cast. The second gauge of plaster (containing enough size to retard the set till the end of the casting operation) is immediately brushed into the canvas and firstings. Perimeter laths, pasted with plaster to aid adhesion, are now positioned all round the cast. The rest of the wood lath reinforcement may be positioned and covered with a second layer of hessian, or the hessian applied first and the laths positioned and then covered by strips of hessian. The cast is kept wet by brushing on plaster 'seconds' during every stage. Finally, the back of the cast is shaped to fit the on-site fixings. Lines of plaster are placed on the ribs formed by the wood laths, are ruled to thickness and shaped off the specially shaped edges of the mould.

In the one-gauge method, one mix of plaster is gauged to a thicker consistency than for two-gauge casting and enough size retarder is added to keep the mix workable to the end of the casting operation. As with the two-gauge method, a layer of plaster is first applied to the mould. To prevent the reinforcement being worked through to the face of the cast, the first layer is dusted with a fine layer of dry plaster, sifted by shaking from a bag made from two thicknesses of 6 mm mesh canvas. When the surface of the plaster has toughened sufficiently, the hessian is applied and the rest of the casting operation completed as for the two-gauge method.

Models made by the plasterer can be formed by sections of run moulding mitred and jointed together. Enrichment can be carved from plaster, modelled in clay or plasticine or dressed on to plain run mouldings in the form of composition.

Moulds for plaster casts or cement-bound mixes may be made of various types of material which belong to one of two groups:

1   rigid materials that are used where no undercut exists or when the mould is made up of pieces that are demountable from the cast;
2   pliable materials that will bend away from, and pull out of, undercut sections.

The most commonly used rigid material for moulds is plaster of Paris, although Keene's cement and other special hard plasters may be used. The mould may be a single unit or made up of loose pieces sitting in an overall cast. Glass reinforced plastics may be used to form moulds in the same way. Plaster of Paris

PLATE 1.

GRECIAN ORNAMENTS.

Fig.1.

Fig.2.

Fig.3.

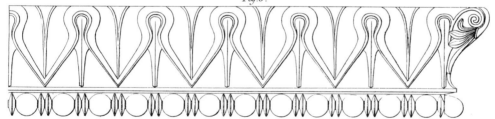

Fig.4.

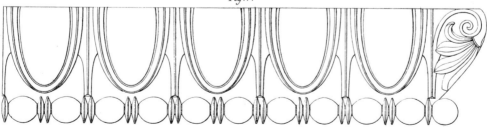

349

may be formed into mouldings by the use of running moulds, these mouldings forming the plaster moulds from which casts are made. Undercut sections may be formed by dividing the full section of a mould into more than one moulding.

Where only one cast is required, a 'waste' mould may be used, both the model and the mould being destroyed in the process. The model is made of clay, plasticine or wax and is a modified version of a plaster of Paris cast. Clay and plasticine models are removed from the mould by scraping and wax models by melting. A cast is made in the plaster mould in the usual way and the mould removed with a hammer and chisel, chipping it away from the cast, piece by piece. The firstings of the mould is usually coloured to act as a warning for when the cast has nearly been reached. The back of the firstings is seasoned so that the reinforced seconds may easily be chipped away from it.

Pliable moulding materials are either thermoplastic polyvinyl chloride (PVC) or a two-pack rubber compound. The special grades of PVC for mould-making range in flexibility and their melting points vary from 140° to 170°C. They are melted in thermostatically controlled electric coppers and poured over the model to be moulded. The rubber compounds each have a curing agent that is added and thoroughly mixed in before pouring. To be held to shape, all pliable moulds need to sit into a plaster back. A back is not used, however, if a mould is to be bent or distorted intentionally.

The simplest type of pliable mould is the flood mould. Flood moulds are taken from relatively flat units, for example ceiling roses. A retaining wall is erected round the model some 40 mm away and splaying inwards. The mould material is poured on to cover the model by about 10 mm at the highest point. When the material has solidified the retaining wall is removed and a fibrous plaster back is cast over the whole.

A skin mould is used for larger and more deeply contoured models, such as coats of arms. It is produced in the same way, except that the mould is not flooded but the moulding material made to follow the contours of the model. Hot-melt compounds chill and form a natural skin when poured sparingly over a model. As the material solidifies, thicknesses on high spots may be increased with scoops of excess material from the low areas. Cold-cure rubber compounds are produced in thixotropic grades that are painted on to a model in layers, between cures, until the required thickness is built up.

A case mould is used for items such as enriched capitals and is produced by first making a plaster back or case. Placed over the model, this leaves a cavity which is then flooded with a pliable mould material.

An insertion mould is a rigid mould with inserts of pliable moulding material to reproduce the enrichment.

Squeeze moulds are taken directly from in situ mouldings. They may be in the

Fig. 1.

Fig. 2. *Fig. 3.*

Fig. 4.

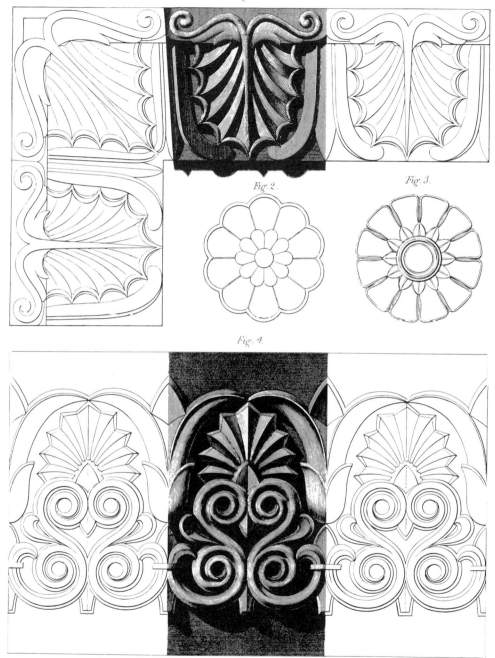

351

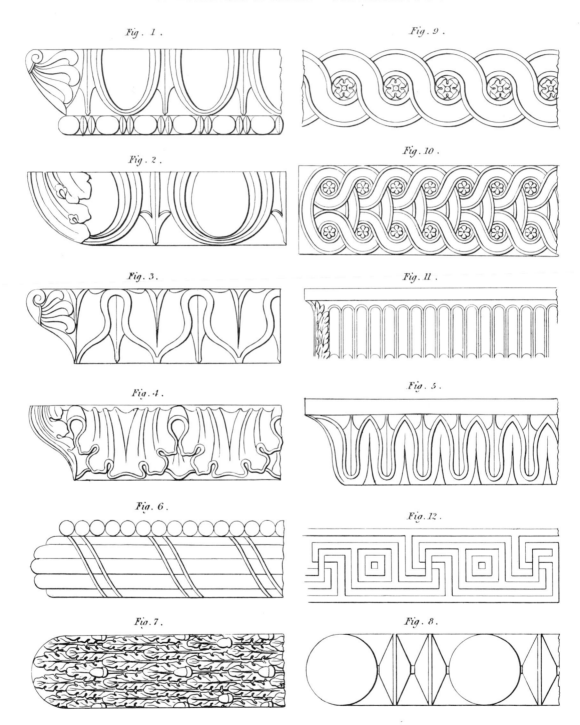

Fig. 1.

Fig. 9.

Fig. 2.

Fig. 10.

Fig. 3.

Fig. 11.

Fig. 4.

Fig. 5.

Fig. 6.

Fig. 12.

Fig. 7.

Fig. 8.

form of fibrous plaster casts (one-piece or loose-piece), cold-cure rubber skin moulds, or simple pressed impressions in clay or plasticine.

Materials in which Casts are made include:

Gypsum plasters — these are for internal use only as they are very vulnerable to attack by the elements, especially rain and frost.

Scagliola — this is also for internal use only and is an imitation marble consisting of a hard plaster and alkali-resistant powdered dyes. The coloured plaster is mixed to a thick, dough-like consistency and produces the best imitations of marble by working in a way that imitates the stone's formation (for example lamination). The process is finished by polishing with paraffin and beeswax or by the application of a two-pack polyurethane varnish.

Cement-bound mixes for external use — for balusters, copings and trusses cement-sand mixes are used in imitation of Portland stone.

A combination of stone-dust and particles with coloured cement that can produce a close imitation of any specific stone.

9. Painting

Ian Bristow

To comment on the house-painting chapter of Nicholson's book presents a number of difficulties. As a text it is comparatively unimportant, being a work of plagiarism from other, often much earlier, sources. It therefore contains much that is misleading with respect to early nineteenth century practice. The text is based directly on the house-painting article contained in Thomas Martin's encyclopedic work *The Circle of the Mechanical Arts*, 1813 (pages 460–4). Nicholson makes several omissions together with a number of minor alterations, and the only notable addition is the list of colour mixtures. These came originally from the second edition of a late seventeenth-century work, John Smith's *Art of Painting in Oyl*, 1687 (pages 51–2) although it seems quite likely that Nicholson worked from William Butcher's crudely revised re-issue of this book as Smith's *Art of House-painting*, 1821 (2nd edition 1825, pages 23–4). By this date, however, these suggestions may be regarded as generally obsolete, at least as far as many of the names given to the various combinations of pigments are concerned. Nicholson's role was, therefore, merely one of editor; and as will become clear, an editor none too critical of the texts from which he worked.

Martin's essay in its turn is also a compilation, although he drew from a wider variety of earlier sources. He mentioned, for example, T. H. Vanherman's method for preparing fish oil as a paint vehicle 'lately laid before the Society of Arts', and noted the names of two London grainers in a way which suggests that he may have been familiar with their work, or at least their reputation. These items were however omitted by Nicholson. Martin also gave a recipe for a drying oil (Nicholson repeated this in his text) which is very similar to one proposed by the late eighteenth century writer, J. F. Watin, in his book *L'Art du peintre, doreur, vernisseur*, first published in 1772 (4th edition, Paris 1785, page 85). The majority of the information which Martin provided on pigments was, on the other hand, derived from *The Handmaid to the Arts* published by Robert Dossie in 1758 (Vol. 1, pages 8–9 and 42–132), and it is here that one of the greatest pitfalls lies for the reader of Nicholson's *Practical Builder*. In describing the range of pigments available during the mid-eighteenth century, Dossie was not merely concerned with house-painting and, amongst other subjects, treated of fine-art techniques besides the preparation of marbled papers and other decorative products. Hence, his pigment list included several which were far too expensive for house-painting, such as ultramarine, besides a number of more esoteric pigments like pearl white which might be prepared on a small scale by the individual artist for his own use in miniature painting. In repeating this without qualification, Martin and Nicholson betray a lack of immediate intimacy with the subject of house painting and omit several important pigments introduced during the second half of the eighteenth century, such as Scheele's green and patent yellow. Consequently the whole article in the *Practical*

CHAPTER XIII.

HOUSE-PAINTING.

HOUSE-PAINTING is the art of colouring and covering with paint all the several kinds of wood, iron-work, &c. either as an external finish or for protection from the weather. This practice may be divided into four branches; that is to say, COMMON PAINTING, GRAINING, ORNAMENTAL PAINTING, and INSCRIPTION WRITING.

WHITE LEAD, is the principal ingredient used in house-painting; and this is a calx, obtained by rolling sheets of lead into coils, with their surfaces, about half an inch distant from each other, and then placing them vertically in earthen pots, with a portion of good vinegar at the bottom, in such a way that, when set in a moderate heat, the vapour of the vinegar corrodes the lead, so that the external portion will come off in white flakes when the lead is beaten or uncoiled. These flakes, being bleached, ground, and saturated with linseed oil, form the *white lead* of the shops. This composition, if genuine, improves by keeping, and for the best whites it should be, at least, two or three years old. The Nottingham white lead is the most esteemed for what is called *flatting*, or dead-white. This article is so frequently adulterated with common whiting, that it cannot be too carefully examined, before it be used.

LITHARGE is composed of the ashes of lead, and is a kind of dusky powder that first appears in the oxydation of the lead. It is mixed with linseed oil, and used to give the paint a greater capability of drying quickly.

Builder is clearly a second or third hand account, rather than an authoritative work by a craftsman versed in his subject. Each statement it contains must therefore be tested and receive independent confirmation before its reliability in reflecting early nineteenth century practice can be accepted.

Although Nicholson's preliminary definition of house-painting is concerned immediately with external work, he later describes techniques such as clearcole and finish, or flatting, which were restricted to interiors. At first glance, therefore, it may appear surprising that nowhere is there mention of size-bound distemper, a technique widely employed in interiors, and indeed, essential to the achievement of a number of bright colours which had been fashionable during the second half of the eighteenth century. On the other hand, the pigment list copied from Dossie included several pigments whose use was by their very nature most often restricted to distemper. This apparently major omission of Nicholson was clearly not on account of any change in taste. At least since the beginning of the seventeenth century, oil paint had been regarded as the prerogative of the painter, a state of affairs prescribed by Act of Parliament in 1603 (1 jac. 1, c.20), while distemper on the other hand could be, and frequently was, applied by the plasterer. The convention that distemper was measured as a plastering item, oil alone being included in pricing painter's work, was perpetuated throughout the eighteenth century and well into the nineteenth. This is emphasized by the division of these between the two trades in many price books of the period including, for example, the 'Perpetual Price-book' (pages 138–42 and 148–53) originally provided at the end of the *Practical Builder*. In omitting distemper from his painting chapter therefore, Nicholson simply reflected current trade practice. On the other hand, in common with Martin, he did not include information on distemper in his section on plasterwork.

Although lead paint now enjoys a strictly limited use, oil paint for buildings continued to be based on white lead well into the present century. Nevertheless, modern formulae for its employment resemble early nineteenth century practice closely and, where used, lead paint is still made up from white lead, linseed oil, driers, and a thinner (*see* Albert Beckly, 'If it was good enough for the Prince Regent . . .', *The Painting and Decorating Journal* (February 1979) pages 26–9). The pigment was accorded proper status by Nicholson, although his description of its manufacture was rather vague. Rather than merely being 'saturated' with linseed oil, the most commonly used medium, it had of course to be ground into this by mechanical means (*see* Ian Bristow, 'Ready-mixed paint in the eighteenth century', *The Architectural Review*, vol. clxi, no. 962 (April 1977) pages 246–8). As it is today much of the oil employed seems to have been hot draw, that is extracted from the seed in a heated press. It is by no

LINSEED OIL, which is used in every kind of house-paint, is obtained, by pressure, from the seed of flax, and then filtered to free it from feculæ. This oil should be kept for two or three years, that it may precipitate its colouring particles; as the more transparent it is, the better is the paint, of which it forms a component part. In Holland they whiten linseed oil by the following process, which gives it the effect of age. Having put the linseed oil into a well-glazed pot, they add to it fine sand and water, each of the same quantity as the oil, and having covered the vessel with glass, expose it to the sun, and stir it once every day. This process soon renders it very white; after which it should rest for two days, and is then fit for use.

DRYING OILS are usually prepared from litharge, white lead, plaster, and umber, in the following manner: to one pound of linseed oil add half an ounce of each of the above ingredients, and then boil the composition over a gentle fire, taking care to skim it from time to time. When the scum begins to rarify, and becomes red, the fire should be stopped, and the oil left to clarify and settle, when it is fit for use. The scum is called *smudge*, and is used for outside work. Oil, thus prepared, may be bought at colour shops under the name of *boiled oil*, and it is always used for the best house-painting.

OIL OF TURPENTINE, or TURPS, is made from the resin of that name, which is obtained from all larch and fir-trees. *Venice Turpentine* is obtained from the larch, by fixing pipes in a hole made in the trunk, and thus conducting the liquid turpentine into buckets. In this state the turpentine has a yellowish limped colour, a strong aromatic smell, and a bitter taste. When this liquid or juice is distilled, by means of a bath, an oil is obtained, which is called *Essence of Turpentine*. The residue of the distillation is the boiled turpentine of commerce. This oil improves much by age, as the older it is the longer will the work performed with it retain its colour. It is much used in what is generally called *flatting*.

All the prismatic colours are occasionally used by the painter, and he varies these, according to circumstances, into almost every gradation of tint. They may be thus classed :—

RED.
- Vermilion,
- Native Cinnabar,
- Red-Lead,
- Scarlet-Ochre,
- Common Indian-Red,
- Spanish Brown,
- Terra di Sienna, burnt, } Red tending to Orange.
- Carmine,
- Lake,
- Rose-Pink,
- Red-Ochre,
- Venetian-Red. } Crimson tending to Purple.

GREEN.
- Verdigris,
- Crystals of ditto,
- Prussian-Green,
- Terra Verte,
- Sap Green.

ORANGE.
- Orange Lake.

PURPLE.
- True Indian-Red,
- Archil,
- Log-Wash.

BLUE.
- Ultramarine,
- Ditto, ashes,
- Prussian-Blue,
- Verditer,
- Indigo,
- Smalt.

BROWN.
- Brown-Pink,
- Bistre,
- Brown-Ochre,
- Umber,
- Cologne Earth,
- Asphaltum.

YELLOW.
- King's-Yellow,
- Naples ditto,
- Yellow-Ochre,
- Dutch-Pink,
- English ditto,
- Light ditto,
- Gamboge,
- Masticot,
- Common Orpiment,
- Gall-Stone,
- Terra di Sienna.

WHITE.
- White-Flake,
- White-Lead,
- Calcined Hartshorn,
- Pearl White,
- Tray White,
- Eggshell White,
- Flowers of Bismuth.

BLACK.
- Lamp-Black,
- Ivory-Black,
- Blue-Black.

These colours are nearly all that are employed by the house-painter, and are those which experience has taught him to mix so as produce almost every teint that can be required.

VERMILION is a bright scarlet pigment, formed of common sulphur and quicksilver, prepared for use by a chymical process. It has a delicate body, and will grind as fine as the oil itself, but is too expensive for common use.

CINNABAR is a similar pigment, differing only from vermilion by having a more crimson teint.

RED-LEAD, or MINIUM, is lead calcined till it acquires a proper degree of colour, by exposing it with a large surface to the fire.

SCARLET-OCHRE is an earth, with a base of green vitriol, and is separated from the acid of the vitriol by calcination.

COMMON INDIAN-RED, is of an hue verging to scarlet, and is imported from the East Indies.

VENETIAN-RED is a native ochre, rather inclining to scarlet; this is the pigment which is selected for graining of doors, &c., in imitation of mahogany.

SPANISH-BROWN is a native earth, found in the very state and colour in which it is used.

TERRA DI SIENNA is a native ochre, and is brought from Italy, where it is generally found. It is yellow originally, and in this state is often made use of, and is accordingly placed among the yellow colours. It changes to an orange-red by calcination, though not of a very bright teint, for which property it is sought to produce a pigment of that colour.

CARMINE is a bright crimson colour, and formed of the tinging substance of cochineal, with nitric-acid. It is not well calculated to mix up with oil, as its colour changes rapidly by exposure to the air and light.

LAKE is a white earthy body, as cuttle fish-bone, or the basis of alum or chalk, tinged with some vegetable dye, such as is obtained from cochineal, or Brasil-wood, taken up by an alkali, and precipitated on the earth by the addition of an acid.

ROSE-PINK is a lake, like the former, except that the earth or basis of the

means clear whether the then well known Dutch process for its refinement was 'in common use' (Nicholson quoting Martin), and the majority of linseed oil available today is refined by other means.

The 'boiling' of linseed oil with driers such as litharge and others he mentioned had been practised for many years in order to improve its drying properties. Oil prepared in this way, which was and continues to be commonly available from shops selling painters' materials, is much darker in colour than raw linseed oil and Nicholson's suggestion that it was always used in the best work is misleading where interiors are concerned. For external work, however, boiled oil seems to have enjoyed wide use in combination with raw linseed oil; but for more delicate tints in interior work the addition of a drier, such as litharge or lead acetate in paste form, was the rule. To thin the paint, oil of turpentine was employed in the same way as today, but it seems doubtful whether this would ever have been distilled from Venice turpentine (which Nicholson correctly distinguished as obtained from the larch tree) since this was much more expensive than oleo-resins from the pine. Crude Venice turpentine was generally reserved for the manufacture of certain varnishes.

To colour the basic lead paint, tinting pigments ground into linseed oil were added and it is here that the greatest differences from modern practice appear. Although ready-mixed tints had been sold in London since the 1730s, it is likely that even a century later the majority of colours, at least in better class work, were tinted up on site using a range of pigments including many of those listed by Nicholson. Of these, however, only a handful are still in commercial use and less than half the others remain available for artist's use. Many he listed were never used for house-painting. To find substitutes is not easy, and so the restoration of interiors in a completely authentic manner is a matter requiring extremely specialized knowledge, particularly since many pigments, especially those of an historical nature, react chemically one with another. It must also be borne in mind that many of the now obsolete pigments became so for very good reasons, either on account of their toxicity, fugitive nature, or other undesirable characteristic. While it is an invaluable exercise to aim for complete authenticity where museum interiors are concerned, this is impractical in the vast majority of rooms. The use of paint colour in the early nineteenth century depended largely on the relative costs and working characteristics of the tinting pigments available and their individual properties are not necessarily matched by modern stainers of similar colour (*see* Ian Bristow, 'Cost constraints on historical colours', *The Architect* (March 1977), pages 40 and 55).

Although vermilion was employed well into the nineteenth century, the native form of pigment, cinnabar, was unimportant. Scarlet ochre, common Indian red, Venetian red, and Spanish brown were different varieties of red ochre described

pigment is principally chalk, and the tinging substance extracted from Brasil or Campeachy wood.

RED-OCHRE is a native earth; but that which is in common use is coloured red by calcination, being yellow when dug out of the earth, and the same with the *yellow-ochre* commonly used. This latter substance is chiefly brought from Oxfordshire, where it is found in great abundance.

ULTRAMARINE is a preparation of calcined *lapis-lazuli*, which is, when perfect, of a brilliant blue colour; it has an extremely beautiful and transparent effect in oil, and will retain this property with whatever vehicle, or pigment, it may be mixed. It is excessively dear, and is frequently sold at the colour shops in an adulterated state.

ULTRAMARINE ASHES are the residuum, or remains, of the calcined *lapis-lazuli*.

PRUSSIAN-BLUE is a brilliant pigment; it is the fixed sulphur of animal or vegetable coal, chymically combined with the earth of alum.

VERDITER is composed of a mixture of chalk with the precipitated copper, formed by adding the due proportion of chalk to the solution of copper, made by the refiners in precipitating silver from the nitric acid, in the operation called *parting*, in which they have occasion to dissolve it in order to purify it.

INDIGO is a tinging matter, extracted from certain plants, which are found in both the Indies, from whence the Indigos of commerce are mostly imported.

SMALT is a species of glass, of a dark blue colour, being coloured with zaffre, or oxyde of cobalt, and afterwards ground to a powder. This beautiful colour carries no body in oil, and can be strewed only upon a ground of white lead.

KING'S-YELLOW is a pure orpiment, or arsenic, coloured with sulphur.

NAPLES-YELLOW is a warm yellow pigment, rather inclining to orange.

YELLOW-OCHRE is a mineral earth, which is found in many places, but of different degrees of purity. See *Red-Ochre*, above.

DUTCH-PINK is a pigment formed of chalk, coloured with the tinging par-

by Dossie, the last term being generally applied to the cheapest native varieties. However, although his nomenclature may reflect mid-eighteenth century practice accurately, by the 1820s these terms were also applied to artificially prepared pigments, and it seems extremely doubtful, for example, whether much native Indian red was being imported. Raw and burnt sienna were in use, but were expensive and reserved for applications such as graining where their comparative transparency was an advantage. Carmine was, and remains, an extremely expensive commodity and the cheaper lakes would normally have been employed in its stead, rose pink, the least expensive of these, finding special use in distemper. Ultramarine was again so expensive as to be reserved for artist's use and it seems doubtful whether, after the introduction of Prussian blue during the first quarter of the eighteenth century, smalt would have enjoyed much application in house painting, gamboge and gallstone being exclusively artist's water colours. At the time Dossie described it, Prussian green was made by varying the process for the manufacture of Prussian blue; but although by the late 1820s the name was applied to chrome yellow 'Brunswick' green, the latter was not widely available at the time Martin compiled his text. As Dossie himself had observed that its use was neglected, the earlier pigment is unlikely to have been used to any extent. Terre verte may have enjoyed strictly limited employment in house painting, but sap green was clearly an artist's pigment, and orange lake was Dossie's own particular invention, not a commercially available pigment.

Archil seems to have been employed as a blue dye to correct any tendency to yellow in a white pigment used in the manufacture of wallpaper, but is unlikely to have been purchased for direct use in house painting. Logwood was again the source of a dye which could be used in pigment manufacture, but there is no evidence that the pigment produced from it would have been used in house painting. Brown pink was an expensive commodity, possibly employed to a limited extent in graining, but bistre was again an artist's pigment and Cologne earth (Vandyke brown) was also expensive and unlikely to have been used in common work. Asphaltum does not appear to have been used as a house painting pigment but was employed in gold-size and certain varnishes. Flake white was regarded as a fine variety of white lead, but since it was often double the price of the ordinary pigment the extent to which it was used in house painting is an open question. Nottingham white, which Nicholson had already mentioned, was generally specified instead by the 1800s. Troy white was a term used to imply a fine grade of whiting. The other white pigments contained in the preliminary list can be ignored. (For further detailed information *see* R. D. Harley, *Artists' Pigments c. 1600–1835* (Butterworth 1970)).

These defects in this part of Nicholson's text emphasize its inadequacy as a

ticles of French berries. It is not well adapted for work in oil, because it fades speedily.

ENGLISH and LIGHT PINK are merely a lighter and coarser kind of Dutch pink.

GAMBOGE is a gum brought from the East-Indies; it is dissolved in water to a milky consistence, and is then of a bright yellow colour.

MASTICOT, as a pigment, is flake-white, or white-lead gently calcined, by which it is changed to a yellow, which varies in teint according to the degree of calcination.

ORPIMENT is a fossil body, of a yellow colour, composed of arsenic and sulphur, frequently with a mixture of lead, and sometimes of other metals.

GALL-STONE is a concretion of earthy matter, formed in the gall-bladder of beasts: it is but little used.

VERDIGRIS is an oxyde of copper, formed by a vegetable acid: it is used in most kinds of painting where green is required.

CRYSTALS of VERDIGRIS is the salt produced by the solution of copper, or common verdigris, in vinegar.

PRUSSIAN-GREEN is, in composition, similar to blue of the same name.

TERRA-VERTE is a native earth; it is of a bluish green colour, resembling the teint called sea-green.

SAP-GREEN is the concreted juice of the buck-thorn berry.

ORANGE-LAKE is the tinging part of anata, or annotto, precipitated together with the earth of alum.

TRUE INDIAN-RED is a native ochrous earth of a purple colour, but so scarce as seldom to be met with at the shops.

ARCHIL is a purple tincture, prepared from a kind of moss.

LOGWOOD is brought from America, and affords a strong purple tincture.

BROWN-PINK is the tinging part of some vegetable, of an orange colour, precipitated upon the earth of alum.

BISTRE is a brown transparent colour of yellowish tint.

BROWN-OCHRE is a warm brown or foul orange colour.

COLOGNE EARTH is a fossil substance of a dark blackish brown colour, a little inclining towards purple.

ASPHALTUM is sometimes employed by the painters to answer the end of brown-pink.

WHITE-FLAKE is a ceruse prepared by the acid of the grape.

TROY-WHITE is simply chalk, neutralized by the addition of water in which alum has been dissolved.

LAMP-BLACK is properly the soot of oil collected as it is formed by burning; but, generally, no other than a soot raised from the resinous and fat parts of fir-trees.

IVORY-BLACK is composed of fragments of ivory or bone, burnt to a black coal, in a crucible or vessel, from which all access of air is excluded, and then ground very fine for use.

BLUE-BLACK is the coal of some kind of wood burnt in a close heat, to which the air can have no access.

Of the COMPOUND COLOURS, *Lead colour* is of indigo and white: *Ash colour*, of white-lead and lamp-black: *Stone colour*, white, with a little stone-ochre: *Buff*, yellow-ochre and white-lead: *Light willow green*, verdigris and white: *Grass green*, verdigris and yellow pink: *Carnation*, lake and white: *Orange colour*, yellow-ochre and red-lead: *Light timber colour*, spruce ochre, white, and a little umber: *Brick colour*, red-lead, with a little white and yellow-ochre.

All the simple colours may be bought at the colour shops, either in a crude or prepared state. They are prepared by saturating them with linseed oil or water, as either is to be used with them, and then grinding them on a slab of porphyry, marble, or granite, till they are perfectly levigated.

All colours are derived from either vegetable or mineral substances; but though the former kinds have a more brilliant effect at first, they soon change when exposed to the atmosphere, which the latter never do.

The painters' tools are few in number, being almost entirely brushes. The *pound brush* is made of hogs' hair, and is used as a duster, till the soft part is worn away. This previous wear adapts it better for spreading the colours for which it is afterwards used. The other brushes vary in size according to the work they are intended for.

COMMON HOUSE-PAINTING may be divided into the following kinds:

CLEARCOLE AND FINISH, which is the cheapest kind of painting; it is performed by first dusting and cleaning what is to be painted, and filling up cracks and defects with putty, called *stopping*.

The whole is then painted over with a preparation of whiting and size to form the ground. Over this a coat of oil-colour, prepared with lead, called the *finish*, is laid. Where work is not very dirty, this may answer pretty well, but not for outside work.

TWICE IN OIL means when the work is twice painted over.

THRICE IN OIL, means when the work has been twice painted over with oil-colours, and once in colours prepared in turpentine.

THREE TIMES AND FLAT means three coats of oil colour and one of turpentine. This is generally used for new work.

BRINGING FORWARD is a term applied to priming and painting new wood added to old work, or old work which has been repaired, so that the whole shall appear alike when finished.

GRAINING is the imitating, by means of painting, various kinds of rare woods; as satin-wood, rose-wood, king-wood, mahogany, &c., and likewise various species of marble. For this kind of work the painter is furnished with several camel's-hair pencils, and with one or more *flat* hogs' hair brushes. An even ground is first laid of a composition formed of ceruse, and the colour required diluted with oil of turpentine. This is then left for a day or two to get fixed and dry. The painter then prepares his pallet-board with small quantities of the colour required; and, being furnished with some boiled oil and oil of turpentine mixed together, tries the effects of the teint by spreading it over a panel, and if it suits, perseveres by doing a panel at a time. The shades and graining is then produced by dipping the flat hog's-hair brushes in the mixture of oil and turpentine, and drawing it down the newly-laid colours. The other particular appearance required is produced by means of the camel's-hair pencil. When all is fixed and dry, the whole is covered with one or two coats of good oil varnish. This kind of painting is not much

basis for pigment selection in any restoration specification today. The mixtures he suggested antedated early nineteenth century practice by a century and a half, although the majority of the pigments mentioned in it were still in use. In many ways it is a pity that Nicholson did not use the colour mixtures contained in his *Architectural Dictionary* (1819) (vol. ii, s.v. PAINTING, Economical, page 417) since those, although not providing a complete coverage of the subject, reflected contemporary practice to a much greater extent.

In contrast, however, the remainder of the essay in the 'Practical Builder' is a better account of early nineteenth century practice. The brushes described were of course round in shape rather than flat — as Nicholson indicated the latter was used in varnishing. The various paint systems he describes were those commonly in use. The first two are more or less self explanatory, but the last two, requiring the finishing coat to be 'prepared in turpentine', need a little explanation. This rather delicate finish, known as flatting or dead white, was simply prepared by dilution of the white lead paste (not the dry pigment) in oil of turpentine without the further addition of linseed oil. It required some skill in application, so that it was reserved for finer interiors and those not subject to everyday wear and tear. Nicholson's account of graining technique, on the other hand, represents a cheap method. Graining systems more closely resembling modern practice, although often water-based, were in use for finer work.

Unfortunately there is no complete and authoritative source which describes fully contemporary house painting practice in England in the early nineteenth century. Instead information has to be pieced together from a large number of scattered and often conflicting publications together with tradesmen's accounts and other documents in manuscript. It is essential too that a study of them is supplemented by the scientific examination of contemporary paint specimens. In general, however, the practice of Nicholson's day may be summarized concisely as follows. Ceilings in common interiors would have been whitened, that is finished simply with a wash of whiting in water without the addition of size or other binder. On walls where abrasion could be expected and on ceilings to be coloured the use of size-bound distemper would have been usual. Joinery would have been painted in oil and in fine interiors this medium would have been employed for walls and ceilings, except where the use of distemper was essential to make use of one of the more brilliant pigments only suited to that medium. Normally oil paint would have possessed a slight sheen but flatted oil finishes were fashionable and used in finer rooms where their expense could be justified. Graining, frequently varnished, had become popular on joinery elements, in particular doors, windows, and architraves and was often used too on dados and skirtings. To this basic scheme, many embellishments could be added by the ornamental painter in the way of marbled walls, or trompe l'oeil

dearer than good work in the common way, but it will last ten times as long, by being occasionally re-varnished, without losing any of its freshness.

ORNAMENTAL PAINTING embraces the executing of friezes and the decorative parts of architecture, in chara-obscura, or light and shade, on walls or ceilings. It is performed by first laying a ground of the colour required, then sketching the ornament with a black-lead pencil, and afterwards painting and shading it, so as to give the required effect.

INSCRIPTION WRITING is similar in process to ornamental painting; the painter sketching out the letters in pencil and finishing the outline with colour. If the letters are to be gilt, they are covered with leaf gold, while the paint is wet. After the whole is dry, the superfluous gold is removed with a moist sponge, and the work covered with a coat of good oil varnish.

VALUATION OF PAINTERS' WORK.

PAINTERS' work, in general, is valued at the yard superficial of nine square feet. Sash-frames are valued at per piece, and sash squares at per dozen. Inscription writing is charged by the inch, *viz.* the height of one letter being taken, and multiplied by the whole number of letters, will give the quantity of inches. Shadowed letters are a halfpenny more than plain ones, and gilt letters treble the price. The charges for painting are regulated in London by intelligent surveyors; but, as colours and oils can be purchased at any degree of purity, painting is often done at twenty per cent. less than the prices so regulated; but the value of painters' work, in all cases, depends upon the quality of the materials and goodness of workmanship, and in reference also to the different species of works.

friezes and panels. As in any architectural work, cost was a decisive factor and in contrast to the opulence of many important Regency interors, the majority of ordinary rooms would have been decorated in a simple manner using a restricted range of colours and finishes.

Index